The Townies' Guide to the Countryside

The Townies' Guide to the Countryside

Jill Mason

Photographs by David Mason

Merlin Unwin Books

First published in Great Britain by Merlin Unwin Books, 2003
Copyright © Jill Mason, 2003

MERLIN UNWIN BOOKS
Palmers House
7 Corve Street, Ludlow
Shropshire SY8 1DB, U.K.
Tel 01584 877456
Fax 01584 877457
email: books@merlinunwin.co.uk
website: www.countrybooksdirect.com

British Library Cataloguing in Publication Data:
A catalogue record for this book is available from the British Library

ISBN 1-873674-65-1

Designed and typeset by Merlin Unwin Books and Think Graphic Design, Ludlow, UK.
Printed in Italy by EuroLitho

CONTENTS

ACKNOWLEDGEMENTS

All aspects of the country way of life are subjects very close to my heart. During the last few years I noticed, from talking to country folk, a certain frustration that town people knew so little about the practical things that go on in the countryside. So I set about writing a book which would explain what *does* go on. After more than two years' research, it was completed. However, while trying to get my book published I discovered that country books are written with country people in mind, not townspeople, and this made things difficult and I'd like to thank Merlin Unwin Books for taking me on. Hopefully this book will do what it was intended to do – help bridge the undeniable gap that exists between town and country.

Conveniently, my husband David's hobby has, for many years, been photography and I am very grateful to him for allowing me to raid his extensive collection of countryside pictures to illustrate my book.

I would also like to say how much I appreciate the numerous people whose brains I have picked and who have filled in the bits of information which I lacked. They have meant that I've been able to include many more details than I would otherwise have done and my grateful thanks go to each and every one of them. I also would like to extend my thanks to the Poultry World magazine who very promptly answered my plea for help to illustrate the chapter about poultry and supplied the picture used at the top of page 36 as well as those on pages 37, 38, 40, 41 and 45.

Thanks also go to David Kjaer for the use of the picture of a peregrine on page 182, and to Peter O'Reilly for the salmon on page 222.

*"I have tried
to imagine that I
am a town
dweller passing
through the
countryside and
wondering what
things are and
what people
are doing."*

Jill Mason

INTRODUCTION: FARMING IN BRITAIN

During and after World War II, farmers, in the typical bulldog fashion that prevailed at the time, set to work ploughing up every available acre in order to feed a hungry nation. They did a remarkable job and took pride in their achievement.

The next demand made of them came in the 1960s when consumers expected food to become cheaper. Farmers successfully responded by intensifying their production methods.

Now, at the beginning of a new century, the pendulum has swung the other way and farmers have become the victims of their own success. Public opinion now condemns them for doing what was required of them a few decades ago. Post-war technology has greatly improved crop and livestock production, resulting in over-production and surpluses in the West. Despite this many people in Third World countries are still hungry.

Farming today is manipulated by EU and British Government policies. Grants, subsidies and quotas dictate the direction that farming takes. The poultry and pig industries are the only ones not influenced by subsidies. At present the emphasis is on agri-environmental schemes and making the countryside available for public leisure.

Farming, as an industry, is genuinely on its knees. Health scares affecting humans such as CJD, E-Coli and Salmonella and animal diseases like Swine Fever and Foot and Mouth have taken their toll on livestock production. The epidemic of Foot and Mouth disease that started in February 2001, and continued for seven months, infected over 2,000 farms and was considered to have been very badly handled by the Government. The policy of contiguous culling meant that many of the 4 million plus animals culled may have been unnecessarily destroyed if protective ring vaccination had been used as it was on the Continent. The delays

Above Unloading barley from the combine. 25% of our farming land is for crops

Below Snail on a head of wheat – organic farms are struggling after the initial start-up grants

in incinerating stock after it had been shot and transporting it in lorries for many miles through the countryside to designated sites were appalling. It wasn't until Brigadier Birtwistle and his troops were called in that some semblance of order took place.

Compensation payments at the beginning were far in excess of market values and were no doubt viewed as a golden handshake by a few older farmers who were not sorry to get out of farming. For many, though, it was utterly devastating to see all they had cared for destroyed. Generations of selective breeding were wiped out. Those in areas adjacent to the culling were financially worse off than those who actually lost their stock, for they were not compensated but suffered greatly because of all the restrictions imposed upon them and their livestock. The lives of everyone living in or visiting the countryside were affected. In the aftermath of Foot and Mouth it is difficult to see that many of the recording, bio-security and restrictive measures introduced will ever be rescinded, adding to the already heavy burden of red tape suffered by agriculture.

How the land is farmed

Excessive wet weather, the strong pound and financial returns much lower than they were a few years ago have also badly affected arable and vegetable growers. Under a government that appears to have no notion of what makes the countryside tick, farmers have become very despondent. More than 20,000 people employed in agriculture have quit working on the land annually in the last four years. Were it that number walking, in a mass, for the last time through a redundant factory's gates it would make disturbing headline news. Less than 1.9% of the workforce now work on the land yet they take care of more than 75% of it. Of the areas classified as agricultural holdings, 24% is used as rough grazing, 25% is used for growing crops, 29% is improved semi permanent grass and 7% is put down to grass for less than 5 years. Of the rest, 3% has been taken out of production under the 'set-aside' scheme and 11% has other uses, including woodland.

Keeping up with the times

Farming is a complex network of small businesses very individually run and their activities were once limited by the suitability

FARMING
Useful Words

BRITISH FARM STANDARD Logo of a red tractor with blue wheels denotes that the product has been produced in Britain and meets recognised standards.

CLA Country Landowners' Association.

DEFRA Dept for Environment, Food and Rural Affairs. Formed in 2001 to bring together environmental, rural and food related issues and incorporating MAFF (Ministry of Agriculture, Fisheries and Food).

FARM ASSURED stamp means farmers comply with DEFRA recommendations for welfare and legal requirements.

FREEDOM FOOD is defined as meat from producers who conform to standards set by the RSPCA. Animal based protein in feed, with the exception of milk products, and growth promoters, are banned and transport times are limited.

FREE RANGE chickens must have continuous daytime access to open air runs for at least half of their lives. No restrictions on the use of animal products in the feed or proper use of antibiotics.

HECTARE One hectare equals 2.47 acres or 10,000 sq. metres.

NFU National Farmers Union.

ORGANIC means produce supplied by farmers registered with a recognised organic inspection body which demands strict standards for production.

OUTDOOR BRED/REARED When applied to pigs this means that they spend the first 12 weeks of their lives outside and the remaining time, about 10 weeks, inside.

of the area in which the farm was situated. Now, though, because of grants, subsidies and sophisticated machinery, the scope is much broader. Diversification has become the key word lately but there are only so many ways in which to diversify and many of them are proving unprofitable.

Organic produce is much in demand but after the initial boost of government grants to get started, many farmers are now finding it difficult to maintain their business. It is ironic that conservation measures such as the Countryside Stewardship scheme and grants and set-aside payments, which have taken a percentage of land out of production, can provide a farmer with a greater income than that he receives from livestock and crops.

Agricultural holdings in the UK vary greatly in size. Only a small percentage are in excess of 500 acres (200 hectares) but small ones are getting fewer as they become absorbed into larger enterprises. Well over half are owned and the remainder tenanted. Unlike on the Continent, British farms are generally run as individual units whereas in Europe farmers form co-operatives to share costs and capital outlay.

Many British estates that come on the market are now being purchased by foreign or city investors, and land prices are on the increase, having doubled in the last ten years.

Sophisticated employees

Today there is no place for the country 'yokel'. Modern farming requires highly skilled people to operate hi-tech machinery and to manage the large number of livestock now allocated to the care of one person. Most agricultural workers live in 'tied' accommodation. Housing is supplied free or for a nominal rent as it is necessary for employees to live near to their place of work in rural and sometimes isolated areas. Accommodation is taken into account as part of their wage deal, and in return agricultural workers are expected to be available to work long hours when required and often at unsociable times such as weekends. Land work has to be done when conditions are right and livestock require attention seven days a week. Many landowners now rely on contractors to do the work in preference to employing their own full time staff. 70% of farms are family run but on many of the smaller ones, there is insufficient income to support both

To prevent the spread of Foot & Mouth disease more than 4 million animals were culled

Use of heavy horses declined after WW II: today's farm workers usually have to operate hi-tech machinery

Over 20,000 agricultural workers per year have quit working the land in the past 4 years

father and son, so the son leaves farming to find other work. When father decides to retire from the struggle of running the farm, there is no one to take over. The farm is sold and bought by a larger concern, becoming amalgamated with it. Its identity and those of the family who have worked it for generations are gone forever.

Small farms, for a variety of reasons, are falling by the wayside at an alarming rate. Countryside communities are changing as people cease to work on the land. Far fewer people do the work and understand how and why it's done. Fifty years ago, a quarter of the population were connected with farming; now that figure is less than one in ten.

Farmers no longer know what is required of them. Powerful supermarkets have a big influence on production and marketing issues. Farmers can't cut their costs because, like other employers, they have to pay a minimum wage as well as having

Land prices in Britain have doubled in the last ten years

Below British farms are generally run as individual units whereas in Europe farmers form co-operatives to share costs and capital outlay

to comply with animal welfare and health and safety standards, yet they are trying to compete with imports from countries who pay scant regard to such things.

The future for those working in British agriculture is very uncertain. For the first time in history, it almost seems as if they aren't needed any more. Farm incomes have fallen by 25% in the last three years while costs have increased. Tenant farmers are at a particular disadvantage as rents continue to rise. While some farmers are only in it to make a living, for many others there is a traditional pride in raising good crops and healthy livestock. There's a lot more to being in farming than the amount of money that is made out of it but a farmer still needs sufficient to feed his family and invest in his farm or neither will be able to carry on for very long.

Britain produces some of the highest quality, best value and safest food in the world, and appreciates it has to remain competitive, but the difficulty is to know how.

Farm incomes have fallen by 25% in the past three years

Holsteins in the parlour: the farmer will receive about a quarter of the price of the pint on your doorstep

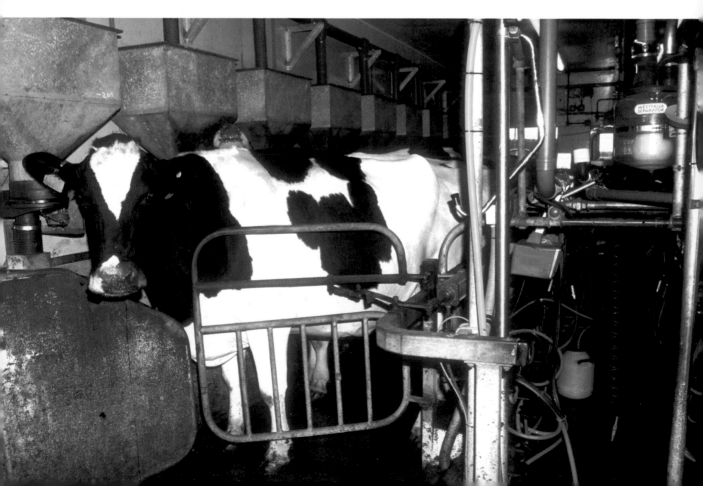

CATTLE FARMING

The plethora of regulations that have followed in the wake of BSE and the epidemic of Foot and Mouth disease which struck Britain in 2001 have cost the British cattle farmer dear. EU rules had already made life difficult for all livestock farmers but the introduction of a ban on the human consumption of any cattle over the age of 30 months meant that the financial value of older heifers and barren cows became greatly reduced. Beef and dairy farmers were also both badly affected by the long ban on exports following the outbreak of Foot and Mouth disease.

Strict EU regulations have enforced very high standards of hygiene as well as increased paperwork, which have also added to the financial burden. In addition to this, the price a dairy farmer receives for his milk has actually fallen. He is paid only about half of what a four pint container costs in a supermarket or a quarter of that charged for a pint delivered to the doorstep. For that he has had to bear the cost of rearing a calf for two years before she gives milk, then feeding her, keeping her healthy and generally looking after her during her productive life.

Quota systems now operate in the dairy industry and can prove to be an added expense if the dairy farmer wrongly estimates his level of production. He can find himself in the situation of pouring surplus milk down the drain at a time when maybe as much as 40% is being imported from France.

Because of high overhead costs it is vital that optimum performance is achieved from each animal. There are over 2 million dairy cows in the UK and 95% of them are the familiar black and white Holsteins. In the last few decades this breed has superseded all the native British breeds which have now become little more than collector's items to be found on parade at agricultural shows. Very few are now kept on a commercial basis.

A 'store animal' is one that needs to be fattened

A heifer is a young female cow up to the time she gives birth to her second calf

Above Silage is used to supplement the diet of cattle

Designer breeds

The Holstein, preceded by the very similar Friesian, is a breed that has been developed solely to produce milk. Its metabolism is such that its body converts the food it is given into milk, not fat on its back. In fact a high yielding cow cannot eat a sufficient volume of grass alone to survive so it is reliant on supplementary rations. Beef cattle have been greatly improved with the intro-duction of different breeds from the Continent such as the Charolais and the Simmental. They have the ability to grow quickly, not lay down too much fat and to develop the largest proportion of meat on the back end, where the most expensive joints are cut from.

The benefits of AI

The now common practice of using AI (artificial insemination) for cattle enables semen from the best bulls in Britain and abroad to be used by any cattle breeder and has greatly improved the quality and output from their herds since the 1950s. Some pedi-gree herds make full use of modern reproduction techniques. AI has even made it possible to select the sex of the offspring. Research has also provided the means to breed several calves from one cow at the same time. This involves injecting the donor cow with a substance that will make her produce several 'ripe' eggs when she would normally only produce one. A further injec-tion brings her into oestrus (heat) and by inseminating her 3 times during the critical period it is possible to fertilise several of the eggs. These are left to develop for about 7 days before being removed by a vet, carefully checked under a microscope and then each individual embryo is either implanted into a surrogate heifer or cow or frozen at this stage and stored for future use. This is an expensive procedure but several calves from an exceptional cow can be produced or stored each year, speeding up the process of selecting the best or preserving the bloodline.

It may be argued that the dairy industry is a victim of its own success in selective breeding but escalating costs across the board, combined with lower financial returns, have forced it to become increasingly competitive. Apart from food, it costs as much to keep a cow producing 4,000 litres of milk a year as it does one giving twice that amount.

AI has made it possible to select the sex of calves

The Holstein is such a phenomenal milk-yeilder, grass alone cannot support its diet

Herds can be as large as 200 thanks to modern milking machinery

CATTLE FARMING *Useful Words*

AI Artificial insemination.

BARREN Infertile.

BULL Male.

CATTLE GRID An alternative barrier to a gate, consisting of a pit covered with evenly spaced heavy duty metal bars providing a very effective method of preventing cattle and sheep straying where roads are unfenced.

CLUSTER Cups on milking machine that fit on to the teats; an intermittent squeezing action releases milk from the udder.

COLOSTRUM Very rich milk produced by an animal for a few days after giving birth.

CONCENTRATES Supplementary food containing necessary nutrients such as protein and vitamins manufactured into pellets, pencils, nuts or cake.

COW Mature female.

DIS-BUD, DE-HORN Remove horn growth, normally done in first few weeks before the horns develop.

DRY OFF Cease to give milk.

EAR TAG Plastic or metal identification tag inserted in the ear.

ELECTRIC FENCE Thin single strand wire fence electrified by a battery that is charged by a small windmill, solar panels or a transformer to reduce power from the mains.

FREEZE BRAND Permanent identification carried out painlessly by applying liquid nitrogen which turns the marked hair white.

FLY TAG Chemical fly repellent tag inserted in the animal's ear.

FREEMARTIN A female calf that is born twinned with a male and is invariably infertile. Applies only to cattle.

GESTATION Period of pregnancy.

HAY Dried grass.

HEIFER Young female up to the time she gives birth to her second calf.

LACTATION Period of milk production.

LICK Solid mineral or nutrition block.

MAIDEN Animal that has not previously been bred from.

NURSE COW Cow used to suckle calves, foster mother.

PARLOUR Building in which cows are milked.

OESTRUS, HEAT Ovulation period when mating can take place.

SERVE Mate with.

STEAM UP Increase feed rations prior to calving.

STIRK Young female.

STORE Animal that still needs to grow or be fattened.

STRIP GRAZE Allow animals access to a small area of grazing. Usually electric fencing is used and is moved daily to provide fresh grazing.

SILAGE Grass or maize that partially ferments while stored and ultimately provides palatable fodder.

STEER Castrated male.

STRAW The dried stems of cereals. Barley straw can be used for feed but wheat and oat straw are only suitable for bedding.

TURN OUT Given access outside.

UNIT Milking machine.

The number of cattle farmers is dwindling because the smaller ones find it increasingly difficult to remain competitive against the background of crippling overheads. Many small farmers, devastated by Foot and Mouth disease, have chosen new ways of earning a living rather than by going back into cattle.

However large or small a dairy enterprise, much of its success is due to the skills of the herdsperson. There are now many herds in milk exceeding 200. It is stockmanship, attention to detail and dedication on which the welfare, and therefore profitability, of the herd depends.

A female calf which is born twinned to a male is always infertile

CALF REARING

A cow can come into oestrus at any time throughout the year so calves may be born in any month. However to fit in with seasonal growth of natural food, production costs and financial returns, most beef calves are born in early spring and dairy calves in late summer. Calving may take place either indoors or outside; there are advantages and disadvantages with either choice.

Many beef calves are raised outdoors on a 'single suckler' system in which the cow is allowed to rear her own calf naturally. Beef breeds do not give nearly as much milk as dairy, so one calf is enough for her to rear. A dairy breed of cow, if used as a foster mother or 'nurse cow', may produce enough milk to rear up to 4 calves.

It is vital for the health of the calf that it receives 'colostrum' which is the first milk produced by its mother. This is not only extremely rich and highly digestible but it also contains antibodies passed on from the cow which will, to start with, provide the calf with some degree of immunity and resistance to bacteria and other bugs as well as flushing through and activating its digestive system. If it is intended to artificially rear a calf, it is usually separated from its mother after only a few hours. It is given the colostrum for the first 3 or 4 days and very quickly learns to drink from a bucket.

Nearly all dairy calves and some beef calves are reared on milk powder because it costs only half as much as fresh milk. This is fed once or twice a day, occasionally *ad lib*, until the calves are weaned at about 5 or 6 weeks of age. Hand-reared calves are very often housed in small pens separate from each other. This means they can receive individual attention and every calf gets its fair share of milk, hay and the concentrate feed (pellets or pencils) which they are also given. Separating them also avoids them developing bad habits such as sucking one another. If they are not penned separately then they are best kept in small groups of similar ages so that they can put their heads through a 'yoke' (grille) to drink their rations of milk. This prevents the greedy stealing from the slower ones and the milk buckets being knocked over.

A single suckler is usually a beef cow allowed to rear her own calf naturally outdoors

Holstein dairy cow with her calf: but most dairy calves are reared on milk powder which costs half the price of fresh milk

Calves need to be kept in clean, well-ventilated and draught-free conditions. Scours (diarrhoea) and respiratory ailments such as pneumonia are probably the biggest threats to their health.

Ayrshires are a traditional dairy breed that are now seldom seen

Ear tags

Unless a calf is slaughtered before it is 36 hours old, as many unwanted dairy breed bull calves are, an ear tag issued by DEFRA must, by law, be inserted in each ear; a small metal one in one ear and a larger easily-read plastic one in the other. Most farmers also fix a large plastic numbered identification tag in the ear with the small metal one for their own records. The compulsory DEFRA tags are registered so that every calf can be tracked throughout its entire lifetime in conjunction with a passport. This is issued at the same time and has to accompany the animal whenever it leaves the farm, even if it is only taken to a show for a few hours. This requirement was instigated as a direct result of the BSE health scare and enables every single animal to be traced at any time and its whereabouts recorded.

All beef animals destined for human consumption must be killed before they are 30 months old

Castration

Male calves, unless they are wanted for breeding purposes, are normally castrated. When this operation is carried out by the stockman, it has to be done within the first week of life. Either of two methods can be used by an experienced person. The first is by placing a strong elastic ring around the scrotum above the testicles with a special tool. The blood supply is cut off and in a short time the scrotum and testicles shrivel up and drop off. The initial pain when the ring is put in place lasts only a few minutes until the restriction causes numbness. After that the process is painless. The alternative method of castration is to crush the spermatic cord with a tool known as a 'Burdizzo'; this also seems to cause little discomfort to the animal. If a bull calf has not been

Before it can give any milk, a cow has to give birth

castrated by the time it is a week old then it is necessary for the surgical removal of the testicles which can only be carried out under anaesthetic by a vet. When a bull calf is kept for breeding it must, by law, have a ring put in its nose before it is a year old as this is the only safe way of restraining such a large animal.

Dehorning

Dehorning (or disbudding) is usually done when the calf is between two and three weeks old and the horns are just beginning to grow. Many breeds of cattle naturally grow horns, and by removing them there is less possibility of them harming each other or the people looking after them. A specially designed tool heated by either propane gas or electricity is used to burn away the soft growth after a local anaesthetic has been administered. At this stage heifer calves are carefully inspected to see if they have any extra teats. A cow's udder, which doesn't develop until she is close to giving birth to her first calf, is divided into four 'quarters' and there should be only one teat for each quarter. It is quite common for there to be extra, and surgically removing them when the calf is young and the teats are very small saves problems later in its life.

While beef calves suckled by their mothers are several months old before they are weaned, those reared artificially are weaned at approximately 6 weeks old. They are then usually 'loose housed' in straw bedded yards or barns, in groups of similar ages, until 4 to 6 months old. They continue to be fed on concentrates and good quality hay or silage but after this period it is likely they will be turned out to grass between April and October before being brought inside again for the winter. Occasionally in drier areas yearling stock may be left out for their second winter. When they reach breeding age, most heifers are freeze branded to make identification easy.

Cattle farmers often insert yet another ear tag when the animals are turned out to grass: a fly tag. This acts like a flea collar on a cat or dog, and protects cattle from the summer plagues of biting flies. Fly tags inserted in May will last for 4 or 5 months and provide some relief during the worst period.

Cows have a strong maternal instinct

Very little fat is wanted on the carcasses of beef animals today which is why the Continental breeds are so popular

BEEF CATTLE

Many beef herds are what are known as 'single sucklers'. Each cow gives birth to a calf which she rears herself. This is a popular system on poorer grazing land such as hills and moors. Calving is usually timed for late winter or early spring so that the calf grows along with the grass. Very often a bull is put to run with the cows and their calves when they are a few weeks old, so natural mating takes place to produce next year's crop of calves.

Favoured breeds

Continental breeds such as the Charolais, Simmental and Limousin are generally the most popular choice for beef production because of their conformation: lean meat and plenty of it. However, unlike some of the native breeds, they are not always hardy enough to thrive on poorer ground although the weaned calves make a better price if they are sold as stores to be fattened on good grazing or in straw yards elsewhere.

Smaller native breeds such as the white faced Hereford and the all-black Aberdeen Angus still have their place and are sometimes better suited to certain conditions. They are often the choice of dairy farmers to cross with their cows and especially heifers as, being smaller, calving is generally easier. The resultant calves are reared in a similar way to dairy replacements although they may have increased rations so that they gain weight faster. Likewise they may have a summer out at grass before being brought in to straw yards for the winter and fattened to be sold.

The same stringent regulations regarding identification and marketing apply to beef cattle as to dairy. All beef animals destined for human consumption must be killed before they are 30 months old.

DAIRY FARMING

Before it can give any milk, a cow has to give birth. A young cow continues to be called a heifer until it has had its second calf.

Heifers are usually mated when they are between 15 and 18

When a bull calf is kept for breeding it must, by law, have a ring put in its nose before it is a year old

Continental breeds such as the Charolais are a popular choice for beef production – note the compulsory ear tags required by DEFRA

months old and weigh approximately 450 kgs. Pregnancy lasts for 9 months. To be profitable a cow needs to have a calf every 12 or 13 months, so she will be mated again within 3 months of giving birth. A natural substance that can be artificially produced called Prostaglandin is frequently administered to bring young heifers into heat. Using Prostaglandin on maiden heifers synchronises the heat period, making subsequent management easier.

Artificial insemination

Cows come on heat for approximately 1 day every 3 weeks all year round. AI is used extensively in the dairy industry and many herdsmen and stockmen are trained to do this. Young heifers that have not been got in calf by AI are often run with a bull for a few weeks because natural mating will sometimes succeed when AI has failed. As there is no assurance that the calves from young unproven heifers are worth keeping, a small beef breed such as an Aberdeen Angus or Hereford, for easy calving, is often used because unwanted pure bred dairy calves are of no value. Cows that do not fit into the selected calving pattern are also often crossed with a beef breed and their calves sold so that the next batch of replacement heifers will all be of a similar age making management easier.

Pregnancy checks

Even though summer milk prices are slightly higher, many dairy farmers choose to have their cows calve in autumn. This is because the silage and concentrates they receive as winter feed is utilised to the best advantage during the period in which they are yielding most milk. Because it is so important that a cow or heifer is got in calf, pregnancy tests are routinely conducted. Pregnancy can be determined either by scanning after about 5 weeks or manually after 6 weeks by a vet who puts his arm inside the cow and is actually able to feel the developing foetus. Dairy farmers do not welcome twins; they are often small and can give rise to various complications. If twins of differing sexes are born, the female is inevitably sterile and therefore useless for breeding; she is

Of the two million dairy cows in the UK, 95% of them are the familiar black and white Holsteins

Below In addition to the 'herring bone' milking parlour (shown below)there is another design, the 'abreast', where the cows stand on a slightly raised platform directly in front of the operator

known as a 'freemartin'. After giving birth the cow will quickly come into full milk, reaching peak production after about 5 weeks when it is possible that she will give as much as 65 litres a day. Soon after this peak, her yield will gradually decline until after about 10 months she will give only a few litres and be milked once a day. At this stage she will be 'dried off' by cutting back her food allowance for a short while. This gives her body a chance to replenish itself and build up reserves to produce plenty of milk during her next lactation. After a month or so at a low level, her feed will be increased 4 or 5 weeks prior to the birth of her next calf although care has to be taken that she does not get unhealthily fat.

Enormous milk yield

Commercial cows may average about 7,000 litres in a lactation but the very best dairy Holsteins can produce up to 12,000 litres of milk each year. The lower yields from commercial herds can still prove to be economic if a low cost and streamlined system of management has been adopted. Many dairy farmers, for their own records, have their cow's yields officially recorded for two consecutive milkings once a month.

Although some extremely high yielders may be milked three times a day, most herds are milked twice, as near to 12 hour intervals as is tolerable. This means that a herdsperson starts work very early in the morning, usually about 5am, and often doesn't finish until after 6pm or later. However if their other chores are completed it is sometimes possible for them to take an extended lunch break. Cows also have to be milked at the same times on weekends and bank holidays, so herdspeople have to be prepared to work long and unsociable hours often only having one day off a week in lieu of working Saturdays and Sundays and one weekend off a month. Many small-scale farmers have to do all the work themselves, so holidays are unknown. Besides the long hours, it is physically demanding, repetitive and dirty work; cows are not housetrained.

To lessen back strain, the herdsperson usually works from a pit often between two rows of cows. If he is busy he does not always notice the tell tale sign of a raised tail and has to suffer the unpleasant consequences!

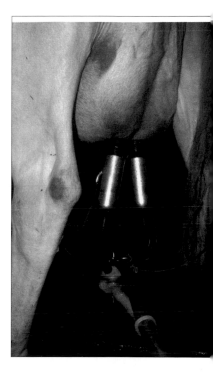

Below A cow will reach peak milk production about 5 weeks after calving. It is possible for a cow to give 65 litres a day, but only the very best ones do

To be profitable a cow needs to have a calf every 12 or 13 months

Milking parlours

Modern dairy herds are generally milked in specially designed, hygienic milking parlours with raised floors although some very small herds may still be kept in stalls on the same level, where cows are tied up individually to be milked. Occasionally where cows are grazed away from the farm buildings in summer, for example on water meadows such as the Somerset Levels, a portable structure known as a 'milking bail' may be used.

Whatever the system used, the milk from each cow is first collected in a container or large glass jar before it is released into an overhead pipe conveying it to a bulk tank. There are several designs of milking parlours. The most popular is the 'herring-bone' where the operator works from a pit approximately 90cms deep. The cows are let in one end in batches of 6 or 8 alternately either side, and stand with their backs to the pit at an angle of 30 to 35 degrees hence the name herringbone. When they have received their individual rations of food and been milked, they are let out the other end and a fresh batch let in.

Portable bucket machines are also available for milking individual cows when they are taken to agricultural shows or being kept in isolation. Some very large commercial dairy herds have invested in 'rotary' parlours or 'carousals' where the cows enter onto a circular raised platform that moves very slowly round the operator who is working from a central pit. The cow exits near to where she entered and another takes her place.

Other duties

All the designs have evolved to make milking cows quicker and easier, but it has often meant that one person is expected to milk many more cows. There is also a lot of muck that has to be cleared up each day from the parlour, from the collecting yards where the cows wait prior to milking and the dispersal yards where they are let out of the parlour afterwards.

There are now extremely high standards of milk hygiene that have to be met and a refrigerated bulk milk tank is a modern necessity. Here the milk is agitated, cooled quickly to a temperature not exceeding 4C and stored until it is collected by a milk tanker and taken to a distribution centre before either being packaged and sold fresh or sent for butter or cheese making or yoghurt production.

Cows come on heat for about 1 day in every 3 weeks – all year round

Dairy calves are usually housed in straw yards when they are weaned

Random testing

Samples are taken each day by the tanker driver. These are randomly tested several times a week for the presence of bacteria, traces of antibiotics, to make sure that there is no evidence of blood or water and to do a cell count to detect the presence of mastitis, a common infection in the udder. If a cow or heifer has been treated with antibiotics or any other drugs a detailed record has to be kept of the medication used and the milk has to be thrown away both during treatment and for a fixed number of days afterwards. The premises and equipment are regularly inspected. Dairy farmers face stiff penalties if their milk is found to be contaminated, so they adhere to the strict rules.

Keeping cows fit is vital, not only because drugs are expensive but also because of the lost revenue from milk that has to be tipped down the drain, although there are times when this can be used to feed calves. An experienced stockman or herdsperson performs many veterinary procedures such as giving injections, treating foot problems and assisting with difficult births.

Grazing cattle

Grass is a complete food providing for the basic needs of a cow and supplies the bulk of its food between March and October. During the winter when grass stops growing and the weather is cold and wet, dairy cows are usually kept inside although some farms grow kale for extra feed in the autumn or even the winter in drier areas. Cows are usually turned out for only a few hours a day and fed a small strip at a time. Electric fencing is used and has to be moved daily. Strip grazing in this manner is also used on some farms for grassland management, others use small paddocks, while many others opt for the traditional method of fenced or hedged fields. Cheap electric fencing has replaced much of the barbed wire once found on dairy farms; it is less costly, easily and quickly erected and the risk of stock being injured by it is greatly reduced.

Cattle cake

Supplementary feeding is given to high yielding cows and those nearing calving in the form of large pellets (often called cow cake) or a muesli-type mix. This concentrate ration is high in

Cattle 'out at grass' in a water meadow where the wide range of grasses provides an excellent dietary balance

The very best dairy Holsteins can produce up to 12,000 litres of milk each year

Summer milk prices are higher than winter ones

protein and contains vitamins and minerals; the latter is also often made available to animals in the form of blocks known as licks.

Concentrates for milking cows are usually fed in the parlour while the cow is being milked; it is convenient and is also an encouragement to enter the parlour. The herdsman identifies each cow by a number on its rump and dispenses the appropriate amount of food either manually with a lever or by punching in the number on a keyboard of a computerised system that automatically apportions the correct amount. More sophisticated systems are sometimes used where the cow is recognised by a sensor attached to a collar.

Winter quarters

There are two main systems for housing cows in winter. Some are housed loose in covered straw yards with access to a feed area and mangers. Alternatively the covered area may be divided into individual 'cubicles' narrow enough to prevent a cow turning round and soiling its bedding. There are 'dunging' passages between the rows of cubicles, a 'loafing' area and feed mangers. Cow 'kennels' are very similar.

Straw yards have to be littered up each day; and all the open areas of concrete as well as the collecting and dispersal yards for the parlour have to be cleaned. A scraper mounted on a tractor is used to move the rather liquid muck into a storage pit (slurry lagoon) or to where it can be pumped into a large circular storage tank prior to its being spread or sprayed on the fields. Sometimes a system similar to that used for irrigation is used to spread this valuable source of fertiliser. Chopped straw, sand or sawdust may be used for the bedding-in cubicles and much less litter is needed than the 2 to 3 tons of straw per cow used each winter for those loose housed in straw yards. Cows keep cleaner in cubicles although there is often an odd one that prefers to lie in the passageway. There is more chance of bullying in straw yards and it is a major task to remove the compacted straw several feet deep by the end of winter.

While cows are kept indoors, their basic maintenance rations are fed in mangers or, on some farms, they are allowed direct access to the face of a silage clamp where the amount they have available is controlled by an electric fence. Their food may

On average cows are kept for 6 lactations, ie until they are about 8 years old

The ring in a bull's nose is used to restrain him when necessary

After calving a cow can yield as much as 65 litres a day

consist of hay, silage, barley-straw treated with an alkali, crushed cereals and human food by-products such as sugar beet pulp, maize gluten or biscuit waste. Much research and analysis is carried out into the value of rations, as a healthy and well balanced diet is essential. High-yielding cows have very specific nutritional requirements and soon suffer detrimental health problems if these aren't met. The quality of hay and silage very much depends on weather conditions during the growing period and at the time when the grass was cut.

Barren cows

Housing cattle in winter is expensive and time-consuming. It is always a relief when the herd is turned out in the spring.

Normally it is uneconomic to keep a cow if she does not conceive within a certain period; any that don't are sold as 'barren'. Exception may be made in a pedigree herd if a cow, because of its breeding, is valuable. Cows are often culled too if they have anything wrong with them that will potentially reduce their milk yield. On average cows are kept for 6 lactations, ie until they are about 8 years old.

Incineration for cattle over 30 months

Because of the BSE scare in the 1990s, new regulations were brought in. The dairy farmer, like the beef farmer, is paid a set amount for any animal over 30 months old sent for slaughter. This is much less than he would have previously received for similar animals. The animals have to be sent for slaughter at designated slaughter houses and the carcasses incinerated. Before these regulations the animals, if not used for human consumption, would have been utilised as pet food or processed into meat and bone meal that was used as a protein source in animal feed rations. This is believed to have been the link between BSE in cattle and CJD in humans. Without this source of essential protein for cattle, an alternative has to be used, resulting in increased pressure on fish stocks and a bigger demand for plant protein providers such as soya to fill this need.

Cows and calves that die or have to be put down on the farm need to be disposed of. The knackerman can now only take dead stock if it is under 24 months old and casualty stock under 30

Most herds are milked twice daily, as near to 12 hour intervals as possible

Charolais bulls on show. The use of AI has improved the quality of cattle

months; anything older than this has to be incinerated. He now charges to collect dead or 'fallen' stock because transport costs are so high and the only money he can make from most of the animals is from their hides. Local hunts collect cattle within a certain radius of their kennels and provide a free means of disposal but they too are governed by strict regulations. It is estimated that 400,000 animals each year are collected, skinned and fed to hounds offering a valuable service to farmers who can ill afford any extra costs.

The knackerman can only take dead stock if the animal is under 24 months old and 'casualty stock' under 30 months

SHEEP FARMING

There are an estimated 36 million sheep in Britain and 80 different native breeds. Some of these are very local to an area such as the Herdwicks found only in the Lake District. All the native breeds have been developed over the centuries for their capacity to thrive in the many different environments they are expected to live. Sheep are one of the most adaptable species of animal in the world, able to exist in arid deserts as well as high on the tops of mountains.

Nearly all sheep in Britain are kept primarily for meat production. The quality of the fleece varies greatly with the breed and the coarser ones can only be used for carpets etc and are almost worthless. The finer ones are of more value but the market for wool of any sort is minimal as the demand for cheap man-made fibres increases. Ironically the popular 'fleece' material today has nothing to do with a sheep.

Herdwicks are local to the Lake District. Only the rams have horns in this breed

Upland sheep

Hill sheep are small and slow maturing but are able to withstand the rigours of the open mountains. They can thrive on poor grazing and provide the main source of income for hill farmers. Upland breeds are slightly larger and hardy enough to live out all year on the hills. Since the 1950s, because of market trends and more recently EU subsidy payments per sheep, numbers are reckoned to have quadrupled. The uplands of Britain, which cover

SHEEP *Useful Words*

AGE The age of a sheep is indicated by its teeth. A 'shearling' is a 2-tooth and over 5 years is 'full mouth'.

BROKEN MOUTHED Ewe with damaged teeth but otherwise fit and able to survive where the living is easy.

COUPED or **CAST** When a sheep has rolled on to its back and is unable to get up.

DAGG or **CRUTCH** to remove soiled wool from the rear end of sheep.

DRAFT EWE Term used when older ewes are sold, often applied to 4-year-old hill ewes that can no longer withstand the harsh conditions but can still be used for breeding in the lowlands.

DRENCH To administer medicine orally.

EWE A female sheep.

FEED BLOCK Supplementary food is sometimes provided for sheep in the form of a compressed block.

FLUSH To increase food prior to mating or lambing.

FOLD To enclose sheep for grazing over a small area at a time.

FLY STRIKE Attack from flies that lay their eggs in the wool. These hatch into maggots which then work their way through the fleece and eat into the flesh.

GIMMER, THEAVE, CHILVER Young female sheep.

HEFT An area or territory on open hillside grazed by a certain group of sheep.

KEEP SHEEP Sheep kept on a temporary basis, eg. those taken off the marshes or hills for the winter.

MULE A crossbred sheep popular in the North.

RADDLE Coloured paint or crayon put on ram's chest to identify the ewes he has mated with.

RAM A male sheep.

SHEAR Remove wool by cutting close to the skin.

SHEARLING Sheep between its first and second shearing.

TEG, HOGG or HOGGETT Sheep in its first year between December and its first shearing.

TUP A male sheep.

TUPPED EWE One that has been mated by ram.

WETHER A castrated male sheep.

27% of the land area, have taken the brunt of these increased numbers and now hold 70% of the national sheep population. As a result of over-stocking it is estimated that 40% of heather on the hills has disappeared. Numbers are likely to be reduced when the headage payment is replaced with an area aid scheme.

Hill sheep live a fairly wild existence. They may be confined for a few weeks when the rams are first put in or when they have their lambs but for 10 or 11 months of the year they roam completely free. Sheep possess a strong herding instinct but those loose on the open hillsides naturally divide into groups and live in certain areas or territories. This instinct is known as 'hefting' and the knowledge is passed from one generation to the next. The loss through Foot and Mouth of so many of these hefted sheep flocks has caused great concern to hill farmers for, although the animals can be replaced, their intimate knowledge of the hills can't. A natural system which has worked so well for hundreds of years could die out.

Hill sheep are often the only way of utilising the very impoverished ground of the British uplands although grouse

Below Blackface ewe with her new-born lamb

Ten-day-old lambs enjoying the spring sunshine

shooting and deer stalking can also provide an income in those places where the conditions are right. It may need as much as 10 acres of rough grazing to sustain a ewe and her lamb while the lush lowland pastures can be stocked at up to 5 sheep per acre.

Grazing habits

Sheep are tidy grazers nibbling the grass very short. They only have front teeth on the bottom jaw and a hard pad on the top. They eat quickly and then regurgitate the cud (grass) when they are resting as cows do, it is then chewed again thoroughly before being swallowed. Many conservationists make use of the sheep's neat grazing habits to create ideal, almost bare ground, conditions for certain species of flora and fauna. Their droppings are evenly distributed and can add fertility to the soil.

Many lambs are weaned off of hill sheep flocks in autumn and sent to the lowlands to fatten or overwinter on grass, unsprayed stubbles or arable crops. East Anglia is a popular area for this as stubble turnips sown directly after harvest and sugar beet waste left on the fields is utilised. Sheep are often 'folded' over turnips restricting access to a small area that is cleared up before they are moved. As many as 100 sheep may be kept like this per acre (·405 hectares). Providing winter keep for sheep enables arable farmers to supplement their income and benefit the soil while providing a service to hill farmers. Sometimes lambs are sent as 'keepers' where payment is made per head or per week

Some breeds of sheep have horns on both sexes, others only on the rams and many of the lowland breeds have none at all

Sheep have front teeth on the bottom jaw and a hard pad on the top

and then they are returned. Otherwise they are sold as 'stores' at September lamb sales and bought by dealers or farmers themselves to fatten. Besides feeding on roots, 'keep' sheep are used to tidy up grass in the cow paddocks after the cows have been brought indoors for the winter.

When they have had 3 or 4 crops of lambs, hill ewes are often sold to lowland sheep farmers where they continue their productive lives in less extreme conditions; here they may last until they are about 8 years old. Usually it is their teeth that fail, becoming broken and making it impossible for them to feed on grass properly.

Breeding

Many of the sheep kept in Britain are what are known as 'half-breds' which are a direct cross of two pure breeds. These have been deliberately chosen to possess the best attributes of the two breeds selected. Ewes come into oestrus in late summer or early autumn although one or two of the lowland breeds such as the Dorset Horn will come in earlier than this. Hill ewes are not usually lambed until April or May when it is hoped the weather should be less unkind. Larger lowland sheep generally begin to lamb in early March. Some farmers wishing to produce lambs for the Easter market will lamb theirs as early as Christmas. Although the grass will not be growing then and the lambs will need additional feed, the cost is offset by the premium prices obtained. The black faced Suffolk is a very popular breed for producing quality fat lambs both from lowland flocks and by crossing with hill sheep breeds.

Lambing

Most lowland farmers start to lamb in March so that the new growth of grass will help the ewe to produce plenty of milk and so that the lambs will have plenty of grass to fatten on through the summer. A single, fast growing, well fed lamb can be ready for slaughter as early as 12 weeks but most lowland farmers prefer to have twins even though they are slower growing. When talking about a lambing percentage of 175%, shepherds mean that they have had 175 lambs from a hundred ewes. Early lambs are sold fat straight off the ewe but the main crop are separated sometime

A well-fed lamb is ready for slaughter in 12 weeks

Shearing a Swaledale ewe in the Yorkshire Dales

A mature ram will mate with up to 50 ewes in lowland flocks

in July or August. They are weighed regularly and are ready for sale when they weigh about 80lbs (36kgs) providing they are fat enough, although it is possible for them to get too fat. Experts can tell by feeling their backs through the wool at the base of the tail whether they have the correct 'finish'. The value of later lambs is considerably less than early ones but they are low cost to produce, having grown on only grass and their mother's milk.

Lowland sheep

Ewe lambs are not generally bred from until their second year when they will be at least 18 months old. Ewes, whose lambs have been weaned, are kept on poorish ground so that their milk dries up, before being turned onto good grazing just before the rams are put in. This is known as 'flushing'. Being on a rising plane of nutrition helps to improve fertility.

One mature ram will mate with up to 50 ewes in lowland flocks but a lesser number out on the hill where it takes time for him to find those that are receptive. AI is rarely used. Ewes are on heat for about 2 days and have a 17-day cycle. The gestation period is about 150 days (5 months) and the rams are put in according to which day lambing is planned to commence. Coloured paint is frequently put on the rams' chest or a crayon held in place by a harness so that the ewes are marked on the rump when he mates with them. The colour is often changed after 3 weeks or so to identify those that have been served later or not held the first time. This practice is known as 'raddling'.

A few weeks prior to lambing, ewes may be given supplementary food to ensure a well-developed lamb and a good milk supply. Some shepherds have their ewes scanned to determine whether they are pregnant to avoid the unnecessary cost of feeding those that aren't.

Many shepherds provide their ewes with some form of shelter for the first few days after giving birth. Some early lambing flocks may be kept for several weeks in large sheds temporarily divided into pens. Simple shelters can be made out of straw bales and hurdles. For those ewes that are lambed out of doors the weather can have a disastrous effect. Cold weather combined with prolonged rain or drifting snow causes the damage, especially to any lambs that are weak. Occasionally

A hefted sheep is one allowed to roam free on the hill and yet it has an instinct to stay within its territory

Below Routine dosing is carried out to control intestinal worms in sheep

shepherds put on the young lambs specially designed polythene jackets which will disintegrate after a short time.

Lambing difficulties
Shepherds are frequently faced with lambing difficulties such as malpresentation and weak lambs so have to be ever vigilant. Any lambs that have lost their mothers or are one of triplets can sometimes be fostered on to another ewe. As a ewe recognises her new born lamb by smell, this can be done by putting the skin of the ewe's dead lamb on to the one that needs fostering, making her think it is her own lamb. If not fostered, they are hand-reared on a bottle and become very tame.

Early days
Temporary numbers are often painted on the sides of lambs to identify them with their mothers and it is now a government requirement that they are ear-tagged to register the place where they were born.

It is very important that new born lambs receive the first milk (colostrum) which is a rich source of energy and contains a laxative that gets the bowels working and also antibodies to disease that are passed on from the ewe. Hill lambs are not docked, those kept at intermediate levels may have half of their tails removed and those on lowland grazing are docked quite short so that their wool does not get soiled by their softer droppings and attract flies. Both castration and tail docking is carried out usually using the elastic band method during the first few days. If it isn't done within a week an anaesthetic has to be administered and the operation done surgically.

Lambs destined for the early markets are often 'creep' fed. Supplementary pelleted food is provided in a trough surrounded with hurdles or fencing that denies access to the ewes but allows the smaller lambs to pass through. This system is also sometimes used to allow lambs access to fresh grazing ahead of the ewes. Hill sheep on high ground are not fenced in. Those at intermediate levels are often kept in by stone walls; these are constructed to have a small gap at intervals in the base to allow small animals and birds to pass through. Strong, large meshed, galvanised wire netting is erected in the lowlands where a permanent fence is

> It takes 10 acres of rough upland grazing to support a hill ewe and her lamb

A hoggett feeding on beet in the winter

required but where temporary fencing is needed electrified, lightweight mesh is used. Another popular method of sheep fencing is the use of 3 separate strands of thin electrified wire. This is quickly put up using an apparatus mounted on a quad bike or barrow pushed by hand. All types of electric fencing are supported with insulated metal or plastic posts. Power is provided by mains electricity reduced through a transformer or a battery that is sometimes charged by a small windmill and solar panels.

Shearing

Lambs are not sheared (clipped) in their first year. Mature sheep are normally sheared in May or June; hill sheep a month later. Different sheep have different grades of wool varying from the really coarse texture of the Herdwick to the finer and more valuable fleece of Cheviots and Shetlands. The value of low grade fleeces does not even cover the cost of shearing. Wool in recent years has been displaced by manmade fibres. The best quality wool is used for clothing and knitwear while the lesser goes into making carpets and mattresses. Poor wool is also being used as a mulch for gardening use. In recent years some farmers have been forced to burn their fleeces because there has been no market for them.

However it is vital that a sheep is sheared each year. Apart from the obvious problem of over-heating there is also a serious risk of 'fly strike'. Blow flies are attracted to the wet, greasy or soiled wool and lay their eggs in it. In a few days these eggs hatch out into maggots which work their way through to the skin and begin eating the flesh. This is difficult to detect and causes the sheep severe discomfort and, if left untreated, results in a horrific lingering death. At other times of the year if the wool has grown long round their rear ends it may be clipped away. This is known as 'crutching' or 'dagging'.

Large sheep farmers often employ contractors to do the shearing. There are gangs of men and women who come over from New Zealand especially to do this and travel around the country. They are expert at shearing and rolling up the fleeces, shearing a sheep in one minute and hundreds of sheep in a day. However the sheep need to be dry when they are sheared or the fleece deteriorates when it is stored, so it is not possible to do the

Farmers are always looking for new markets for low grade wool and a new product for house insulation called Thermafleece is now being produced

Owners of 4 or more sheep are obliged to sell their wool through the British Wool Marketing Board

shearing every day unless the sheep have been penned in doors for a while to dry off if it is raining. Lowland sheep that are kept inside for the winter are sometimes sheared prior to being housed.

Sheep ailments

It is no longer compulsory to dip sheep to protect them from contagious parasites such as scab mites and ticks as well as fly strike but some sheep farmers still do. Dipping is carried out a few weeks after shearing and the sheep have to be submersed for at least a minute. Organo Phosphate dip was cheap and effective but because of its potentially harmful side effects it has now been replaced with other chemical compounds. A pour-on treatment similar to that used as an insecticide for domestic pets is now available for sheep.

In early autumn the lambs are weaned. Those that are to be retained for breeding are usually fitted with a farmer's own identification tag or a tattoo in the ear. Other more visual methods of identification are made by putting a notch in a certain place on the edge of the ear or permanently marking the fleece by putting a spot of coloured paint on the rump, shoulders or elsewhere.

Sheep with horns may have coloured insulation tape put on one horn or a number burned into it.

A low-grade fleece does not cover the cost of shearing, but it must still be done for health reasons

Below Swaledale and Cheviot ewes gathered for checking before being put with the rams

Sheep are notorious for having bad feet. Those kept on stony ground wear their hooves down but those on lowland pastures tend to develop soft overgrown hooves and a condition known as 'foot rot' caused by an organism living in the soil. Long grass can also cause sores on the skin between the cloven hooves, particularly in wet weather. A sheep kneeling down to graze is often an indication of it having sore front feet. Lowland shepherds have to pay regular attention to the feet of their flocks. Any overgrown hoof must be pared away with a sharp knife or specially designed cutting tool and treated. Often a diluted solution of formalin is used for this purpose. Many shepherds regularly pass their flocks through a foot dip both for treatment and prevention.

Intestinal worms are another ever-present problem for sheep farmers. Routine dosing (drenching) is carried out for lambs and regular moving to fresh pasture can help to break the reproductive cycle of these parasites. Ewes are usually dosed prior to mating and again just before they lamb. Liver fluke can affect sheep in certain areas and it can also affect cattle, goats, deer and rabbits. Grouse can become severely debilitated from infestations of strongylosis worms and ticks they pick up from sheep. Several species of birds and animals gain some protection from parasites because of the regular treatment of sheep.

Ewes are vaccinated against several diseases 2 to 4 weeks before lambing and protection is provided for the new born lambs through the ewes' milk for up to 6 weeks. At this age the lambs receive a multi-dose vaccine which protects them from as many as 8 diseases for several more months.

Sheep and grouse share the same parasites on the moor

The shepherd's year

The shepherd's year traditionally begins in autumn, when lambs are separated from their mothers. Young sheep are selected for breeding stock and the rest sold or put on better grazing to fatten. Breeding ewes are checked over, the condition of their teeth and udders being most important and any not fully fit will be sold.

There are a number of sheep farmers who specialise in keeping pedigree sheep, and rams from these can be quite valuable. Suffolks are probably the most popular sire for early fast growing lambs although several continental breeds are also gaining in popularity. In the north of Britain, rams from breeds

Small sheep farmers and hill farmers often help each other out at busy times such as gathering, shearing and dipping

such as the Blackface and Cheviot, whose lambs are hardy enough to survive the rigours of the uplands, are much sought after. In the Western Isles of Scotland as well as Shetland there is still a strong demand for wool from the local breeds to make the traditional Fair Isle and Shetland knitwear and of course the famous Scottish tweeds. All the wool used to make Harris tweed is actually spun on the island of Harris.

Dairy sheep

A few sheep in Britain are kept for milk production. These are usually a breed originating in Holland called the Friesland. The milk is very rich and in an 8 to 10 month lactation period a ewe can produce up to 125 gallons (570 litres). The milk is used to make cream, yoghurt and cheese. One gallon of milk (4.55 litres) is needed to produce 2lbs (900gms) of cheese. The ewes are milked twice a day with specially designed milking machines (they only have two teats whereas a cow has four). The actual cheese-making is a complicated procedure which, by law, has to have very high standards of hygiene.

Besides being kept for meat, wool and milk, sheep are also kept for functional and decorative purposes, especially in parks surrounding stately homes. Their manner of grazing produces a short even sward that gives a most attractive appearance to the grounds. Breeds such as the Jacob with its double set of impressive horns and black and white markings can add an extra dimension to the landscape.

A ewe has only two teats, whereas a cow has four

One gallon of ewe's milk is needed to produce 2lb of cheese

A Blackface ram is a popular choice for hill farmers

PIG FARMING

Pig production is one of the few aspects of British farming that receives no grants or subsidies from either the British government or the European parliament although several other countries within the EU offer cheap loans to their pig farmers.

BSE, Swine Fever and Foot and Mouth Disease epidemics in recent years have imposed much hardship on commercial producers. As a result of overcrowding caused by the movement restrictions imposed on farmers who were not able to send their pigs for slaughter when they should have gone, serious outbreaks of PDNS and PMWS in weaners followed, causing wasting and losses of up to 40%. As usual it was the smaller producers who were hardest hit by all the problems and many went out of business. The national pig herd has been decreasing annually and the total breeding stock now kept amounts to about 483,000 sows producing nearly 9 million pigs for slaughter annually.

Outdoor herds have become a common sight in recent years and although labour and feed costs are higher, there is not the need to invest in expensive buildings. Production methods appear to be more acceptable to the consumer and most outdoor units supply the quality assured schemes operated by supermarkets and have to meet stringent rules imposed as part of this system of marketing.

Young pigs are often kept on a bed of chopped straw

Pig welfare

As more pigs are kept outside and the welfare of those kept indoors has been improved, production costs have risen putting a severe strain on an already beleaguered industry. In addition, veterinary expenses incurred as a direct result of the BSE health scare in cattle, and directives from the European Parliament, have had to be met. Sows can no longer be kept tethered in stalls in the UK although this is still permitted on the Continent. Instead, pigs of all ages kept intensively must now be kept unrestricted in houses having either slatted floors or a strawed area with a dunging passageway. Despite its reputation, a pig has clean toilet habits and will not soil its bedding if it can avoid doing so.

The only time a sow can be confined at present is when she

Rings are put in pigs' noses to prevent them from digging

30

is about to or has just given birth and she is put in a 'farrowing crate' which is similar to a stall. This prevents her from squashing her ten or more tiny babies by lying on them. The crates are set in individual pens to which the piglets have free access. Sometimes a heat lamp is provided to keep them warm. A few losses in piglets are inevitable as with such large litters there will always be odd ones that are small and weak and others that are accidentally trodden or laid on.

Outdoor pig rearing

The outdoor system is more complicated than indoors as batches of pigs are continually moved round. Small groups of sows are kept together in paddocks fenced with 2 or 3 strands of electric wire. These fences are not high because pigs make no attempt to jump over them. As a group of sows near the end of their pregnancies they are moved into paddocks with individual huts. When they have sorted out amongst themselves who will have which hut, they proceed to make a nest out of the straw provided before giving birth to normally 10 to 14 babies. Some sows can be quite aggressive in protecting their young so the stockman has to be very careful each time he goes to check on them.

Soon after birth the tips of the piglets' tails are snipped off as routine practice and if it is the sow's first litter, the piglet's sharp canine teeth will be cut off. This is a skilled job and if it isn't done properly, the sow's teats will become cut and sore and she will be reluctant to let her babies feed. A small barrier is put around the doorway to each hut so that the tiny piglets do not wander away and get lost. By the time they are 3 weeks old they can scramble over this.

The piglets are weaned when they are about 25 days old and are moved into what are known as 'long huts' (outdoor kennels). These comprise a covered area at one end in which the feeding and watering systems are located and an open boarded run on the other. Both are littered with chopped straw. About 35 similar-sized piglets are put in each hut. At first they have plenty of room but as they grow they fill up the space. They are confined until they are approximately 11 weeks old and weigh about 88lbs (40kgs). The supermarket stipulation for pork to be sold as 'outdoor-reared' is that it spends a minimum of 40% of its life

PIG FARMING
Useful Words

AI Artificial insemination
BOAR Mature male pig
FARROW to give birth
FMD Foot and Mouth Disease, affecting cloven-hoofed animals
GILT Young female pig
HYBRID Mix of breeds
PMWS & PDNS Wasting diseases in weaners
SERVE to mate with
SOW Mature female pig
WEANER Young weaned pig

Piglets are weaned off the sow when they are about 25 days old

Outdoor boars are seldom dangerous but those kept indoors can sometimes be quite vicious

outside but this doesn't mean that it can't be kept in small pens. When weaners have reached the required weight, they leave the outdoor unit and are transferred to indoor yards to be grown on for a further 10 to 12 weeks until they reach a slaughter weight of approximately 200lbs (95 to 100kgs).

Because the part of a pig which is in most demand by the consumer, whether as pork or bacon, is the loin with as little fat on it as possible careful selective breeding has engineered a hybrid that is long and lean. The young pigs will not inter-breed true to type, so replacement sows have to be bought in along with pure bred Large White boars to provide the foundations for the production system. Combined with scientifically produced food rations, pig production has very much been refined to suit the customer.

Inquisitive young outdoor pigs kept behind a barrier so that they don't get lost

Breeding again from the sows

When the piglets are taken away from their mothers, the group of sows are moved to another pen and after a day or two their milk dries up. After 5 days they will come into oestrus (season) and be served by one of the boars running with them. The sows are left in with the boars for about 10 weeks to make sure they get pregnant. 17 weeks after mating they are due to give birth and will once again be moved to the farrowing paddocks. Commercial sows are expected to produce an average of 10 weaned piglets per litter and 2.2 litters each year; on average they will have 6 litters before becoming uneconomic and due for slaughter. Most ex-breeding sows in Britain end up being exported to Germany.

Seventeen weeks after mating, a sow will give birth

Boars are kept at a ratio of one to every sixteen sows. A small group, maybe four boars, will be reared together and remain together for the rest of their lives. This way they will have established a hierarchy and will rarely fight over the sows they are run with. Outdoor boars are seldom dangerous but those kept indoors can be quite vicious. Young sows are known as 'gilts' and are first mated when they are about 8 months old. If they do not conceive, they will come into oestrus again after 3 weeks. Outdoor pigs are mated naturally but AI is quite often used in intensive units.

As in every aspect of animal husbandry, medication is not given unnecessarily because it is expensive but there are certain preventative treatments that are beneficial. Drugs are avoided where possible, but if used, there is a statutory requirement that detailed records are kept and withdrawal periods prior to slaughter adhered to.

Weighing the young pigs

Farmers with contracts to supply supermarkets are ensured a market for their products provided they meet strict guidelines laid down by the buyers and are open to frequent inspections regarding the health and management of their stock. Producers can also qualify for the premium offered by being part of an Assured Scheme, in which the onus is on the producer to guarantee a quality supply as and when it is required. Stocking rates per acre are set and all the pigs are provided with weatherproof shelters and large flat water troughs in which they can bathe. Water which overflows from this creates a muddy area relished by pigs as a wallow. It is their instinct, especially in hot weather, to coat themselves with mud which acts as a sun screen, for pigs are susceptible to sun burn.

The part of a pig which is in most demand by the consumer is the loin which has little fat on it

Although outdoor pigs have plenty to occupy them, unlike those kept inside, through wallowing and searching for the large pellets of food that are scattered in their paddocks each day, they still like to chew on objects. Most outdoor pigs are kept in drier areas of the country where the soil often contains a liberal amount of stones or flints. The pigs will spend many hours chewing on them, rather like a human chewing gum. The reason for this behaviour isn't clear but it is very unlikely to be as a result of boredom.

Why pigs have rings in their noses

Another perfectly natural instinct in pigs is to dig up the earth with their noses. The resultant mess they make is intolerable as it ruins the field. Holes fill up with water and can become stagnant and a breeding place for harmful bacteria. Piles of earth may also be heaped against the electric fence and short it out. If allowed, sows prepare a nest prior to giving birth, digging a deep hole in the ground into which the tiny piglets roll and are squashed by the weight of their mother when she lies down. For these reasons rings are put in pigs' noses: to prevent them from digging. Sows are fitted with two or three small ones in the tops of their snouts while boars (like bulls) have one larger one put through the membrane dividing the nostrils. Although this is not so effective as the smaller rings, it prevents injury during the pre-mating ritual that involves the boar prodding the sow's body with his snout.

Pigs very much enjoy digging with their noses

Tail docking is necessary when pigs are housed intensively, as nearly all commercial pigs are at sometime in their lives. It involves snipping the tip of the tail off when they are very young. The tail ends in a tassel, something the other pigs find fun to play with and this can lead to serious injury, pain and sometimes even to cannibalism. Pigs are truly omnivorous, hence the canine teeth, and given the chance will eat almost anything including meat, even that of their own kind. Many country folk in the past always kept a pig; it was the original form of recycling, producing much-needed meat for very little cost while disposing of household and garden waste. Commoners in some places held rights to turn them into the forest in autumn to feed on fallen acorns. It is said that the only part of a pig that is of no use is its squeak.

Indoor or outdoor rearing

Conditions for intensively kept pigs have improved because of recent legislation and there are times when their management can be easier and more humane than in outdoor units. As many as 5,000 pigs can be looked after by one skilled person in large sheds that are fully automated. While outdoor rearing may seem ideal, conditions can often be difficult. In especially wet areas of the country, the paddocks may become a slurry in winter. Prolonged bitterly cold spells can freeze up the entire water system meaning that watering has to be done by hand. Strong

Sows can no longer be kept tethered in stalls in the UK although this is still permitted on the Continent

winds can damage huts and when it's very dry, the dust can be most unpleasant. Pest species are also a greater problem outdoors and are more difficult to deal with. Straw filled shelters provide a comfortable home for rats who share the bonanza of free food with flocks of jackdaws, rooks and feral pigeons. In places where fox numbers are not controlled, these too soon discover an easy living can be had from raiding farrowing huts and stealing young piglets. All these pests can add significantly to the overall costs. On the credit side, there is no great capital expenditure for housing or manure disposal. Light, free-draining land benefits greatly from the straw and manure used and produced by outdoor units and pigs often form part of crop rotation plans, being left on the same ground for only one or two years. The move from one field to another is a mammoth task and an expensive part of outdoor pig management.

An industry that relies on buying in hybrid breeding stock that needs replacing every three or four years obviously requires a regular supply of healthy animals and there are units that specialise in producing these. There are also breed enthusiasts with pedigree pigs who take pride in maintaining and showing native breeds. It is vital for the future of the industry that a nucleus of pure breeds is preserved, for the genes of the old fashioned pigs may still have an important part to play in the future.

Pig production receives no grants or subsidies from the British government or the European parliament

It is their instinct, especially in hot weather, to coat themselves with mud which acts as a sun screen, for pigs are susceptible to sun burn. Here, a water trough serves as the perfect bathing pool

POULTRY FARMING

An estimated 105 million chickens are produced annually in Britain for the table, 29 million kept for egg production and over 7 million as breeding stock to produce the table and laying birds. Ducks, turkeys and geese amount to approximately 11 million. The vast majority of chickens kept today are hybrids, bred for specific purposes. Fortunately, poultry fanciers are dedicated to preserving the native breeds once common across Britain before intensification took over.

Animal welfare regulations set certain minimum standards under which livestock must be kept to provide a humane environment. Stocking densities, management controls and many other factors are strictly regulated and inspected. Freedom Foods (RSPCA approved) and organic farming organisations lay down their own sets of rules and every poultry keeper has to be familiar with the regulations in place for his own operation.

Safety in British eggs

British produced eggs are stamped with a lion logo and a sell-by date 21 days after they were laid. 40% of eggs, including almost all the white shelled ones, sold in Britain are imported, but to be certain that eggs have been produced to the highest standard always buy British. Most foreign countries do not have, or comply with, the strict rules for hygiene and animal welfare that exist in this country.

Laying hens with trimmed beaks to stop 'feather pecking'

105 million chickens are produced annually in Britain for the table

Farmyard hens are a rare sight these days

Poultry meat, especially in the form of portions, is also imported and, like eggs, home grown products excel over foreign imports in production, hygiene and welfare standards.

There are two groups of hybrid laying hens: lightweight ones which are usually white and lay white eggs; and heavier ones which are predominately brown and lay brown eggs. There is no difference in the nutritional quality of either brown or white shelled eggs but when the hens have reached the end of their productive

Laying cages like these used to be called battery cages

POULTRY *Useful Words*

BARN/PERCHERY Large enclosed intensive shed system for laying hens equipped with perches, nest boxes and dust bathing area.

BEAK TRIMMING The removal of the tip of the top beak at about 3 to 10 days of age to prevent feather pecking and cannibalism. Only a very small part is removed and this causes little distress to the chick. In poultry this only has to be done once as the beak does not grow again. The procedure was once called 'de-beaking' which gave a false impression of what was actually being done.

BROILER Fast-growing, intensively reared chicken which is ready for table at 6-8 weeks old.

CANDLE A bright light shone through an egg, making it possible to detect cracks in the shell, blood spots or development of the chick within.

DEEP LITTER Large enclosed intensive shed system where poultry are kept on a floor of chopped straw or wood-shavings. Used for rearing poultry for the table, breeding stock, also occasionally for laying hens.

EGG INCUBATION The time it takes for a chick to hatch. Quail 17 days. Chicken 21 days. Partridge 23 days. Pheasant 24 days. Duck 28 days. Turkey 28 days. Goose 30 days. Muscovy 35 days.

FREE RANGE System of keeping laying hens (and very occasionally broilers) which allows them limited access to grass paddocks.

LAYING CAGE Wire mesh cage in which a small number of hens are kept for laying. Sometimes called battery cages as designed in long tiered rows. Floors are slightly sloped enabling the eggs to roll out of the front; food and water is supplied automatically.

ENRICHED laying cages allow more space per bird and provide perches, nest boxes and dust bathing facilities.

NIPPLE DRINKER Small water dispenser activated by a bird pecking at the valve on the end.

P.O.L. Point of lay. The stage at which hen birds will be approaching the age to lay their first egg, about 16 weeks for a chicken.

POULT Term used to describe the period between a chick's losing its fluff and becoming mature, applied to young game birds and also to day-old turkeys.

PULLET An immature female chicken.

TUBE FEEDER A circular hanging feeder holding 15kgs or more with a trough round the bottom of it.

40% of eggs, including almost all the white-shelled ones, sold in Britain are imported

lives the carcase value of the heavier birds is marginally higher. Cockerels are only kept for breeding purposes; they are never put with hens producing eggs for human consumption.

The majority of laying hens in Britain are kept in laying cages which is the most economic system but EU legislation has prohibited the installation of new 'barren' laying cages and is prohibiting them entirely after January 1st 2012. 'Enriched' cages will be permitted but will have to meet strict welfare standards. At present there are management difficulties with this system. The number of laying hens kept free range is increasing as consumers are becoming more aware of welfare issues and are prepared to pay premium prices. Laying hens are also kept intensively in barn, perchery and sometimes deep litter systems. Certainly it is often easier to care for poultry kept indoors rather than free range because, with good management, it is possible to provide perfect conditions regarding temperature and the availability of food and water. Any medication that may be needed is normally given in the water supply and this is much easier to administer if the birds do not have access to an alternative water supply as free range birds do when it is raining.

Nutrition is extremely important for both layers and table birds, to ensure good growth and production as well as general health. A bird's nutritional needs alter at different stages in its life, so vitamins and minerals as well as protein in the correct balance are necessary to maintain body condition and food conversion throughout its life.

TABLE OR BROILER CHICKENS

Very few table chicken are reared on a free range organic system. Feed, management, and labour costs incurred are excessively high and customers are not usually prepared to pay for these (*see free range layers*).

Almost all chicken destined for the table are reared intensively in large sheds. Broiler chicks arrive on site in plastic chick boxes when they are one day old directly from specialist hatcheries where they will have been counted out and quickly checked over. Broiler chicks are bred to be white feathered and it is only

> *Cockerels are only kept for breeding purposes, they are never put with hens producing eggs for human consumption*

Broiler chicks arrive on the farm when they are one day old

very rarely that a coloured one appears, a throwback to some distant ancestor from which the modern fast-growing, well fleshed strains have been developed. Sometimes the chicks will have been sexed but generally they arrive 'as hatched.'

A temperature of at least 88F (31C) is needed for the first few days; this is controlled by a thermostat and gradually reduced as the chicks grow older. Natural light is excluded from within the shed and artificial light provided on a time switch for up to 22 hours a day. Ventilation is either automatic or controlled manually by the stockman. Depending on the size of the sheds, up to 30,000 chicks may be put in each one. To ensure the chicks find food and water quickly, vital for their well-being, corrugated paper may be laid on top of the litter for the first 4 days. Crumbs of food are sprinkled on this and extra water provided in flat dishes. After 4 days the chicks will have gained strength and found their food in the automatically-supplied trough which encircles the shed. They will also have discovered water in nipple drinkers that they have to peck at to get a drink. From these there is no spillage to wet the litter.

Invariably a few chicks will die between the fifth and seventh day. These are known as 'starve-outs'. They are weak chicks that, for one reason or another, have either not fed or drunk. Until this age they have been able to survive on remains of the egg yolk still left inside them that nurtured their development before hatching.

Broiler chicks are not normally beak trimmed to stop them feather pecking for it is not a problem. As a safeguard, the chicks receive some standard medication in their food at a low level to prevent outbreaks of coccidiosis disease and may be vaccinated against others. Antibiotics are used only if there is a serious outbreak of disease requiring treatment but never on a routine basis. Artificial growth promoters are now banned and have marginally increased costs to the poultry industry, because the bird has to eat more to achieve the same weight. There are very strict standards in force in Britain regarding medication and statutory withdrawal periods prior to killing to ensure there is no possibility of residues remaining in the meat.

A broiler will reach 4lbs (1.8kgs) body weight (the minimum acceptable size) in about 38 to 40 days. Young chicks

The bantam hen is not cost-effective if farmed for laying or consumption but fortunately poultry fanciers are dedicated to the preservation of rare breeds, like this Hamburgh

A broiler will reach 4lbs body weight in about 38 to 40 days

when they are first put in the sheds have plenty of space and it is only in the last few days that they appear to be seriously over-crowded although there is legislation regarding the amount of space provided. When contracts demand larger birds, a batch is reduced by selection. About one third of the largest will be taken out, allowing more space for the ones that are left to grow bigger. This may be repeated 2 or 3 times until the chicken that remain are about 52 days old and weigh 6.25lbs (2.8kgs) the maximum size required to sell.

Some broiler units are expected to fulfil contracts directly to supermarkets. They have to supply what is required when it is demanded, rather than offering what they have available, which puts a lot of pressure on the producer.

Chicken-catchers

Although there are now machines which catch chicken by a gentle sweeping action, most of them are still caught by hand. A gang of 4 or 5 people usually begin work very early in the morning at about 4am. Modern handling facilities mean that the modules (crates) the birds are put in for transportation can be taken inside the shed. With lights dimmed the chicken can be handled with minimum disturbance and stress and the modules loaded immediately onto a waiting lorry with a small fork lift.

Once the shed is emptied it is cleaned out, disinfected and fumigated. When it has dried out it is then prepared for the next arrivals. This usually takes approximately 7 to 9 days, allowing the stockman to have a few days off. Some of the bigger companies employ relief staff so that their poultry men can take a day off a week. The routine for smaller concerns is that the stockman works every day caring for a batch of chicks until they are gone, maybe 7 to 8 weeks, and then has a few days off. Very young chicks need a lot of attention and even when they get bigger the person caring for them has to be on call 24 hours a day, in case there is a breakdown of equipment or some other emergency. One person may be expected to manage up to 150,000 broilers at any one time and it is a big responsibility.

Chicken deaths

Apart from the previously mentioned losses at 5 to 7 days, deaths

One stockman can manage up to 150,000 broilers

Below Intensively-farmed laying hens in a barn or perchery

that occur are rarely caused by disease or poor stockmanship. They are most frequently due to the incredible growth rate achieved from selective breeding and specialised food rations. These have been developed over the years to satisfy the consumer who wants the plumpest chickens for the least amount of money. If these aren't supplied by competitive broiler units in Britain then they will be imported from abroad where welfare and hygiene standards are seldom as high as those in this country.

At every stage of a broiler's short life, legislation is in place to ensure optimum bird welfare, and to protect the consumer from exposure to any medication that the bird has received, or transmittable diseases such as salmonella.

EGG PRODUCTION

Laying cages

Laying hens are usually reared in sheds similar to broilers from a day old until 16 weeks. Sometimes these sheds are partly slatted and occasionally the birds may have been raised in wire cages. They will probably have had the tip of their top beak trimmed when they were a few days old, to prevent them pecking their companions for the rest of their lives.

The pullets are put into the tiered cages at about 16 weeks of age, a month before they begin to lay. No cockerels are kept with them because it isn't necessary. The large sheds in which the laying cages are situated are windowless but very well ventilated. Lighting is limited to about 9 hours a day for the first month, after which it is increased. This stimulates the hens to lay, but if they are given too much light too soon, they will quickly come in to lay but will produce small-sized eggs and would probably do so for the rest of their lives. By waiting until the hens are about 20 weeks old and gradually increasing the light to 16 hours a day, they can be expected to produce plenty of good quality eggs. Each hen will be kept until it is about 15 months old during which time it will have produced about 300 eggs.

The laying cages are 4 tiers high and in rows extending the length of the shed; fewer than 10 hens are normally kept in each cage. The statutory minimum allowance of space per bird has

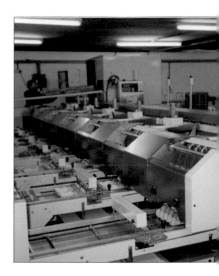

Egg packing unit in which machines can carry out the work traditionally done by many people

Nearly all commercial laying hens are brown and lay brown eggs – the shell colour British housewives prefer. Chicken for eating are white

been increased since 31st December 2002. A weld mesh floor allows the birds' droppings to fall through onto a conveyor belt which, when activated, deposits the droppings into either a collection pit or a manure spreader outside from where it can be spread straight onto the land. Because the hens have no direct contact with any excreta, they are cleaner and are at less risk of contracting diseases, many of which are passed from bird to bird through contact with contaminated droppings. Owners of flocks of over 100 hens must have them tested for salmonella.

The weld mesh floors of the cages are slightly sloped so that eggs roll out of the front when they are laid, preventing them from getting damaged or dirty. In smaller units they may be collected by hand but in large units the eggs will roll directly onto a conveyor belt which carries them from the shed to the egg packing department. Here each egg is passed over a bright light to check there are no blood spots inside or that the shell isn't cracked, before continuing on to a grader where they are sorted, by weight. Any dirty eggs are removed and the rest are packed ready for dispatch. These first quality ones go directly to supermarkets or wholesalers. Dirty eggs need to be washed in a sanitising fluid or dry cleaned and cannot be sold for consumption in the shell. Instead they will be sent to processors and end up being used for such things as dried cake mixes.

Owners of flocks of over 100 hens must have them tested for salmonella

The lion logo and stamp date on every British egg

Feeding the layers

Food is provided *ad lib* automatically and often a coarse meal is fed so that it keeps the hens occupied longer than if a pelleted food was used. Egg yolk colour is determined by the food, and maize or grass meal is often included in the rations to ensure a rich colour. Water is provided through nipple drinkers. The disease risk factor in chicken kept in laying cages is low. Vaccination for some diseases is carried out when the birds are very young and gives a lifetime immunity.

Because of the small number in each cage, the hens suffer much less stress from aggravation caused by the 'pecking order' regime under which poultry kept in large numbers have to survive. Providing there is adequate ventilation, respiratory ailments are not common. Problems are normally due to the weather – either damp fogs or exceptionally hot, oppressive days when the air temperature outside is no cooler than that inside. Even so, the chicken is a remarkably resilient bird and can cope with most things. Very cold weather is not a concern because the body heat given off from the birds themselves ensures that the shed is always warm inside.

Although it may appear that everything in a laying cage shed is automated, it still requires labour to run it. A unit of 70,000 layers may well be producing 50,000 eggs a day and employ several people full time as well as some part-time to pack the eggs. This is often a welcome opportunity for rural mothers with school-age children to earn some money. Each cage has to be carefully inspected every day. If a chicken has died or looks sick, it is removed immediately for, like any intensive operation, great care has to be taken because trouble can spread very quickly. Profit margins are so tight that it is vital there are no hitches.

It may not seem a very happy life for hens kept in cages but they show little signs of stress and such good results wouldn't be obtained if they were not content for it does not take much of an upset to put them off lay. There is no competition for food and water and even the meekest bird does not have many above her in the pecking order. However it is the birds' welfare which is the contentious issue because within the confines of a laying cage they are unable to perform such natural behaviour as stretching their wings, scratching for food and dust bathing. How important it is to a chicken to be able do these things isn't really known.

Free range layers

Free range laying hens arrive on farms from rearing sheds when they are about 16 weeks old, just before they begin to lay. They are always predominately brown in colour and lay brown eggs. They will also have had the tip of their top beak trimmed when they were very young, for free-range chicken are as likely to feather peck and even become cannibalistic as hens kept under other systems. Vaccination will have been given against several diseases including salmonella. This is particularly important for free range hens because, unlike chicken in laying cages, they are exposed to possible infections through contact with excreta. Free range birds may be kept in various sized flocks. Some may be very small, while large enterprises may house thousands of birds

The regulatory indoor space for ordinary 'free range' hens is a minimum of 11.5 hens per square metre. 'Organic' hens are allowed twice as much space

Below Free range hens will lay about 300 eggs each during their lives

in big sheds similar to those used for intensively kept layers. Whatever size, their accommodation food, either in tube feeders which are filled daily or automated chain-supplied troughs, is supplied inside as is water from nipple drinkers. Most of the floor space is slatted with a droppings collection pit beneath. The shed is also equipped with perches, a dust bathing area and a plentiful number of nest boxes.

At first the pullets are kept shut inside for a few days to acclimatise them to their new surroundings. Because they have been reared intensively in sheds, they are not used to green grass, wild birds and vehicles etc and are very tentative about venturing outside at first. They are given access outdoors only during the hours of daylight. Often a covered verandah area over the access pop holes and a mixture of sand and gravel is used in front of them allowing the birds to have some shelter without going inside and also helping to keep the interior cleaner and drier.

> *It is about twice as costly to produce 'free range' eggs compared with those from caged hens*

Space restrictions

Inside the sheds, the hens are quite tightly packed. Even when they are given the option to get away from their companions by going outside, they still don't seem to mind being crowded together. Free range may seem to be an idyllic existence but weather conditions often mean that it is not. Hens don't like rain or snow. Free range hens need to consume more food just to keep warm in winter, so the largest sheds provide most comfort to the birds because of accumulated body heat.

At present the inside space for ordinary free range hens is a minimum allowance of 11.5 hens per square metre while organic hens are allowed twice as much space. Wet weather obviously creates problems for cleanliness. Areas close to the sheds can become very muddy especially in winter when the grass does not grow.

Nest boxes are often lined with 'astroturf' and designed so that the eggs roll away. These are collected regularly between 8am and 4pm by hand or by conveyors in the largest

Below A modern broiler unit

sheds. Some systems are designed so that the nest boxes are automatically closed at night by slowly tilting at a set time, and opened again early in the morning. This prevents the hens from sleeping in them and also empties out any dry dirt. Dirty eggs have to be discarded.

As with intensively-kept hens, artificial lighting is used when needed to provide a minimum number of hours. This starts at about 10 hours a day when the birds are coming into lay, increasing to 15 hours. Obviously in mid-summer, natural daylight extends this period. The hens should reach full lay at 20 to 22 weeks of age and peak at about 24 weeks although the best quality eggs will be laid when the hens are about 32 weeks.

Free range hens are kept until they are approximately 72 weeks old, during which period they will have laid about 300 eggs each. Organic eggs are collected daily from the producers for distribution to various outlets.

Although called free range, the hens are actually confined to grass paddocks outdoors with 6ft (2 metre) high wire netting to keep them in and electric fences to keep foxes, and stray dogs out. To meet set standards, the density outdoors must not exceed 2,500 hens per hectare. Organic and Freedom Food/RSPCA initiatives reduce the stocking density to 1,000 hens per hectare. Ground has to be rested for at least 2 months between batches. The grass/clover mix in the paddocks is normally kept short by mowing or grazing with sheep which can also be managed organically within this system.

Labour intensive

Keeping free range chicken is very labour intensive compared with those in laying cages. One full-time person is needed to care for every 5,000 or so hens. A large enterprise of 25,000 hens is likely to employ 4 full-time people plus 2 or 3 part-timers as well as someone to look after the inevitable paperwork. Not only are there feeding and water systems to maintain but there is also cleaning and disinfecting. To ensure a continuous supply of eggs, keeping batches of hens of different ages is part of the management system so there will be fresh pullets arriving regularly, old birds being despatched, sheds and equipment to be cleaned.

Frequent egg collection, especially in small non-automated

Below Broiler chickens near to slaughter age

One full-time person is needed to care for every 5,000 or so free range laying hens

sheds, is time-consuming. Another job, which is very important, is to shut the chicken inside sheds at night after dark (which is very late in summer) and to let them out again early in the morning. If this is not done, the hens are very likely to fall victim to foxes, one of which may account for a hundred or more hens in one night. A determined fox is quite capable of negotiating the protective 6 foot high wire netting and electrified fencing.

Disease and free-range hens

Disease too is a greater problem for free range poultry than for caged layers. It is far more difficult to prevent and treat because many pests and diseases can live in the soil which is impossible to disinfect thoroughly. Medication for poultry is often administered in the drinking water. If it is raining, free range chicken can find an alternative water source outside, thus reducing their intake of medicine. Swabs are taken regularly from the birds and nest boxes to check for evidence of salmonella. Free range poultry eat more and lay less. The weather and predators such as rats can be a real nuisance, causing problems which do not affect birds kept in sheds. It is about twice as costly to produce free range eggs compared with those from caged hens and up to four times more expensive if the birds are subject to organic standards.

A laying hen will be kept until it is about 15 months old during which time it will have produced about 300 eggs

POULTRY HATCHING AND REARING

To have a national supply of poultry and eggs to eat, farmers must keep a 'breeding stock' available. All birds are hatched from eggs and this in itself is a complicated procedure. Obviously parent stock are needed, but not in equal numbers because one male bird will mate with several females. These stock birds must be kept in conditions where this act can comfortably take place, namely a solid floored area, usually inside large sheds with automated feeders, drinkers, ventilation and lighting systems.

Fertilised egg production

Plenty of nest boxes must be available so that the eggs are laid in a clean and safe environment. These are collected regularly and then checked. Dirty ones are either dry cleaned or washed in a sanitising fluid. The eggs are often fumigated as well before

Modern hybrid hens have lost the instinct to go broody and sit on eggs

being stored in a cool place prior to being despatched to the hatcheries. Here they are checked again and put into trays, pointed ends down. The trays are then slid into trolleys and fumigated before being stored at a temperature of about 55F (13C) for up to a week.

The embryo inside the egg will not begin to develop at this temperature. It is only after the trolleys of eggs are wheeled into 'setters' (machines which provide a controlled environment) that development starts to take place. Temperature inside the setter is kept at fractionally below 100F (37.6C), air inside is circulated, the trays are regularly tilted from one side to another, and a certain level of humidity inside the machine is maintained. All these functions are controlled automatically. From time to time a sample of eggs will be 'candled' so that development of the chicks inside can be monitored. This will also show up any eggs which are 'clear' (with no chick inside).

A few days before the chicks are due to hatch, the eggs will be taken out of the setters and transferred to a 'hatcher'. They will probably be 'candled' again and clear ones removed. The eggs will be placed on their sides in chick proof trays. The temperature inside the hatcher is marginally lower and the humidity slightly higher than in the setter. The trays of eggs are not tilted once they are inside a hatcher.

The hatching

The last few days inside the egg are critical for a chick for it has to manoeuvre into a certain position so that it can peck its way out of the shell. This is an amazing feat because the chick has to have its head under one of its tiny wings and use a small 'tooth' on the top of its beak to chip right the way round the shell, about two-thirds of the way up from the pointed end. It then has to have the strength to force the lid open and scramble out of its prison, a process which takes many hours. At all stages of the embryo's development during incubation, humidity plays an important role, for there needs to be an air sac in the top of the egg for the chick to survive. If there has not been enough moisture, the chick will be small and under-developed; if too much it will have grown too big and probably be deformed.

When the chick has eventually struggled free, it will be very

Free range eggs from small producers can often be bought by the roadside

To 'candle' an egg is to check its developing contents using a bright light

wet and weak but a few hours more inside the warmth of the hatcher and it will soon change into the familiar fluffy chick or duckling. Because of this drying off period, freshly hatched chicks are known as 'day olds'.

The importance of cleanliness

Cleanliness of the eggs and equipment is vital throughout because the moist warm environment which is needed to hatch eggs also provides ideal conditions for bacteria to multiply. Many of these can easily penetrate the shell and infect the chick inside or get into its body through contact with its wet navel immediately after hatching.

Chicks can be sexed at a day old by two or three methods. As a result of selective breeding, the male chicks can be a different colour to females which makes sexing easy. Experts can tell the difference by carefully inspecting the rear end of each chick and sometimes it is possible to tell the difference by the length of the tiny wing feathers. For table poultry, both sexes are needed, but only females are retained for egg laying. Breeding flocks require both sexes but only at a ratio of 1 male for between 4 and 8 females.

Day olds are transported in cardboard or plastic chick boxes, often for long distances. These are specially designed to retain the chick's own body heat while providing adequate draught-free ventilation. They are lined with either wood wool or shredded newspaper and divided into compartments holding between 25 and 50 chicks. Because day-old chicks still have some unabsorbed egg yolk inside them, the part of the egg which provided their nutrition before they hatched, they are able to survive many hours, even days, without food or water, although obviously the sooner these are provided the better.

First weeks

The majority of chicken, ducks and turkeys spend the first few weeks of their lives in large environmentally-controlled deep litter sheds as their parents did. They are kept warm by specially designed radiant gas heaters called 'brooders' which they can lie beneath when they get cold. Alternatively, some rearing houses are space heated to the necessary temperature. Vaccination of

A buff cochin cockerel – a popular 'rare' breed

Unwanted chicks are usually gassed or killed by some other method and used as food for predator species kept as pets, in wildlife centres or zoos

laying and breeding birds is carried out when the chicks are a few days old and is often administered in the drinking water, giving them protection against certain diseases for life.

Bedding on the floor is usually either wood shavings, chopped straw or a mixture of the two and it is important for the young birds' health and welfare that it is kept dry. Poor air flow or badly adjusted drinkers can result in high humidity within the shed which can lead to a build-up of ammonia from damp litter. Under the right conditions, a chemical reaction takes place between the birds droppings and the litter which works it into a fine dry composition. When the sheds are cleaned out between batches, this is either used as a fertiliser on the land or as fuel in the new generation of environmentally-friendly power stations where it is burned to produce steam, which in turn is used to power turbines to generate electricity. The ash residue is then used as fertiliser. Many poultry farms (or units) adopt an 'all in, all out' policy in their sheds. These are thoroughly cleaned, disinfected and fumigated between batches.

Poultry feed is manufactured in three basic forms: a meal, crumbs (which are usually fed to young chicks) and small pellets which may be of varied sizes. As the young birds grow, the composition of their food rations is altered to take into account their changing nutritional needs.

Food conversion rates (the equation relating to weight gain or eggs produced from the amount of food consumed) is continually being improved through selective breeding. Light plays a very important part in the bird's growth and maturity rates, and windowless houses with artificial lighting mean that adjustments can be made accordingly.

It is only after the first few weeks that rearing methods radically change, depending for which purpose the birds are destined. Genetic selection has made huge changes to the poultry industry since intensification (or factory farming as it used to be called) evolved in the 1960s.

Because the reproduction cycle of poultry is comparatively short, i.e. 3 to 4 weeks for an egg to hatch and about 6 months to maturity, improvement in developing a strain to lay more eggs or grow faster is rapid. Intensive research into nutrition as well as breeding and disease has produced hybrids that meet with the

Excess dampness is lethal in a poultry shed: it produces ammonia

Below The yolk of an egg provides nutrition for the developing embryo and continues to do so for the first few days of the chick's life

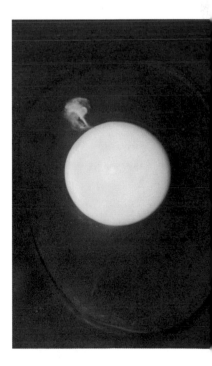

consistently high standards required. However, as with all livestock, the ultimate results are down to the quality of the person who is responsible for looking after them. Observation, attention to detail, conscientiousness and experience not only add to the profit but also to the birds' well being.

GEESE

Goose is not in great demand in the UK but it is gradually becoming more popular, especially at Christmas. Consequently little research and genetic improvement has been done. Commercial table geese are usually white in colour and will reach a minimum killing weight at about 12 weeks of age. They are usually kept outside in grass paddocks and besides their normal food rations, will also graze on the grass.

While young birds fatten relatively quickly, it is the egg production of the parent stock that is the problem and makes them uneconomic. One male (gander) is needed for 4 or 5 hens. They need to be put together at least 2 months before mating in the spring, but once bonded they can be kept as a 'set' for several years within a larger group.

The females are seasonal layers, i.e. during the spring and summer, and will lay between 30 and 80 eggs during this period. Geese are not so messy to keep as ducks and are relatively disease free. The most stringent organic body, the Soil Association, stipulate a maximum outdoor stocking rate of 600 geese per hectare.

QUAIL

Diminutive quail and their eggs were once a popular delicacy for the rich, and some are still kept commercially today. They are reared in a similar controlled environment as broiler chicken and are ready for table at about 40 days old, when they weigh approximately 8ozs (250 grams). They are very susceptible to respiratory diseases and require a high standard of management.

Quail mature quickly and will come into lay when only 6 to 8 weeks old. A ratio of 1 male to 3 females is kept for breeding, and hens will lay about 200 eggs during the course of a year.

Those retained to produce eggs for human consumption do not have males kept with them.

Wild greylag goose, ancestor of the domestic goose

Quail are ready for the table at about 40 days old

Below The Norfolk Black turkey, an old traditional breed

TURKEYS

Research and selective breeding have developed a reasonably priced table bird which has become popular at other times of the year besides Christmas. Commercial turkeys are reared in a similar way to broiler chicken but sold in a wider weight range. Females are more compact and do not reach the proportions of the much larger males. Mini turkeys reach approximately 8lbs (3.5kgs) at about 12 weeks of age, but the most popular choice are hen birds weighing between 10 and 15lbs (4.5 to 7kgs) when they are 20 or so weeks old. Stags, as the males are called, can be grown on for several more weeks and may reach weights of 45 to 50lbs (20 to 23kgs). These giants are cut up and used for processing by big companies such as Bernard Matthews.

Of the 15 million or so turkeys produced annually for the table, over half are used for processing and the majority of the rest are frozen. Only a small proportion are sold fresh. Those supplied for the Christmas trade are usually killed between December 5th and 10th and left to hang in chilled conditions; this maturing greatly improves the flavour and is no way detrimental to the quality of the bird.

What makes turkeys costlier to produce than chicken is not their inability to grow as quick but the poor prolificacy of the breeding stock. Because of the disproportionate body size, modern turkeys bred for the table are unable to mate naturally so fresh semen has to be collected from the stags and used to artificially inseminate the hens. This is carried out once a week during the laying season and is obviously a very labour-intensive and time-consuming chore.

All mass-produced turkeys are white in colour. Breeding stock are usually housed in 'pole' barns which have open sides covered with small mesh wire netting to exclude pests such as rats and starlings and littered with straw. Stags and hens are kept separately and the laying season extends from April to August.

Laying turkeys

Artificial lighting ensures a minimum of 13 hours daylight during this period and commences when the stock birds are about 21 weeks old, bringing them into lay at 32 weeks, sooner than they would naturally have done. Nest boxes are provided at ground

Male turkeys are called 'stags'

Modern turkeys bred for the table are unable to mate naturally

Below All turkeys are descended from the wild turkey of North America

level at a ratio of one for every 4.5 hens. Eggs are collected at least six times a day to make sure that they are as clean as possible and to avoid damage to them. Most producers achieve about 70 eggs from each hen turkey during the 18 week laying period but the bigger companies who require birds for year-round processing extend this to 22 weeks and obtain about 120 eggs from their stock.

It is as cheap to replace breeding stock each year as it is to over-winter them. Sometimes hens are kept for a second year but they do not lay so many eggs.

Day old chicks, which have often been sexed, arriving from specialist hatcheries are reared like broiler chicken in environmentally-controlled sheds usually on wood shavings, although some of those to be grown on may be kept in 'pole' barns. Sometimes they are beak trimmed or kept in subdued lighting to avoid feather pecking.

Occasionally young turkeys are purchased when they are 4 weeks old and no longer require supplementary heat: these are known as poults.

Turkey husbandry

It is possible for one skilled man to rear as many as 100,000 turkeys in a fully automated environment but a very high standard of stockmanship is needed to avoid problems. Preventative drugs for two diseases are often used in the food rations for the first few weeks and the young birds are tested for salmonella. Leg weakness, which was once a common problem, has now been selectively bred out of commercial turkeys.

Some farms rear especially for the Christmas trade. Hatching takes place between May and September and turkeys are 'finished' at 11 to 17lbs (5 to 7.75kgs) for hens and 18 to 40lbs (8 to 18kgs) for stags. Organic standards specify a minimum slaughter age of 20 weeks for commercial turkeys.

A few producers specialise in the old traditional breeds such as the Norfolk Black and Broad Breasted Bronze. Although commercial turkeys are invariably white, all the hybrids and pure breeds in Britain originated from the black wild turkey of North America.

About 90% of table ducks are reared in East Anglia, many intensively but also 'free range' as well

Duck farm in East Anglia: no pond is required, but they do need a plentiful supply of drinking water

DUCKS

Ducks, like chicken, have been the subject of selective breeding which has produced a placid, white feathered, fast growing table bird and prolific breeding stock. Although they are good layers, there is very little demand for duck eggs. They are rich, but there is a recognised risk of salmonella transmission, so cleanliness is essential at all times for egg production, whether for human consumption or for hatching.

Ducks do not need swimming water in order to mate but a plentiful supply of fresh cool drinking water is necessary. The most popular way of keeping them for breeding is in controlled-environment intensive housing, similar to chicken but incorporating a slatted area where the ducks are watered. For breeding purposes one male (drake) needs to be kept for every 8 females.

Indoors, ducks are either reared on chopped straw or on weld mesh. Because of their messy habits many are reared on weld mesh for the first 4 weeks and then transferred on to straw to finish. Often they are also given access to an outside area. Ducklings grow rapidly and at 7 to 10 weeks old will weigh 4.5 to 7.5lbs (2 to 3.5kgs).

Outdoor ducks require only rudimentary shelter and a low fence to keep them in

Farmed ducks don't like rain

The light sandy soil in parts of East Anglia is ideal for rearing ducks out of doors during the summer months. Put out when they are about 3 weeks old, they only require rudimentary shelter. This is adequate for their needs as their fluff, and later their feathers, are naturally oily and give enough protection from the weather, although domestic ducks, unlike those in the wild, do not like the rain. The ducklings are put out in groups of about 200 at a stocking density of no more than 2,000 per acre (5,000 per hectare). Organic standards however specify a stocking rate of no more than 2,000 ducks per hectare. Low mesh fencing is all that is needed to keep them in, because they cannot fly. Additional electric fencing may also be used as a precaution where there is a high risk of attack by foxes.

The pens must be moved between batches on to fresh ground to avoid a build up of disease in the soil.

Outdoor ducks are very vulnerable to attacks from predators particularly foxes which can cause serious losses. Younger duck-

Most domesticated breeds of duck can't fly

lings are also at risk from rats and marauding black-backed gulls. As with free range chicken production, costs are high and management can be very difficult. The economic success depends on the consumer's willingness to pay a higher price for duck that have been reared outside.

ANIMAL WELFARE

Animal welfare is a contentious issue and 'anthropomorphism', that is, crediting animals with the same feelings as humans, is the bane of livestock farmers' lives. Every species of animal and bird has different temperaments and behavioural needs, so it is pointless to compare them with those of humans.

All creatures react to their present situation. They possess no imagination so the future is of no concern to them. They survive through their natural instincts, learn by past experiences and live only for today. They certainly don't lay awake at night worrying about tomorrow. Only a few species such as dogs, apes and elephants show any great degree of intelligence and some dogs show signs of being telepathic in certain situations. For example hounds and gun dogs seem to be able to tell the difference between days they will be worked or merely exercised even though their handler follows exactly the same routine each morning before taking them out. Sheep are not known for their intelligence although they might be credited with some for sheltering from the wind or hot sun but that is in fact a purely natural instinct. The need for food and the urge to reproduce are the main influence on the behaviour of animals and birds.

Animal welfare is a sensitive topic but it is often misunderstood. It can be interpreted as meaning the physical and mental well-being of any creature and is represented in Britain by the Farm Animal Welfare Council (FAWC), a government-appointed body to advise ministers. It oversees farm animals kept on agricultural land and in buildings, at market, in transit and at slaughter houses. Whenever animals are owned there is a responsibility towards their care. Allowing an animal to overeat can be

Taking care of livestock can be difficult at times because of the vagaries of British weather

'Battery' hens wouldn't lay so well if they were not content for it doesn't take much to put poultry off lay

as unkind and bad for its health as not feeding it enough. Many pet owners are guilty of this and over indulgence is certainly not a kindness. Even though the British are considered to be a pet loving nation there are thousands of cases of cruelty and mistreatment reported each year.

World opinion holds very differing views about animals. Dogs are pets in Britain but are eaten in China; British cows are a commercial investment but in India they are sacred animals.

Farm animals more protected than pets

There is much more attention paid to how farm animals are kept than to domestic pets and there is a vast amount of legislation concerning their welfare. The majority of the population think that farm animals are best kept in natural conditions but nature can be very cruel. Creatures in the wild are exposed to cold, wet and hunger as well as parasites, infections and being eaten or injured. Young lambs look happy gambolling in the sunshine but many born outdoors may perish if there is a prolonged cold, wet spell when they are born. Weak ones are at risk of being killed by foxes or having their eyes pecked out by crows. If, as some people believe, animals have 'rights' that need protecting, who passes judgement on the owl that preys on the mouse: whose right needs protecting, the prey or the predator? This a dilemma that also faces many conservationists.

Animal welfare embraces the Five Freedoms. Freedom from: 1) hunger and thirst, 2) discomfort, 3) fear and stress, 4) pain, injury and disease, and 5) the ability to express normal behaviour regarding space, facilities and the company of its own kind. The latter causes the most problems. Certainly this requirement is conveniently disregarded by pet owners who keep for their own pleasure a horse (herd animal), a dog (pack animal) or a budgerigar (sociable flock bird) without company of their own kind. It can be costly to provide farm livestock with more space, and housing and land are expensive capital investments. The faster the through-put, the higher the returns and the financial crisis in the farming industry means that management has to be finely tuned.

There is a natural balance for stocking levels, for if farm livestock is grossly overcrowded it does not grow or yield to its full potential and therefore becomes unprofitable. Too much freedom

Many veal calves are now being humanely destroyed at birth due to public demonstrations against the use of veal crates and the BSE scare

Below Which of these two animals has rights?

can lead to deaths of the newborn and stress levied on older animals or birds by their companions. Every creature is either territorial if solitary by nature or has a 'pecking order' if gregarious; both result in fighting to establish dominance. It is often management policy to keep groups together for most of their lives so that they will live in harmony, but if you mix groups, stress results.

The media often report on the transport of livestock and it is unfortunate they always seem to be on hand when an incident occurs as it inevitably will.

Delays are unavoidable on Britain's overcrowded roads. The Foot and Mouth outbreak in 2001 exposed big failings in the marketing of sheep, with some being moved from one market to another within several days: a practice which will have to end, on both welfare and health-risk grounds.

Livestock crammed into trailers is frequently depicted and it may appear to be cruel but in actual fact, tightly-packed animals are far less likely to be knocked about or fall over and be trampled on. Hundreds of thousands of livestock are transported annually without coming to any harm.

While EU legislation sets humane standards for animal welfare, it has also meant many small local slaughterhouses have closed down, unable to meet the stringent regulations for health and hygiene. Ironically this now means that livestock destined for slaughter often has to be transported long distances.

There are rules in force regarding the provision of food and water for animals in transit and of regular stops. Animals seem to settle down quietly once on the move and most stress is caused to them at the stops when they are unloaded and loaded up again, which also extends the journey time. Unlike humans, many animals have the ability to rest or sleep standing up.

Veal crates were banned in Britain in 1990. This adversely affected the market for new born calves, as did subsequent very public demonstrations over the export of live calves to the Continent. Combined with the BSE health scare, the long term result has been that there is no longer a market at all for the leaner bull calves of dairy breeds, so many are now being shot or otherwise humanely destroyed at birth.

To give milk it is necessary for a dairy cow to have a calf every 12 to 14 months; about half of these will be male and there-

Many who protest about the way animals are kept in Britain have little conscience about buying cheaper imported meat from countries using dubious methods

There is little demand for dairy bull calves, so many are put down soon after they are born.
At least these can be used to feed hounds

fore of no use to the industry and surplus to requirements. It is now possible, but very expensive, to select the sex of a calf from the semen used for AI. On the face of it this may seem to alleviate the problem by using a beef breed bull on inferior cows to produce offspring that will fatten better. However this would not reduce the number of calves born each year to milking cows and sales of calves of any kind meet a poor demand. Possibly more might be exported to Continental veal producers who still raise calves in crates and the situation would be back to square one.

Mutilation is another matter that concerns many people but unless animals were to be given unlimited freedom (which would be impossible) certain practices are a valuable aid to welfare management. Recently there have been objections to putting rings in pigs' noses although oddly it is acceptable for human parents to have an earring put in their babies' ears. All so-called mutilations are strictly regulated by FAWC who recognise the benefit from existing practices.

Castration is probably the most common because it not only means that animals will fatten quicker but it also minimises aggression and unwanted sexual activities. At present many pigs and sheep destined for early slaughter, being smaller and more manageable than cattle, are often not castrated but this can lead to problems if they are left to reach maturity and have to be segregated from the females.

Nearly all dairy breeds of cattle and some beef are born with horns that begin to develop soon after birth. Cattle have horns for fighting and self-protection. If these aren't removed they are a danger not only to humans but also to each other. Calves are 'de-horned' or 'dis-budded' when they are a few days old. A local anaesthetic is given and the emerging 'buds' are either burned off with a hot iron or a caustic substance is used. At their young age it causes them little distress and the small wounds quickly heal.

Sheep are born with long tails but those intended to be kept on lush grass in the lowlands (which makes their excrement more liquid) will be docked soon after they are born. If they weren't their wool would become soiled and attract flies which would lay their eggs on the dirty fleece and in turn hatch out into maggots which bury themselves into the skin and flesh beneath. If not detected, and it is very difficult to see, then the unfortunate sheep

Many breeds of cattle naturally grow horns. These are removed soon after birth, before they develop – for safety reasons

Castration means that animals fatten quicker but it also minimises aggression and unwanted sexual activities

would literally be eaten alive and suffer a slow and horrific death so to dock a lamb is more humane than to leave it with a long tail. Sheep kept in the uplands have poorer vegetation to graze so their tails are not docked as short and those kept on high ground aren't docked at all because their excrement is dry and a long tail offers them some protection from the harsher weather conditions.

Pigs are appearing in larger and larger numbers out of doors. The breeding stock are kept in large paddocks which gives them plenty to occupy themselves, but the young ones born outside do not enjoy for very long the freedom offered to their parents. Although kept in natural conditions, pigs still need protection from the sun and prolonged rain which can turn their paddocks into a quagmire.

Best interests of the animals

Nose ringing of the breeding stock is necessary not only to prevent them digging up their paddocks but also when a sow is about to give birth. She not only makes a nest but she also digs a hole in the ground, a certain death trap for the tiny piglets because the sow is about 250 times larger and will inevitably crush them when she lays down if they have rolled into the hole. 3 or 4 rings in the top of each nostril is sufficient to stop a pig from digging with its snout. Farrowing crates in buildings, limiting the sow's movement, are also designed to minimise the risk of piglets being squashed. In the first few days of their lives it is important that piglets are confined close to their mothers, indoors and out, so they don't get lost. Very young piglets sometimes have the points of their canine teeth clipped off so they don't make the sow sore when they suckle. Because they like to chew the tassel on the ends of each others tails which can lead to soreness, pain and even cannibalism, the tip of the tail is often docked.

It is extremely difficult for the farming industry to find solutions that will assuage public opinion and maintain moral standards while being both practical and economic. There are 'fors' and 'againsts' for everything to do with animal welfare – nothing slots neatly into place. Even the best systems can fail if they are badly run or there are unforeseen circumstances such as an outbreak of disease when orders are made restricting the movements of livestock. The outbreak of swine fever in East Anglia in

Below Rings are put into pig's noses to prevent them from digging up the ground

Docking lambs' tails may seem cruel but it can prevent them from being eaten alive by maggots

2000 and Foot and Mouth throughout Britain in 2001 created huge backlogs of animals waiting to leave farms. Such is the economic situation that rearing programmes rely on a tight schedule for throughput and many animals had to be destroyed on welfare grounds because there was no room left to keep them or no fodder available to feed them on.

The huge majority of people working with livestock are compassionate towards their animals and do their best for their welfare but this can be made extremely difficult at times due to the vagaries of the British weather. It is not in any livestock farmer's interest to neglect or mistreat his animals. Sick animals neither fatten or yield to their full potential so it is uneconomic not to care for them properly.

British farmers are some of the most progressive in the world regarding animal welfare and, unlike many countries, believe legislation and moral standards are an obligation, not something to be ignored.

Many people who protest about the way animals are kept in Britain have no conscience over buying cheaper imported produce from countries using dubious methods. However our own welfare standards sometimes appear to be extreme at times and influenced by ignorant public opinion rather than practical common sense. A broad view of all animal welfare issues has to be taken, and judgement should not be made on a few isolated incidents.

It is not in any livestock farmer's interest to neglect or mistreat his animals

Idyllic scene: cattle of different ages seeking shade under the trees

ARABLE FARMING

The farming year traditionally ends and begins at Michaelmas time, the last week in September. This is particularly relevant to the arable farmer who has harvested most of his crops and is about to sow the seeds for next years.

Nearly all farmers use a system of rotating crops because some, such as legumes, will put nitrogen back into the soil while others take it out. Crop rotation has been practised for hundreds of years. Not only does it help preserve the structure and fertility of the soil but it also prevents a build-up of pests and diseases.

There are a wide variety of crops grown in Britain, some of which are only suited to particular areas. Sometimes this is because of soil type, of which there are many across Britain, and sometimes because of climate. There are also many different breeds or strains of each crop which have been developed to meet specific requirements. The most valuable cereal crop is wheat but because the straw from it is of little value, plant scientists have developed strains that do not grow very tall.

Farmers maximise the potential from each crop for a variety of reasons including the necessity to remain profitable and competitive as well as for personal pride. Land values are not relative to the present state of the agricultural industry because owning part of the British countryside is regarded as an attractive investment for foreign and city money. Rents (if applicable),

Britain produces just over half the amount of sugar consumed in the UK each year

Above Straw bales, rarely seen today, are the small ones once hand-lifted by the farmer. These large round ones require special machinery

ARABLE FARMING *Useful Words*

ANNUAL A crop that completes its life cycle in one year or less.

AWNS The 'whiskers' on ears of cereals.

BALE Hay, straw or grass compressed into round or rectangular shapes and fastened securely with string or mesh.

BI-ANNUAL A crop that is sown one year and harvested the next.

BINDER Old fashioned horse or tractor-drawn implement that cuts and ties cereals into sheaves.

BOOM The fold-up 'arm' of a sprayer.

BREAK CROP A rotational crop that helps prevent a build up of disease, may add organic matter to the soil and replenishes certain nutrients.

CHITS The new growth on seeds or plants. Potatoes are deliberately exposed to the light to encourage growth prior to being planted in order to hasten development.

CLAMP A large heap of a root crop or fodder crop such as maize or grass.

COMBINE Large self-propelled machine that cuts crops and separates the seeds from the stalks.

CULTIVATOR A tined (spiked) implement that breaks up the soil.

DESICCATE Spray with paraquat to quickly kill off every plant.

DISC HARROW An implement that consists of round discs used to break up the soil.

DRILL An implement for the precision sowing of seeds.

EAR Grain bearing head of cereal.

FALLOW Land that is ploughed but left without a crop.

FUNGICIDE Chemicals that destroy fungal diseases of plants.

FURROW The number of blades on a plough or the narrow channels left in the soil by it.

GAME COVER Crop grown to provide food and shelter for pheasants and partridges, very often a mixture of seed bearing plants.

HARROW An implement for levelling the soil or 'combing' grassland.

HAY Dried grass.

HEADLAND The ground forming the perimeter of a field.

HEAVY LAND Water-retaining soil such as clay.

HERBICIDE Chemicals applied to kill plants.

INSECTICIDE Chemicals that destroy insect pests of plants.

LAID/LODGED Standing crop that has been flattened, usually caused by heavy rain.

LEGUME Pod bearing plant such as pea or bean.

LEY Area sown with grass.

LIGHT LAND Free-draining soil such as sandy types.

MOLE PLOUGH An implement that cuts deep into the ground and leaves a mole-run effect to improve drainage.

PERENNIAL A crop that will keep producing for more than 2 years.

PESTICIDE General term for herbicide, fungicide and insecticide.

PLOUGH An implement that slices through the soil and turns it over.

PRESS An implement attached to a plough and which levels and compacts the soil.

ROGUEING The pulling up by hand of unwanted plants, usually applied to removing the weed known as wild oat from cereal crops.

ROLLER A heavy implement for compacting the soil, either with a flat surface or solid rings.

ROTATION System of management where crops are grown in a certain order.

ROTOVATOR An implement that breaks down the soil into a fine tilth.

SELECTIVE SPRAY Herbicide that kills certain species of plants while leaving others unharmed.

SHEAFING Old fashioned method of harvesting cereals where they were cut and tied into small bundles.

SILAGE Fresh grass that has been compressed and partially fermented.

SPINNER An implement that dispenses seeds or fertiliser over a wide area.

SPRAYER An implement, either tractor-drawn or self-propelled, for the precise application of liquids. Used for crop protection and applying fertiliser.

STOOK A group of sheaves stood together and left outside to dry.

STRAW Dried stalks of cereals.

STUBBLE The remaining stalks left in a field after a crop has been cut.

TILTH Broken down condition of the soil.

TOP DRESS Spread fertilizer on to the ground.

TRAMLINE Evenly spaced gaps left in a crop the exact size of the machinery wheels used as a management tool to make spraying and fertilising easier.

labour, fuel and production costs are high, making it necessary to obtain the optimum use of the land with expensive machinery and the highest-yielding crops. As a result, farmers have become the architects of their own demise by over-producing. The government has tried to rectify this with a system of allocating specified quantities (quotas), such as those for sugar beet, and the reduction of productive land by making grants available for tree planting and many other conservation schemes. The new 'set-aside' where perimeter strips or even whole fields are left unused or sown with non-food crops is also aimed at curbing over-production.

Stubble is often sprayed with a herbicide or disced over soon after harvest and then left for a while. Deep 'mole ploughing' is done on heavy land to help drain the ground prior to any other cultivations. Most fields are ploughed, an action which turns the soil completely over, burying the weeds and trash. Then cultivations are carried out to break down the soil to a fine tilth before the next crop is drilled.

Plough and press, on sandy soils the press is often used to settle the soil after ploughing

The crop-sowing year

The seeds are nearly always sown in straight lines several centimetres apart, the spacing depending on the crop grown. Sometimes rows are deliberately missed to leave tracks or 'tramlines' so that machinery used for spraying or applying fertiliser can run along them without causing damage to the crop. Seeds are often treated with chemicals to give protection against pests and diseases before they are sown and the land may also be sprayed with a selective pre-emergence herbicide spray before they germinate, to discourage weed growth. While the majority of crops are for food, some are grown especially for seed.

There is a seasonal order in which crops are sown. The first to be drilled after harvest is usually grass which will have time to become established before cold weather sets in. Stubble turnips are sometimes sown directly into uncultivated stubble. These grow very quickly and will provide fresh green winter feed for sheep. Oilseed rape, rye and winter barley follow on and then winter wheat and beans by which time in some areas the ground will be too wet for tractors to get on. After the mid-winter lull, a few drying days in late February and March will see spring wheat, barley and oats being drilled. March is also the time when

Wheat has the highest protein of all cereals

Soil ridger – preparing the ground for potatoes

sugar beet and fodder beet are sown as well as peas and last of all are the more delicate linseed (flax), maize, potatoes and other crops which cannot tolerate a hard frost.

By May, when the last of the arable crops have been sown, grass is nearly ready to cut for the first crop of silage and fertilising and spraying need to be done. Hay is usually made in late June or July by which time in southern England winter barley will be getting ripe. Oilseed rape will also be ready although this is sometimes desiccated (sprayed with a herbicide to kill the plant) to hasten the ripening. In turn other crops will be harvested through until September, later in the north.

And so the year has passed and the growing cycle begins all over again, for nearly all the crops with the exception of grass are annuals and need to be replanted.

New initiatives

Because of high overheads arable farmers, like livestock farmers, have been endeavouring to reduce their costs. Fertiliser is expensive but it is a necessity for without it, the plants would be puny and non-productive. However, more attention is being paid to the use of sprays both because of costs and because of public concern and these are being used more sparingly.

New crops are also being tested especially ones that prove to be a high source of protein. Eliminating the use of meat and bone meal from livestock feed because of the BSE health risk meant that alternative protein sources had to be found for animals. Fish meal is an excellent substitute but fish stocks are already threatened so cannot bear any increased pressure. Soya bean is high in protein and experimental crops are now being grown in this country. The lupin is another plant that may prove to be useful.

The weather is an important element in the success or failure of each farming year; it plays a key part in the successful sowing and harvesting of most crops and is something the farmer has no control over. Most years his costs are increased by having to artificially dry his seed crops to a level where they can be stored safely and one that is acceptable to the buyer.

Progressive arable farmers are motivated to explore and exploit every possibility that comes their way in order to make a living from the land.

Most potatoes are lifted between September and the end of November

Below Oats: the best quality is used for milling and breakfast cereals and the rest for livestock feed

ROOT CROPS

SUGAR BEET For centuries Britain imported sugar from the British colonies in the West Indies where sugar cane flourished. It wasn't until the early 1900s that sugar beet was grown in Britain. The first factory was opened at Cantley in Norfolk in 1912. Production rapidly increased until levelling out in the 1970s at about 195,000 hectares but new varieties and improved farming practices have now reduced this area to around 150,000 hectares. There are now about 7,000 growers producing approximately 9 million tonnes annually.

Sugar beet is all grown under contract, ensuring an agreed price on a quota system. This means that in a very good growing year, when the crop is exceptionally heavy, it is guaranteed that the surplus will be purchased but probably at a very low price. On average over 50 tonnes of beet will be harvested per hectare.

There are now about 7,000 British sugar beet growers

The sugar beet industry supports about 20,000 British jobs in farming, processing and transport

Some is grown in the West Midlands but the bulk of it in the dry East Anglian region. In recent years Rhizomania, a sugar beet disease has become a problem in some areas. Rhizomania-tolerant seed is likely to be grown more extensively in future.

Sugar beet seed is drilled in March or April. Harvesting begins at the end of September and continues to February. This period is known as the 'Campaign'. Most farmers prefer to have the beet transported to factories as soon as possible after it is lifted, having tipped it into a heap where lorries have easy access to load up. Loads can only be taken into the factory by permit, which ensures a constant supply. Later in the season, when there is a risk that the ground may become waterlogged or frozen, the remaining sugar beet will be lifted and stored in 'clamps'. Big bales are often used to form a barrier around three sides and if prolonged sub-zero temperatures are forecast, the top may be covered with plastic sheeting or more straw.

Sugar beet needs free-draining soil because the big machinery needed to handle it would get bogged down in wet clay

From harvest to factory

Huge machines complete the harvesting work in one operation. First the green leafy tops are cut off and discarded to one side. The roots are then eased out of the ground on to a rotating turbine or slatted elevator which allows dirt and stones to fall through. The beet is then either stored in a bin on the machine to be emptied later or dropped straight into a trailer driven alongside. The green tops are put back into the soil to provide much needed organic matter, or cattle or sheep may be turned into the field to eat them and any pieces of roots that remain in or on the ground; these they find very palatable.

From September until the end of February sugar beet factories operate 24 hours a day, 7 days a week. Between them they produce about 1.4 million tonnes of sugar which contributes just over half the amount consumed in the UK each year. Sugar is also supplied directly to factories producing cereals, sweets, jams, ice cream, cakes and biscuits. Some of the co-products from the refining process are used for animal feed. 800,000 tonnes of molassed sugar beet feed is produced annually. It is the drying of this animal feed that causes the familiar plumes of steam to be emitted from the large factory chimneys. Lime, another co-product, is used on the land as a soil improving agent.

Root vegetables need to be grown in soil free of stones to allow the roots to grow straight

There are 6 sugar beet factories in UK:
in Shropshire, Nottinghamshire, Yorkshire, Suffolk and 2 in Norfolk

Sugar beet factories

When the sugar beet arrives at the factory it is sampled for its sugar content which may vary but usually averages about 17%. It is then washed so that soil, stones and other debris are removed. Once inside the factory it is sliced before passing into large vessels where it is 'diffused', a process comparable to brewing tea in a teapot. The 'cossettes' (slices) are mixed in hot water at about 70C for a period of time which extracts sugar from the slices. The juice so formed is then purified by mixing with milk of lime and adding carbon dioxide gas.

The resulting lime solids are then filtered off, carrying many of the impurities with them. After this it goes through an evaporation process to concentrate the solution which is then either stored or goes on for further processing. The actual crystallisation process operates in vacuum pans where more reduction takes place before minute sugar crystals called 'seeds' are introduced to form a nucleus on which larger crystals will form.

This mixture of syrup and sugar crystals is then spun in a 'centrifuge' to separate. The crystals are washed and dried ready for storage while the syrup is processed twice more to extract as much sugar as possible before being discarded and used in animal feed as molasses.

Factories are powered by a combined heat and power system producing both steam and electricity. Two of the factories produce an excess of electricity which is fed into the National Grid system.

The British sugar 'Silver Spoon' label markets the white sugar products manufactured from British sugar beet such as granulated, caster and icing sugar

Below One of Britain's sugar beet processing factories – boosting the national electricity grid as a by-product

POTATOES Large acreages of potatoes are grown on the free-draining areas of Britain, mainly on the eastern side and predominately in England and Scotland. Maincrop potatoes average over 40 tonnes per hectare and just over 158,000 hectares are grown annually. There are many varieties, some of which are grown specifically for one purpose eg. crisps or frozen chips.

The land is prepared in early spring and formed into ridges. Any stones are sifted out and put in the dips between the ridges. Early varieties are planted in March and occasionally covered with plastic to protect them from frosts, with the main crop following on after. The chitted tubers are planted quite deeply, one at a time, by a tractor-drawn machine manned by one or two people whose job it is to keep a check on the proceedings. Several young potatoes grow from one tuber. The tops grow tall and green and either white or purple flowers, depending on the variety, appear in July or August. Early varieties are usually dessicated prior to lifting to get rid of the unwanted tops, but the growth dies off naturally on later varieties which are not harvested until autumn.

The earliest of all potatoes are ready about early June and although they are still immature, the high price they command makes a lower yield acceptable. Most potatoes are lifted between September and the end of November. In wet autumns it is sometimes impossible for heavy machinery to get on the land and frozen ground in winter will destroy the crop.

Nearly all potatoes these days are harvested by machine although the old fashioned method of 'spinning' them out of the ground with a small tractor-drawn implement is still used where only a small amount are grown. These are then picked up by hand. It is best if they can be left to dry before being gathered but they cannot be left very long because they will soon turn green when exposed to light.

Potatoes grown in bulk are stored in large, darkened, environmentally-controlled barns. Rejected small or damaged potatoes are used for livestock feed.

STUBBLE TURNIPS are similar to vegetable turnips and are often sown after harvest directly into the stubble. They are fast growing and both the green tops and roots are grazed by sheep in late autumn. Droppings from the sheep add fertility to the soil.

SWEDES and **MANGOLDS** (sometimes called mangelwurzels) are grown in some areas for stock feed. Swedes are also used for human consumption.

FODDER BEET is grown like sugar beet but used as animal feed.

Potatoes being harvested. They are mainly grown in Scotland and the east of England

Potatoes require an inch of water each week

Exposure to light turns potatoes green and they become unusable

CEREAL CROPS

WHEAT grain is on the upright stalk and does not have 'whiskers', although a few varieties do have short ones. The best quality, and therefore the most valuable, is milled into flour to be used for baking bread, biscuits and cakes or used for breakfast cereals. Lesser quality is known as feed wheat and is processed for use in livestock rations or fed as whole grain to poultry or game birds. Wheat has the highest protein of all cereals and by-products from the milling process such as bran can be used for either human or animal consumption. The straw is only suitable for use as livestock bedding. Durum is a variety of wheat grown specially for making pasta. About 8 tonnes per hectare of wheat is harvested and nearly 2 million hectares grown in the UK each year, mainly in England.

BARLEY grain has long barbed whiskers and the individual seeds are encased in a fibrous cover. The best quality is known as 'malting barley' and used in the brewery trade for making beer and whisky; by-products from these processes, called brewers grains and draff, are utilised as cattle feed. The rest goes for livestock feed and is often crushed and used to fatten cattle. The straw also has some value as feed for cattle and is often treated with alkali to make it more palatable and nutritious. Barley can be expected to yield about 5.6 tonnes per hectare and over one million hectares is grown annually in the UK, mainly in England and Scotland.

OATS The dainty seed heads hang down on individual stems and do not have any whiskers on them. Those that do are an unwelcome weed and are removed from crops either by using a selective spray or by hand if there is only a light infestation or the crop is being grown for seed. This removal by hand is known as 'rogueing'. Oats are not so commonly grown as wheat and barley, although Scotland is famed for them. The best quality is used for milling and breakfast cereals and the rest for livestock feed. It often forms part of the rations for sheep and horses. Oat straw has some value as animal feed. About 6 tonnes of oats per hectare can

Below Barley: the best goes to the brewing industry as 'malting barley' and is used for making beer and whisky

Durum wheat, the main ingredient in pasta, is grown in England

be obtained and approximately 125,000 hectares are grown annually, mainly in England and Scotland.

RYE is only grown in a relatively small quantity and is similar in appearance to barley but usually taller. Like wheat and oats, it is used for milling and breakfast cereal production and the remainder is used for animal feed. About 9,000 hectares is grown each year but only in England.

TRITICALE is a cereal; basically a cross between wheat and rye. About 14,000 hectares are grown each year in the UK and the grain is used in live-stock rations. Sometimes triticale is used on shooting estates as a game cover crop.

FODDER CROPS

GRASS is grown as feed for livestock, either grazed directly or cut and preserved for winter use. Many different species of native perennial grasses cover the hills, downs, fells and marshes providing grazing for sheep and cattle. Cultivated varieties, found in lowland fields, are faster growing and more lush. Some leys (grass fields) are left in for several years while others are regarded as annuals. Rye grass is very quick growing and is often planted as a silage crop from which 3 or 4 cuts may be taken in a year; it is then ploughed up.

The traditional method of preserving grass for winter use was to cut it and leave it to dry in the fields. It needed dry weather and turning 2 or 3 times before it was fit to store. Originally this was done by hand. The loose hay would be taken on horse drawn carts to the farmyard where it was unloaded into large stacks which were then

Combining the barley crop

Hay being baled

Below Cutting grass for silage, instead of hay

thatched with straw when complete. In the last century, mechanisation progressed and the baler was invented which gathered the hay into compact round or oblong bundles and tied it tightly with string. The bales were then collected, stacked in a pile and covered with a tarpaulin.

Modern silage

Silage is a comparatively modern way of storing grass for winter feed. Cut and left only a day or so to wilt, the grass is collected and made into a clamp or put in a pit where it is then compressed by a heavy tractor running to and fro over it, sealed with plastic sheeting and weighted down, often with old car tyres. Molasses are sometimes added to it but the effluent which leaks out from the compressed and fermenting grass is a problem to dispose of. Should it pollute a water course it can be very damaging and many people also find the smell obnoxious.

However a new system has revolutionised the production of good quality winter feed for livestock. The wilted grass is now baled into big bales, tightly wrapped in polythene and stored where it is needed. Transporting and handling it is very simple by tractor and nearly every farm now uses this method.

Hay is still needed for calves and horses but as always with the unreliable British weather, it is a gamble. To make top quality hay, the cut grass needs to dry quickly. If luck isn't on the farmers' side, periods of rain can reduce the goodness and even make it unfit for feeding if it becomes black and mouldy in the fields where it lays.

The quality of silage can vary from year to year according to growing conditions but supplementary feed rations can be adjusted to take this into account after an analysis has been

The most popular method of silage making is in the black polythene bags often seen in farmyards and fields

Below Bales of silage are sometimes wrapped in a long tube of polythene

made. With this modern technique for silage-making, the results are much more reliable.

LUCERNE (or Alfalfa) is a perennial which grows well in dry areas. It has a blue/purple flower and is cut green to be used for hay or silage.

CLOVER is a perennial which has a white or red flower. It is not often grown as a crop but can be used for either hay or silage.

MAIZE has become a popular crop for use as silage for winter cattle feed. It is nutritious and bulky, growing over 2 metres high and having 2 or 3 cobs on each stalk similar to sweet corn. It is usually cut and put in a clamp in September or October when the plant is naturally beginning to dry off. The machine that is used to cut it also chops it up into small pieces. Maize is also frequently grown in strips or small blocks to provide food and shelter for pheasants and partridges. Millet is often planted with it and proves very attractive to them and other birds.

MISCELLANEOUS CROPS

OILSEED RAPE is a member of the mustard family and is the crop which provides a patchwork of bright yellow fields across the countryside when it flowers in April and May. It is usually ready to harvest from July onwards, and is often cut or sprayed with paraquat to dry it off prior to combining. The stalks are of no use and are frequently shredded by the combines at the time of harvesting and spread back on to the field. The small seeds are later processed by crushing to extract oil which is used to make vegetable oils (used in margarine, salad dressings etc), for live-stock feed, bio-diesel fuel and also industrial lubricants. Oilseed rape yields about 3.3 tonnes per hectare and over 400,000 hectares are grown annually in the UK.

MUSTARD is planted in late spring and looks very similar to Rape. It is normally grown for culinary use, for game cover or to be ploughed back into the soil while still green.

140,000 hectares of fodder crops are grown annually in England, 10,500 in Wales and 27,500 in Scotland

Oilseed rape is now used to produce bio-fuel for cars and lorries

Flax fibre makes high quality paper, such as bank notes

LINSEED (or Flax) is one of the oldest cultivated crops and is another that paints the landscape in early summer. A small delicate plant growing only about half a metre tall, its pretty blue flowers burst open when the sun comes out only to close up again when it disappears. There are varieties that are grown for either their seed or their stems. More than 40% oil can be extracted from the seed which has many industrial uses including the manufacturing of paints, varnishes, printing ink and linoleum. The residue left from the extraction process is compacted into high protein 'cake' for use in livestock rations. The stalks of flax plants are sometimes chopped and used for animal or poultry bedding and has proved to be light to handle, super-absorbent, not too dusty and it rots down quickly after use. However the fibre is mainly used to produce linen, high quality paper such as that used for bank notes and more recently for car interior mouldings. Because of its excellent insulation value, flax straw has also been used experimentally for house construction. Linseed only yields about 1.43 tonnes per hectare and most of the 13,000 hectares used for growing it are in England.

HEMP is a similar agricultural plant to linseed, and is also occasionally grown for industrial use.

Linseed in flower, painting the landscape pale blue in mid-summer

Linseed (or flax) is one of the oldest cultivated crops

Soya beans are a prime source of protein for both animals and humans

KALE is a popular autumn/winter green feed for dairy cows, which are usually only allowed access to a fresh narrow strip each day so that the crop is not damaged by being trampled on. Kale is also often grown for game cover when it is sometimes left *in situ* for a second year, allowing seeds to develop after it has flowered in the spring. These are particularly attractive to many small farmland birds.

BEANS (Field or Tic) are usually sown into ground that is ploughed but not cultivated to a fine tilth as it is for other crops. The plant resembles the 'broad bean' grown by gardeners and turns black in late summer when it dies off. The beans are crushed and used for animal feed. Beans, when they are harvested, yield about 3.8 tonnes per hectare and almost all of the 164,000 hectares grown are in England.

PEAS are grown commercially as a vegetable and also used for animal feed, in which case the plants are left to dry off naturally before harvesting and then the peas are crushed. When harvested, dry peas average just under 3.5 tonnes per hectare and about 68,000 hectares are grown, mainly in England.

SOYA BEAN is one of the prime sources of protein for both animals and humans but is not grown on a wide scale in Britain although experimental crops are being tried. The plant is similar in appearance to a 'dwarf' or 'french' bean.

LUPIN is another experimental high-protein crop appearing in the British countryside.

HOPS have been grown for centuries for use in the brewing trade and have always been associated with the county of Kent. The plants grow several metres high and have to be tied to supports. Not so many years ago, hops were picked by hand and families would come out into the countryside from London for the season but they have now been displaced by machines. The fields where hops grew were known as 'hop gardens'. Only about 2,000 hectares are now grown in England annually.

Most vegetables and fruit grown in Britain arrive at the super-market within 24 hours of being picked or harvested

Experimental soya bean field in Suffolk

COMMERCIAL HORTICULTURAL CROPS

The commercial growing of vegetable and fruit crops is scattered across the British countryside, wherever there are conditions to suit the crops, although there is very little horticulture in Wales. All root crops need to be grown on light, free-draining land because in early spring a fine seed bed has to be worked in which to sow the seeds.

In autumn and winter, heavy machinery needs to be able to get on the ground to harvest the crops. Vegetable crops are grown mainly in East Anglia and the East Midlands. Campbell's factory in Kings Lynn is the world's largest soup maker and there are many vegetable packing stations there and in such places as Wisbech. The rich black soil of the Fens makes it one of Britain's prime vegetable growing areas. Kent was once famous for its apple orchards, Somerset for its cider while greenhouse produce is grown in many parts of England. Cheap imports however are reducing the amounts grown in this country.

The top quality produce found on supermarket shelves is normally supplied by growers under contract. It is in the supermarkets' interest to deal with big suppliers.

However this puts the producers under enormous pressure as they have to invest heavily in the necessary expensive equipment,

By limiting the number of small farms growing for them, supermarkets reduce their admin costs while ensuring consistent quality and availability

Above Harvesting carrots: supermarkets insist on evenly-shaped carrots and these are best grown on sandy, stoneless soils with no guarantees that all the crop will be used or of the price received for it. Growers have to commit themselves to have available whatever quantity the supermarkets require, exactly when they want it. When seasonal products, such as lettuces, cannot be supplied at certain times of the year, usually winter and early spring, the grower under contract is still expected to supply the goods which is done by growing crops abroad.

Spain is an ideal place, with a warmer climate than Britain and yet relatively close, thus reducing transport costs – a big consideration. In some instances, crops such as parsnips have even been grown as far afield as Australia to ensure a constant supply for the supermarkets during early summer when they cannot be grown here. Even though produce may have been grown on the other side of the world, it can still reach the British consumer in perfect condition. It is sealed in special 'modified atmosphere' plastic bags which expel gases that hasten degeneration while retaining gases that maintain the produce in good condition for as long as 28 days. This type of packaging is seldom used in Britain except when it may be necessary to hold produce over, such as at Christmas time.

Most perishable fruit and vegetables grown in this country arrive at the supermarket within 24 hours of being picked or harvested. The exceptions are things like potatoes, onions and apples which can be stored for several months in a controlled environment without deteriorating.

Producers not directly contracted to supermarkets or other outlets sell to wholesalers who then distribute to smaller shops and traders, which means that the produce is not quite so fresh by the time it reaches the customer. The increasing number of 'Farmers Markets' provide a useful outlet for many of the smaller growers and by selling direct off the farm they cut out the middle man therefore receiving a better price for their goods.

Overall the supermarkets have the easy part of the equation by notifying growers of their

> *About 25% of the cost of horticultural crops is in the actual growing; 75% is in the packaging and transport*

Bunching and tying spring onions (or what the supermarkets call 'salad onions')

requirements and the price they will be paid for it. The hardest part is for the growers who have to estimate what acreage of the crop they need to grow to fulfil the potential orders. They need to care for it in such a way that it is ready for harvesting at the appropriate time and is in perfect condition. The weather as ever is the bogeyman. Other than growing in greenhouses or plastic tunnels where the environment can be controlled, there is little that can be done to combat unseasonal temperatures. To protect early crops in the spring, plastic or spun fleece, a relatively new invention, is spread over them to offer some degree of insulation while allowing water to permeate through. Both plastic and fleece are normally removed by early May although a hard frost later in the month can cause severe damage to some crops.

This type of carrot harvester pulls them out of the ground by their green tops

Too much, then too little

The next problem likely to face the grower is a periodic lack of rainfall. Many vegetable and fruit crops, particularly in the drier parts of Britain, are likely to need irrigating. Carrots and parsnips need a soaking at least once a week, lettuces twice and potatoes require an inch (2.5cms) of water each week. Such irrigation can be supplied by the simple rain gun which swishes water from side to side while slowly dragging itself along; or sophisticated computerised systems delivering a fine mist to more delicate plants.

Farmers' own reservoirs

For many years, water for agricultural use has been abstracted, under licence, directly from rivers or underground bore holes. The drought years in the early 1990s put a severe strain on our water resources and the Environment Agency began to take a close look at the feasibility of selling water for crop irrigation on their 10 year licensing system. Many growers realised that their licenses to abstract water may not be renewed, so rather than put their crops in jeopardy, they began to build reservoirs on their farms and lay a network of underground pipes to reach parts of their land where irrigation might be needed. These reservoirs are

Carrots sold in bunches with the green tops left on are all pulled by hand

filled in autumn and winter, under E.A. supervision, from rivers when they exceed a minimum height. This is an excellent way of preserving unwanted excess winter rainfall until the summertime when rivers are naturally low. Ironically, since the construction of these reservoirs began, the summers have been fairly wet so there has not been the huge demand for crop irrigation as there was in the drought years.

Later in the year, a prolonged wet spell in autumn can make it impossible to harvest potato crops and they cannot withstand severe frosts. A few weeks of hard weather, when the ground is frozen solid, can make picking greenstuff or harvesting carrots or parsnips almost impossible. Polythene and straw laid on top of the rows provide some insulation for root vegetables and help prevent the soil from freezing. It can also preserve the quality of the crop for a little longer by delaying unwanted weed growth caused by warmer springtime temperatures. Laying this, though, is a costly undertaking and a waste of money in mild winters.

Combating pests

Disease and pests are another continuous problem. Supermarkets are extremely strict over what treatments can be used, and when. Regular inspections and testing are carried out to ensure that no residues remain in the produce by the time it reaches the consumer. There is always great public concern regarding the use of sprays, and farmers would much prefer to be in the position where they didn't need to use any at all, because they are costly not only to purchase but also to apply. Pesticide use is decreasing as the chemicals used have become more efficient but even some of those approved for use on organic farms can be potentially harmful to humans.

Commercial trials with plants such as garlic, which can act as a barrier against insects as well as diseases, are producing promising results. All sprays are used to a minimum, and only when necessary, not as a matter of routine. For example, traps are set out amongst the crops to monitor moths that can devastate peas within the pod or flies whose larvae can end up as maggots inside carrots. By checking the traps regularly it is possible to know whether the crop is likely to be at risk from these pests.

While consumers express their grave concerns about the use

> *Pesticide use is decreasing as the chemicals used have become more efficient*

Below Cutting coriander. Many herbs are now grown on a commercial scale

of pesticides, they would be absolutely horrified to find maggots in carrots and peas, slugs and aphids on their lettuces and caterpillars in their cabbages and cauliflowers which would be commonplace if sprays weren't used.

Manual work

Another major problem that large growers are faced with is that of finding sufficient labour. There has been much bad publicity about the illegal use of foreign workers but insufficient British people are prepared to toil out in the fields, laboriously picking by hand, day after day whatever the weather. But with the right attitude and a will to work, good money can be earned. With the introduction of the minimum wage, many foreign workers are able to earn as much in half a day as they would in a week back home and what is more, they are very keen to. 'Piecework', a form of payment for the quantity produced, is another incentive. In areas such as East Anglia, where most of the salad crops are grown, there are many foreigners employed legally throughout the summer. They hold valid permits to work for a certain number of weeks and some are agricultural students on exchange agreements. Many students are provided with hostel accommodation.

Although there are now massive machines to do many jobs, there is still a great need for manual workers. All the carrots sold bunched with the green tops left on have been pulled, tied and packed by hand. Lettuces have to be cut by hand before they are placed in cups on a huge machine known as a 'rig'. As many as 4 or 5 people may be cutting while another team of 15 or more will be on board the rig, trimming, wrapping and packing, putting 10 lettuces into each crate and handling maybe 3 to 4,000 crates a day. There may be up to 4 rigs working on the same farm. Salad onions are all pulled by hand, the roots and tops trimmed and outer skins removed before being bunched together with 2 elastic bands. Celery is cut by hand before being placed on the rig where each head is washed, trimmed, packaged and put into a crate.

Greenhouse produce, soft fruits and flowers have to be very carefully picked by hand to avoid damage and consequently are very labour intensive. Many more people are employed in packing stations sorting, packaging and despatching fruit and vegetables, often working around the clock on a shift system.

Poles and Lithuanians are considered excellent field workers; many come from other Eastern European countries and some from South Africa

Below A machine is used to 'spin' onions out of the ground

78

Only about 25% of the cost of production is in the actual growing; the other 75% goes on packaging and transport.

Rejected goods

Assured schemes guarantee quality but few people realise the incredible amount of work and care that has gone into producing such perfect fresh produce or the amount of waste caused by the rejection of that not-quite-so-perfect. Unless it can be used for processing, the rejected produce is almost worthless and is used as animal feed.

There is probably nowhere else in the world which offers such consistently high quality and safe products as those found on British supermarket shelves. Many horticultural goods cost less now than they did a few years ago, without even allowing for inflation. This is reflected in the large reduction in the percent of earned income actually spent on food. The strength of the pound, the power of supermarkets to fix prices with no guarantees, and cheap imported produce from third world countries who pay a pittance as wages, make the position of the British producer a precarious one. With these factors to contend with it, is very difficult for them to remain competitive. Even within the E.U. British standards are often higher than elsewhere, just as they are with livestock, which all adds to the overall costs.

Loading onions which would have been sown in January or February

The main horticultural crops

Root vegetables need to be grown in soil free of stones to allow the roots to grow straight and there is no risk of damage to the machinery used to harvest the crop. Preparation begins soon after Christmas when the ground is ploughed; it is then ridged up and tractor-drawn stone picking machines work their way slowly along the ridges, sifting the soil and depositing stones into the deep furrows in between. Potato tubers are planted deeply, straight into the ridges, because the developing potatoes must not be exposed to light or they turn green and become unusable. For other crops, the soil is levelled out, burying the stones, and the seeds are sown. Vegetable seeds are usually treated to protect them from pests in the ground and sometimes 'pelleted' (coated with fertiliser) as garden seeds sometimes are. Most of the

Vegetable seeds are usually treated to protect them from pests in the ground

sowing is done with 'precision drills' which measure the seeds out as they are planted so they do not compete for space thus eliminating the need to thin the crop. Drilling of carrots, parsnips and onions begins in January or February and the early crops are usually covered with strips of polythene sheeting to protect them from the weather and encourage fast germination. This is removed in early May when the crop is well established. Parsnips continue to be sown until mid-May and carrots until mid-June.

CARROTS sold in bunches with the green tops left on are all pulled by hand; those sold loose or in polythene bags are harvested by huge machines which lift them or pull them out of the ground by their tops, trim them and deposit them into tractor-drawn trailers. They are then taken from the field straight to factories or packing stations where they are washed and packed. Harvesting begins in mid-June and continues almost throughout the year. Later crops intended for winter use are often covered with polythene and straw.

Carrots reach supermarket shelves within 24 hours of lifting. The grower contracted to supply the produce is given an order by the supermarket late in the afternoon, confirmed the following morning before 10am. The grower is expected to deliver the goods that same afternoon. This means that people employed on the farms or in the packing sheds may have to work shifts, sometimes through the night. Each pack goes out 10% over its marked weight to allow for possible dehydration before purchase.

PARSNIPS are also lifted by machine and handled in much the same way as carrots. Harvesting begins in late July and continues until mid-April. Although more frost resistant than carrots, some late crops are strawed up so that they can be harvested in hard weather. Parsnips need to be kept moist after lifting because if they are allowed to dry out the skins turn yellow making them look unattractive.

LETTUCE are planted out from March, iceberg being the most popular. Using plants purchased from commercial growers rather than growing from seed is the most popular method. Growth is more uniform making it more economic to only have to go over

Only 50% of the crops of carrots and parsnips make the required top grade, the remainder is used for processing or animal food

Below Maize and the small-seeded millet are sometimes sown together as a crop for game birds

the crop once to cut it, when 70-80% will be ready, rather than to have to go over it 2 or 3 times because only one third of the crop is fit to cut at a time. Re-usable fleece is usually put over early crops in March and left on for 5 or 6 weeks. Planting is normally carried out on a weekly basis to ensure a continuous crop for harvesting from the second week in May through until mid-October. As soon as possible after the lettuces have been cut and packed on the rig they are taken back to the factory where they are vacuum cooled to a temperature of about 4C and kept chilled to maintain perfect condition.

SALAD ONION seed is sometimes drilled in August or September under polythene so that early picking can begin in late March the following year. Onions are hardy enough to survive the average British winter. For a continuous supply, sowing resumes in early February, weather permitting, and continues until July. The earliest crops are covered with polythene to hasten growth. Picking carries on until mid-October. Gangs of people are employed for the laborious job of pulling, preparing and bunching. Sometimes floodlights are erected in the fields so that work can continue through the night if necessary to fulfil orders. Ordinary onions are harvested and stored in a similar way to potatoes.

Gangs of land workers are needed to gather salad onions

Garlic can act as a barrier against insect pests, as well as diseases

CELERY is mainly grown in the fenlands of East Anglia. It is cut by hand and washed, trimmed and packed on huge rigs similar to those used for lettuces. Contracts are made between growers and supermarkets and the celery is cut according to their requirements. Often this means working from early morning to late at night. One particularly large grower who is contracted to supply celery all year round employs 500 foreign students. They arrive in April, and regulations require that they have to be under the age of 26, and stay for only 13 weeks before being replaced with another batch for a further 13 weeks. The massive harvesting rigs, which weigh as much as 30 tons, are then transported out to Spain to continue with the harvesting there. This is a massive undertaking and takes a lot of organising.

PEAS are sown in the spring and are inspected regularly and harvested as soon as they are at their best. Selective plant breeding has created strains that are prolific and pods that all mature at the same time. Large machines called 'viners' are used to cut and shell out the peas and they are quickly taken to packing stations where they are quick frozen and packaged within a few hours of being harvested.

BRASSICAS (cabbages, sprouts etc), like lettuces, are best grown from plants supplied by specialist suppliers than from seed. These are normally planted in the spring ready for harvesting in autumn and winter although some varieties of cabbages and cauliflower are gathered throughout the summer. Harvesting any kind of greenstuff when it is wet or frozen during the winter is unpleasant work, some of which inevitably has to be done by hand. However there are now machines that strip sprouts from the main stalk on which they grow instead of having to pick them by hand.

ASPARAGUS is grown in Britain on light land and the tender shoots have to be regularly picked by hand before they grow too big. The asparagus is then washed and sold in bundles. The season is a short one, usually beginning in late April or early May and traditionally ending on June 21st.

SOFT FRUIT (strawberries, raspberries, currants etc) are grown predominantly in the south and east of England although wherever there is a local population within reach of coming to 'Pick Your Own', small enterprises have become established. Such perishable fruits are very much at the mercy of the weather, not only for the harm it can cause but also for the demand it creates. Commercial growers of soft fruits need to be close to handling facilities and have the necessary labour on hand when it is needed. Strawberries and raspberries have to be picked by hand but there are machines available to harvest currants by shaking the bushes.

ORCHARDS are mainly to be found in Southern England, notably Kent, and in Worcestershire and the surrounding counties. Apples, pears, plums and cherries were once grown extensively but are now in serious decline due to a variety of reasons. Many orchards have been grubbed out in recent years because

'Uneconomic' orchards have been grubbed out in recent years with the help of EU grants

Top Men cutting iceberg lettuces and feeding them into the on-site rig. *Bottom* Workers preparing and packing inside the lettuce rig

they have become uneconomic and there have been EU grants to do so. The British weather has always made fruit production difficult. Late frosts in May, when the blossom is out, can devastate the future crop. Although heaters can be placed in orchards to protect the flower from damage, the cost is unlikely to be justified because of such low prices received for the fruit. There are hundreds of native varieties of apples, some over 400 years old, although only ten are still grown on a commercial scale. Fortunately enthusiasts are endeavouring to preserve as many of them as possible even though most of them are not economically viable. Commercially grown apples are used for cider making, apple juice and for cooking or eating, the latter often available to buy as 'Pick Your Own'.

GARDEN PLANTS The boom in TV gardening programmes has created an interest in many kinds of plants and shrubs. Specialist nurseries supply these either directly to the customer, even by mail order, or indirectly through garden centres. Bi-annuals, perennials and hardy shrubs can be grown outdoors. Fields of rose bushes can make an unexpected splash of colour across the countryside in summer.

Bulbs (tulips, daffodils etc), are grown mainly in the East of England particularly around Spalding in Lincolnshire. The growing fields are planted with bulbs in the autumn where they are left to flower in the spring, after which the flower heads are cut off. After the foliage dies later in summer, they are lifted, sorted and packaged. In the West Country, with its milder climate, bulbs are grown for flowers but they need to be picked by hand and there is often difficulty in finding the labour to do this.

HERBS There are 400 different herbs many of which have become big business in recent years. Once again the East of England is a popular area. Colmans, based in Norwich, are not only famous for their mustard but also for the variety of sauces they produce in jars and packets. Crops such as parsley can be cut with a small machine similar to that used for cutting silage grass and then be transported by tractor and trailer. Many herbs however have to be picked and sorted by hand requiring a large labour force. Once again TV has caused an increase in demand

Most annuals and tender plants have to be grown in heated greenhouses or plastic tunnels, to be ready for when the customer wants them

Strawberries & raspberries have to be picked by hand but there are machines for harvesting currants by shaking the bushes

because of the wealth of cookery programmes, creating a great interest in herbs both fresh and dried. There is also an increased awareness of their value as alternative medicines, remedies, cosmetics and for aromatherapy use. Herbs are useful to organic producers as well. Some of them can be used to provide natural treatments for health problems in both plants and animals while others make valuable organic fertiliser. Garlic is particularly useful as it is the most powerful antibacterial and anti-fungal agent but most of it has to be imported. The uses for herbs seem to be never-ending and many farmers have welcomed the opportunity to diversify into an area that shows signs of expanding.

ORGANIC FARMING

Organic farming is a natural method of farming which avoids the use of synthetic pesticides (chemicals that control plants and living organisms) and artificial fertilisers for growing crops. The use of genetically modified material is prohibited as is the routine use of drugs and antibiotics for rearing animals.

There is an increasing demand for organic products as the British population becomes more aware of health and ecological issues. Naturally grown food is considered to be healthier and more flavoursome, and some people feel safer in the knowledge that it is free from genetic modification, artificial chemicals and additives, as well as that the methods used to grow the products are kinder and sympathetic to animals and the environment.

Not very long ago intensive farming and genetic modification seemed to be the answer to providing good quality cheap food but increased affluence has meant that society now demands a choice. At present those demands for organic produce far exceed the supply available in this country. Because of our seasonal climate, legal requirements stipulated by the EU and the fact that crop care is more labour intensive, only about 18% of fruit and vegetables, 30% of cereals and 60% of dairy products are home grown. However, virtually all organic meat and eggs are produced in Britain.

Approximately a quarter of a million hectares are registered

Organic produce: GM material, the routine use of artificial chemicals, drugs and antibiotics are all prohibited

Demand for organic produce is increasing at a rate of about 40% each year while production is only increasing at 25%

for organic food production, representing less than 3% of the land used for agriculture. Financial aid is available for farmers wishing to change but it is a gradual process and there are few large farms that have gone over entirely to organic growing.

Nearly half of the organic land used utilises unimproved grassland such as hills, moors, water meadows and marshes. This land has not been contaminated with chemicals in the past and lends itself readily to an organic system for rearing livestock.

EU regulation number 2092/91 legally defines the standards set for production and processing as well as the requirements for controlling and policing for the UK Organic Food Standards Agency, a government body responsible for implementing EU regulations. Organic products must be certified by an approved body, the largest of which in Britain is the Soil Association.

Conversion to organic farming takes a minimum of two years before a certificate can be issued. When this period has elapsed, a 'Compliance' form stating the conditions and requirements that have to be met has to be signed. This is followed with a detailed inspection of the site before a certificate of registration can be issued. Thereafter there is an extensive annual inspection before the certificate is renewed. A separate processing licence is legally required where on-farm processing is carried out; this is to ensure that rigorous standards are maintained regarding labelling, record keeping and hygiene.

Lower organic crop yields

Crops grown organically are inevitably more costly than those grown intensively. Yields are between 20% and 40% lower and production is more labour intensive. While in theory this may seem beneficial to rural areas by providing employment, there are in fact few people in Britain now willing to do this kind of work which can be repetitive and requires being outdoors in all weathers. The rate of pay is usually basic but a bonus is often paid for hard work. Consequently seasonal foreign workers and students are often brought in on work permits from Eastern Europe and other poorer countries. If it wasn't for these willing and hard working people, organic produce would either be less available or more expensive.

The aim of organic food production is to be self-sustaining,

Conversion to organic farming takes a minimum of two years

Low stocking levels of organic farming, as for these highland cattle, means that native plants and grasses in these areas are not damaged by overgrazing

mainly by utilising crop rotation to improve the fertility and structure of the soil. Different crops have different nutritional requirements and one that has taken a lot of nitrogen from the soil will likely be followed by a crop of legumes (peas, beans or clover) which release nitrogen back into it. Animal manure and plants such as mustard can be ploughed back into the soil to improve both the fertility and the texture. In some instances it is permitted to use certain naturally occurring substances such as rock phosphate, lime, potassium and magnesium.

Any seeds or plants that are bought in must have been grown organically. No synthetic herbicides are allowed so weed control has to be by other methods. Enriched soil not only increases the crop yields but also weed growth. Crop rotation plays a part but the main weapons are mechanical tools or weeding by hand.

Natural pest control

Synthetic insecticides and fungicides are also banned so natural methods of pest control have to be employed. Grass banks, known as beetle banks, may be developed in fields to provide a breeding ground for insects that prey on pests which damage crops, such as slugs, caterpillars and greenfly. Beetle banks are also of recognised value to general conservation. Naturally occurring substances such as sulphur and even some that are toxic can sometimes be used for disease and pest control. Garlic appears a very effective tool in the fight against pests and diseases. Once again crop rotation plays a key role.

Organic meat and eggs

Meat and egg production have been comparatively easy to establish by utilising parts of the countryside where it has previously been impractical to grow crops. Animal welfare standards are very high and natural methods of producing livestock are used wherever possible. When organic animals become sick and need medication, natural remedies are now more widely used, but if all else fails then specified drugs and antibiotics may be administered as a last resort but with an extended withdrawal period between the end of treatment and human consumption of the meat, milk or eggs produced.

Fodder to supplement grazing and other foodstuffs must

Meadow flowers – a sure indicator that organic principles are being applied

Organic crop yields are between 20% and 40% lower than non-organic

contain a high proportion of organically grown material. Organic cereals are not grown on a large scale in this country and 70% have to be imported, adding to the feed costs. Organically raised livestock must have access to natural light and air and be able to conduct their basic behavioural needs. Breeds have to be selected that are suitable to local conditions. Animals that may be bought in, such as calves, must originate from organic holdings.Trout and salmon are also being produced organically, the latter finding a good export market on the Continent.

Having gone to such lengths to grow organic produce to such a high standard, there is obviously an important need to market the results efficiently. Increasingly a broader range is appearing on supermarket shelves and in health food shops. Other marketing schemes are being developed locally to ensure a higher financial return by dispensing with the 'middle man' and reducing haulage costs and pollution. There have always been a few farm shops and market stalls but recently 'Farmers Markets' have sprung up all over the country. These can sell only local produce and have become a useful outlet for organic farmers while giving town people the opportunity to buy fresh locally grown food and at the same time aiding the rural economy.

GENETIC MODIFICATION

Biotechnology is not a new concept, but scientists discovered a short-cut in selective breeding when they finally unravelled the mysteries of chromosomes and then genes. It was in 1953 at Cambridge (England) that Mr Watson and Mr Crick identified the structure of the Deoxyribonucleic Acid molecule, commonly known as DNA, which carries the genetic code.

For centuries growers and farmers have practised genetic engineering by the selective breeding of plants and livestock to continually improve crop management, disease resistance, growth rates and yields. By doing so, they kept an ever-increasing population fed. Farmers improved the milk yields and growth rate of their livestock through cross breeding to develop different strains. In 1694 the method of the sexual reproduction of plants

Many organic vegetable producers now use a 'Box Scheme' whereby boxes of fresh seasonal food are delivered directly to subscribing customers

Potatoes have now been genetically developed that are resistant to the Colorado beetle

87

was discovered and in 1719 the first hybrid plant was recorded. The first cereal hybrid appeared in 1799 and in 1866 an Austrian monk, Gregor Mendel, experimented with crossing varieties of peas and realised that there were certain factors which controlled inherited characteristics. It was nearly a hundred years later before these 'factors' were identified as genes.

Although DNA was discovered in 1953 it wasn't until 1970 that scientists learnt how to move it between unrelated organisms, which was when the public began to realise the previously unimaginable implications and expressed grave concerns over which directions future experiments would take. Instead of the genetic engineering of plants being confined to natural pollination between similar species, scientists could now introduce 'desirable traits' not only from other plants but also from fish and animals. This is probably the most alarming aspect.

Ethical issues of GM

The whole process of genetic engineering is hugely complicated and controversial but because of it plant breeders are able to provide more efficient and economical crops. Straw is an often unwanted by-product from growing cereals, so short-stemmed varieties were selectively bred and the disposal of surplus straw was no longer a problem. However, if modern GM technology was used, crops could also be bred to be drought-resistant. Probably the biggest benefit in Britain would be GM crops which were herbicide tolerant and resistant to virus and insect damage. This would greatly reduce the use of sprays which currently concern the consumer. Argentina, USA, Canada, Mexico, Spain, China, Australia, South Africa and Russia all have commercial GM crops in production. The species currently grown are carnations, chicory, coffee, cotton, flax, maize, oilseed rape, papaya, potatoes, soya bean, squash, sweet corn, tomatoes and tobacco. Sugar beet, rice, and bananas will shortly follow.

The potential for the beneficial use of Genetic Modification is enormous but with such a new discovery the long-term effects are unknown. With such a far-reaching innovation, the potential for a more sinister use of the knowledge of plant engineering techniques is always a possibility and should not be discounted.

Although Britain has played a leading role in biotechnology,

1983: Tobacco was the first GM plant to be produced

1990: First GM cereal crop grown

Women cutting corn in India. With a population of over one billion the appeal of high-yield GM crops is undeniable

there are no plans to grow GM crops on a commercial scale until a full assessment has been made as to the impact on the environment in the countries where it is at present being grown. Experimental trials on a small scale however are being conducted on several sites across the country.

A very simplified example of how genetic modification can be applied beneficially is demonstrated by some of the work done with potatoes. The Colorado beetle is a common pest in some countries causing much damage to crops but GM potatoes have now been developed that are resistant to attacks by this pest. One naturally occurring organism in the soil excretes a substance which is harmless to humans but toxic to insects. This has been isolated and used for many years as a pesticide for crops. However when researchers were able to isolate the gene responsible for the toxin they were then able to insert it directly into the plant which enabled it to generate its own insecticide within its own tissues; hence potatoes that won't get eaten by Colorado beetles.

GM to help mankind?

Besides plant breeding, genetic engineering has produced amazing results using animals and micro-organisms to manufacture medicines such as insulin, interferon and human growth hormone and GM vaccines have also been developed. Chicken eggs are used to produce insulin and antibodies to human viruses. Experimental work is being undertaken to create genetically modified pigs which will provide organs that can be transplanted into humans. A substance called 'rennet' which is a necessary element in the manufacture of cheese could only be found in calves' stomachs and had to be extracted from them after the calves had been slaughtered. Now thanks to genetic engineering it can be produced artificially in laboratories.

Genetically modified crops could be the saviour for many third world countries often stricken by drought and with an exploding population and decreasing resources; countries like India where the official population reached one billion in May 2000 and is still increasing at an alarming rate. It is very easy to be critical and complacent when living in a wealthy and wasteful society. However, the people who live in many African countries unable to produce sufficient food and on the borderline of starva-

Old breeds such as the Longhorn are being revived because of the interest in high-quality rare breeds of beef for the table

Although DNA was discovered in 1953 it wasn't until 1970 that scientists learnt how to move it between unrelated organisms

tion no doubt have a completely different opinion and would perhaps welcome GM crops if they helped to alleviate their plight.

There is obviously a need for caution and very strict controls regarding the use of GM crops. If their development could feed the hungry, reduce the need for so many sprays and artificial fertilisers, enable food plants to adapt to climate changes or be used to produce medicinal drugs and even be bred to absorb impurities from contaminated land – without upsetting the balance of nature – the potential for good may well outweigh the bad.

CROFTING

Crofts in the remote areas of the Western Highlands and Islands of Scotland are the equivalent of lowland smallholdings but they lack the kinder climate and fertile soil. For centuries crofting has provided a subsistence living from hill grazing rights and a very few hectares of 'in bye' land which could be cultivated in summer to provide potatoes for the family and swedes and hay for winter livestock feed. The few cows owned would be kept in sheds during the harshest winter weather and pregnant ewes might be brought into the paddocks to give birth. Most of the year though, both cows and sheep would be expected to survive out on the hill, but in the Western Highlands and Islands this can be a harsh environment even in summer. Tough localised breeds evolved such as the Highland cow and the Blackface sheep.

Ancient crofting

Crofts were traditionally let to tenants by the local Laird who not only gained an income from the rent but also obtained a local source of casual labour. Many crofters were almost self-sufficient. Vegetables and meat were available, wool could be spun and knitted into garments, and peat for winter fuel was dug and dried each summer, but the standard of living was meagre. The winter months were wet and stormy with only a few hours of daylight and was the time for carrying out repairs and tending cattle kept inside for the winter. If the weather was particularly bad, some of the sheep would make their way off the hills and down to the croft in search of food and shelter. They would be

Crofting community at Duirinish, Wester Ross

A fit, strong man can cut nearly one thousand peat turfs in a day

gathered up anyway in late March and the pregnant ones kept in a nearby field, if possible, to lamb.

April saw the crofter busy lambing his ewes and ploughing up what little land he could spare to grow his crops. In May the lambs would be marked for identification and turned back out on the hill with their mothers. Then it was time to start peat cutting. A fit, strong man could cut nearly one thousand turfs in a day while the family stacked them to dry, but 15,000 were needed for winter fuel and not every day could be spent cutting because there were crops to plant and the cows would be calving. June and July was the time to get the sheep back off the hills to clip their wool and then to make hay. Both jobs needed fine weather and were times when the whole community helped each other. In August there may have been time to relax and socialise at the local shows and hopefully win a prize with a beast. There was still work to be done though because the peat, which should have dried by now, needed to be brought home to be stored.

In September, the sheep would again be gathered so that lambs could be separated ready to sell; the ewes dipped and sent back to the hill on their own. The small community would all work together in this and with any cereals to harvest. November and once again the sheep would be brought in and sorted for it was time to put the rams in to ensure a crop of lambs next spring. Some may have been kept in the paddocks to make sure that the ram found them when they came on heat, for out on the hill they were widely scattered. It was also time to wean the calves so that they too could be sold, and to house the cows for winter.

In December the sheep would once again be turned back out to fend for themselves until winter storms raged. It was also time for the crofters to survive on the fruits of their summer labours as the days grew short and to celebrate Christmas. That is how it was a hundred years ago and it is still pretty much like that today.

Government support for modern crofting

The Crofters Commission in Scotland was set up in 1955 with the purpose of protecting the traditional way of life and preserving the identities and cultures of crofters, taking into account the needs of the

Traditionally schools would close for two weeks in October so that crofters' children could help gather in crops of potatoes, swedes and turnips, so vital for the winter months

Below Abandoned crofts, evidence of hard times in the past

crofter and those of the communities as a whole.

The crofting tradition developed out of the old clan system and today there are about 14,000 registered crofts, mainly along the Western and Northern coasts of Scotland and the Islands, supporting around 30,000 people. A new crofting township has been created, the first for 80 years, with the building of 8 ten acre (2.5 hectare) holdings on unused farmland belonging to the National Trust near Kyle of Lochalsh.

Dead lamb – victim of the highland fox which takes a heavy toll from the crofter at lambing time

The majority of crofters are tenants. Some own their own crofts but even when they have been purchased, they are still subject to the provisions of the Crofting Act and it is expected that they be inhabited and used for agriculture. Crofters still have to supplement their income with other work. Those on the coast do this by working on fish farms or sea fishing while those inland look for fencing or building jobs, forestry work or ghillieing for deer stalkers or salmon fishermen. But machines have replaced men in the forests and wild salmon stocks are seriously depleted, making work hard to find. The local postman might be a crofter and the wildlife warden and there is always the tourist to cater for. Crofting is a unique, precarious but tough way of life.

Youngsters are tending to desert rural communities to find work and a social life in towns and cities. However, there is a Croft Entrant Scheme initiative to encourage young people to become crofters and continue to preserve the culture (including the Gaelic language) the environment and heritage and to keep these tiny rural communities alive. Limited grants are available through the Crofting Counties Agricultural Grants Scheme (CCAGS) for such things as building improvements, reseeding of 'in bye' (enclosed) grassland, bracken control, land drainage and the upkeep of roads, dykes (walls) and hedges.

The Crofters' Commission also operate a Livestock Improvement Scheme for crofters where stock bulls can be hired by a community to breed with their cows. These cows are often of mixed breeding containing a proportion of hardy native blood such as the Highland or Luing breeds. Several breeds of bull are

> *A crofter is entitled to bequeath the tenancy of his croft to any one person of his choice*

> *Today there are about 14,000 registered crofts*

available and the continental breeds such as the Simmental and Limousin are popular. However if females from the calves produced are kept for future breeding, another breed such as an Aberdeen Angus will need to be used on them because too much continental blood in future generations will make them unable to thrive under the conditions they are kept.

Hardy Cheviot and Blackface rams are also available for purchase at a subsidised cost. These are the two breeds best adapted to the area. In the Shetland Isles there is also a scheme to subsidise the purchase of pure bred Shetland rams to encourage and support the local wool and craft industries by preserving this specialised breed.

The North-West Highlands is classified as a severely disadvantaged area and as such qualifies for livestock headage payments from the EU and UK Governments. Unfortunately this led to overstocking to the detriment of both the stock and their environment; this has now been rectified by the introduction of a quota system.

In modern times crofts are still very small, usually only a few hectares or less, and rights to graze stock on the open hills are often shared with others in the crofting townships. Less than 10 cows and 100 sheep are often all a crofter owns and each ewe will need access to about 2 hectares in order to survive. It is impossible for crofters to compete economically with their lowland counterparts yet without them the whole ecology of the area would change.

The communities often join together, sharing a tractor and some machinery as well as helping each other out at busy times. The invention of bagged silage revolutionised the production of good winter food and contractors are available to carry out the work. A mix of oats, peas and barley is sometimes grown for silage to provide nutritious winter feed.

Some crofters are able to bring their sheep down into paddocks to lamb while others are forced to leave them out on the hill where they are vulnerable to the weather and predators. Hooded crows will attack weak new-born lambs but by far the worst enemy are foxes who can only be kept under control by shooting them at night using a powerful lamp and a rifle or by searching for places where they spend the daylight hours and

Peat is dug as turfs, dried on the moor, then carried home in late summer

Sheep that instinctively stay on an unfenced area of hill are known as 'Hefted'

dealing with them there. There are 'Fox Clubs' in operation who carry out these jobs but they charge for the service they offer; otherwise the crofter has to do it himself because foxes can take a heavy toll at lambing time.

Lambing, for crofters, is usually organised to begin about April 20th. Those ewes left out on the hill all year may only manage to rear an average of 7 lambs for every 10 ewes, partly due to the fact that some lambs perish soon after birth and partly due to the rams not having found the ewes in the first place.

The ewes and rams are sheared (not the lambs) in July but the invention of acrylic and other man-made fibres has made wool of little value and the price the crofter receives for fleeces does not even pay for the cost of shearing. Sheep older than a year need to be sheared in the summer because flies will lay their eggs in the thick wool and then hatch out into maggots which burrow into the flesh. Dipping a few weeks after shearing also helps to control this problem and a skin disease called 'Sheep Scab'. Organo-phosphorous solutions, the cause of much concern over human health risks were, unfortunately, the most effective treatment but have now been withdrawn.

Lambs are weaned in September when they are sent to special lamb sales to be bought as 'stores' and taken elsewhere to fatten. Replacement ewe lambs retained for breeding are sometimes sent to lowland farms to over-winter, giving them the chance to grow quicker and be in good condition to breed the following autumn. They are individually marked so that when they are returned in spring they can be put back in the area in which they were born.

Ewes from the croft are usually kept for 4 crops of lambs before being 'drafted', which means sold and taken to lowland farms for breeding where the living is easier, for the harsh conditions take their toll and only the fit will survive. Often it is the sheep's teeth that begin to wear, making them unable to cope with the coarse vegetation.

Rams, which have been kept separately all summer, will be turned out with the ewes in late October or November, timed so that lambs arrive at the end of April.

Beef cattle are kept on the single suckler system. They are calved about April time, turned out on the hill with their calves

Twin lambs are not that welcome, for a hill ewe rarely produces enough milk to rear two lambs and bottle feeding is not economic

Below Stone walling in Wester Ross

for the summer and the calves weaned in October; like lambs, these are sold as stores. Occasionally some are kept to fatten but the price of housing and transporting straw and winter feed to remote crofts in most cases makes it not cost-effective. Bulls that have been hired from the Crofters Commission are expected to be returned to their stud farms for the winter. Cows are normally housed through the worst of the weather and a by-product from local whisky distilleries known as 'draff' is often used for part of their rations.

North Sea oil and gas may have proved an easier option to digging peat, and silage is easier to make than hay; otherwise little has changed in crofting during the last century. It is still a hard life but the small crofting townships around the Western Highlands and Islands of Scotland maintain and enrich the environment, giving the area a unique character all of its own.

Highland cow, specially adapted for surviving the harsh Highland conditions

FARMING DIVERSIFICATION

As farmers are becoming increasingly hard-pressed to earn a living from traditional methods of agriculture, they are desperately seeking new enterprises to make ends meet. Not so long ago the farmer's wife would keep a few hens and sell eggs at the gate in order to earn a little 'pin' money. Those days are gone because it is much more than 'pin' money that is now needed.

Some farms invested money into building farm shops selling a wider range of local goods. Farmers Markets have been set up and they are thriving. In 1998 there were only four and by the beginning of 2002 the number had increased to over four hundred. Farmers Markets have brought the countryside back into towns. Usually held once a month, they sell only locally-made or grown produce and have given farmers an opportunity to come into direct contact with their customers. Farmers Markets also provide an outlet for many of the products available as a result of diversification and allow town and country to meet and talk. Buyers can find out how their purchases were grown, harvested or made and enjoy a much more personal experience of the British countryside than they would filling a supermarket

A by-product of whisky distilling known as 'draff' is used to feed cattle

95

trolley. The farmer's wife, instead of keeping a few chicken, may well be selling home produce such as vegetables, cakes, pastries chutney or honey. Many organic producers use Farmers Markets as an outlet for their meat, eggs and vegetables.

Quarrying as a sideline, then using the hole!

The land itself can yield such things as lime and aggregates (gravel, rock, minerals etc). Where these have been quarried, the resulting large holes in the ground can eventually be attractively landscaped and developed into lakes to provide a further income from fishing or water sports activities. The soil in some areas is suitable to grow turfs for laying lawns. Special seed mixes are sown and the process carried out over a period of 14 months. Much care is needed to produce the perfect finished article. Fields of sunflowers or other seeds are grown to supply the huge demand for garden bird food, and some may be crushed to make cooking oil. Herbs such as camomile and lavender are grown to be manufactured into essential oils.

Vineyards have been established for several years in England and Wales. There were over 400 in 1998 but fewer now because of the recent series of bad summers that have made these ventures unprofitable. British vineyards produce between 8,000 and 20,000 litres of wine annually. Small breweries are on the increase creating their own potent special brews.

TV cookery programmes can trigger a sudden demand for things like fresh coriander or flat parsley

Cutting parsley can be done mechanically

Diverse farming methods

Peat (naturally compressed vegetation) was once only cut by crofters as fuel for their fires but now it has become an industry to supply keen gardeners. Instead of it being cut by hand, huge machines cut and package it. This is causing great concern to conserva-

tionists. Now these machines can slice away in minutes what it has taken centuries to form.

A very fast-growing strain of willow is being grown to produce bio-mass as a sustainable eco fuel for the new generation of environmentally friendly power stations. Elephant grass is also being explored for this purpose.

Bees have always been kept in the countryside. They are vital for the pollination of flowers and thus the fruit. The delicious honey they fervently store is distinctly flavoured by the species of flowers they have collected pollen from. They take this back to their hives where it is cached in the honeycomb and later collected by the beekeeper.

Chives being prepared by hand for sale

Maggot farming has always been carried out on a small scale to supply bait to a million or more fishermen but gardening experts and conservationists have awakened an interest in worms as well so worm farms are being set up.

Rabbit farms exist to produce meat; the skins (pelts) are a by-product. As with chicken and turkey meat, farm rabbits are predominately white in colour and have been genetically bred to grow very quickly. There are a few fur farms still in existence but these are quickly being phased out. Mink kept in small cages have been the focus for animal rights groups who believe it is cruel and unnecessary to breed animals for fur. Whatever their views on cruelty, by their misguided liberation of these voracious animals they have caused the destruction of many of our native wild animals, even to the extent of putting some, such as the water vole, in danger of extinction.

The humble goat has always been found tethered in the countryside although there are fewer these days. There are some farms who now keep them in herds for their milk, either sold fresh or made into cheese. Sheep too are sometimes kept to produce milk. Certain breeds of goats and sheep are also kept for their fine wool and it is often used for spinning by their owners. Angora and cashmere from goats command a very high price.

Farmers' Markets are flourishing – there are now over four hundred in Britain

Novelty species

Llamas and Alpacas from South America look very out of place in the British countryside but some farmers are looking to them to earn some extra income. Once mature they can produce a young one annually, will breed at any time of the year and live for 15 to 20 years. Alpacas have soft pads on their feet, like camels, instead of hard hooves, so consequently they cause little damage to grassland when it is wet. They are normally gentle, docile and sociable animals possessing a herd instinct. They choose one area of the field in which to dung so they don't soil their pastures and they do not suffer much from parasites (intestinal worms, fluke etc). They are sheared once a year for their fleece which is not oily like sheep's wool and which is very valuable. Llamas and alpacas are occasionally used as novelty pack animals.

Another exotic animal that has appeared on British farms in recent years is the ostrich although it does not seem to have made much progress as a commercial venture. It is kept primarily for its meat but the skin can also be tanned and turned into leather. Guinea fowl are also being bred to supply restaurants whose customers wish to try something different.

Deer farms have been established to supply quality venison and produce breeding stock. Red deer are usually kept but their profitability, like that of all other cloven hoofed animals, has been badly affected by the regulations implemented because of Foot and Mouth disease.

Wild boar is becoming increasingly popular with consumers who are in search of meat with a more distinctive flavour. Once native to Britain but extinct here for 300 years, boar are once again appearing in the wild, because captive imported animals have escaped from farms and successfully bred. There are now several hundred leading a feral existence in parts of Kent, Sussex and Dorset. The impact of this on the ecology of the countryside has yet to be assessed, although some conservationists are pleased to see a once-native animal returning to the woodlands. In densely populated or intensively farmed areas there is certain to be conflict eventually because wild boar are very strong, sometimes aggressive and often destructive. All members of the pig family are omnivorous, so ground-nesting birds and baby animals will obviously be at risk. Wild boar can also cause damage to

British vineyards produce between 8,000 and 20,000 litres of wine annually

There are now over 5,000 alpacas in Britain and they are well suited to the conditions, such as here in Sussex

plant life with their habit of 'rootling' when they may dig up and eat roots and bulbs.

To keep wild boar captive it is necessary to erect a very strong fence. It needs to be 5ft (1.5m) high and buried into the ground to a depth of 18 inches (45cms). It is recommended that one boar and five sows are given an enclosure of 2 acres (1 hectare) sited in dense woodland which is their natural habitat. They only require the minimum attention. Litter size average about five. A young boar is known as a 'marcassin'. Wild boar are also sometimes used to cross with domestic breeds.

Tourism and farming

As more and more people are encouraged to visit the countryside for leisure purposes farmers are responding to further opportunities to diversify. Riding schools and livery yards are being created. Large rambling farmhouses can be converted into bed and breakfast accommodation, an invaluable chance for visiting guests to learn the ways of the countryside. Outbuildings, redundant piggeries, cow sheds and stables can be converted into self-catering accommodation. Sometimes stables are provided for those wishing to bring their horse or pony with them. Riding may be made available. There are 120,000 miles of trails for the public use of walkers and horse riders in England alone.

Increasingly the British countryside is becoming a leisure area as the population has more time and money to spare. Corporate entertainment now often involves countryside-based activities. Golf has become a popular sport and new golf courses are appearing although these require a substantial long-term investment. Shooting, off-road driving, survival skills training, orienteering and paint ball games appeal to the more adventurous. Open farms attract visitors who are always keen to see young animals. Wildlife viewing and photography opportunities are now big business. Wildlife parks, sanctuaries, woodlands and areas for marriages and burials are being opened to the public in rural areas.

Interest in country crafts abounds. Courses are available and demonstrations given at country shows. Combined with the chance to sell the finished article, this will hopefully ensure that the skills of yesteryear are not lost forever: the blacksmith, the hurdle maker, the basket maker, the weaver, the wood turner and

Honey production is a traditional side-line for farmers, who take the honey then make sure the bees are given enough sugared water to see them through the winter

A young wild boar is known as a 'marcassin'

the carver once fed their families by the skill of their hands.

Diversification is keeping the countryside alive and has awakened interest in some of the traditions that looked at one time as though they would disappear. While ostriches and alpacas may seem alien, the resurgence of natural produce must be good.

Old derelict buildings are being rejuvenated to cater for the holidaymaker and small rural businesses, and the more people that come into the countryside, the greater opportunities there are for employment and for farmers to supplement their income.

The countryside is greatly changed, much to the regret of many country folk, but it is not dying, even though the traditional ways are disappearing. Government grants were available a few years ago to help farmers diversify but the outbreak of Foot and Mouth disease devastated many of their plans and red tape has made other small ventures impossible. Farmers are very disillusioned but as they know no other way of life, nor want it, many will extricate a living from the land by any means they can find.

Animals such as badgers, sometimes a nuisance to farmers, can now generate an income in return for the small cost of erecting a viewing hide and a few dog biscuits and peanuts to entice them near

CONSERVATION

No one doubts that our remaining countryside and the flora and fauna in it needs preserving for future generations, but the way in which it is done sometimes causes disagreement.

There are nearly 60 million people in Britain and each year they encroach onto more and more land. As it disappears under acres of tarmac and concrete, so the wildlife left in it has less space in which to live. At the current rate of development it is estimated that 20% of Britain will have become urban land by 2050. It would be impossible to build on many areas of land, so this means that there will be dreadful pressure on the rest.

The Enclosures Acts in past centuries account for much of the landscape as it is today. In the 1950s and 60s post-war agricultural policies and scientific advances were to blame for the serious deterioration of the countryside. Sheep numbers on moors quadrupled and 40% of the heather was lost. Ancient meadows were ploughed up and the plants in them destroyed. Toxic chem-

Goats are being kept for milk again, uses for herbs are being rediscovered, and the farmer is once again selling direct to his customer

icals used on the land were absorbed by insects, animals and birds and in turn decimated the species that preyed upon them in one way or another. More recently the efficiency of modern farm machinery has meant that no waste is left on the fields for wildlife to glean, corners of fields are now cultivated instead of being left rough and herbicides make a thorough job of killing the weeds on which birds could find food. Farmland and garden pesticides kill off insects and invertebrates depriving birds of their natural food.

Eventually in the late 1980s Britain woke up to what was happening to its countryside and government schemes and policies were introduced in favour of conservation. These have gone from strength to strength and the emphasis now is very much on co-ordinating efficient farming practices with the need to restore and preserve what remains of the countryside. The Policy Commission on Food and Farming has recommended that at least 10% of EU farming payments is re-directed from production-led subsidies to the benefit of the environment and to pay for rural development. Recent EU proposals link future subsidies to environmental standards rather than production.

Conservation groups

However, due to the presence of man, nature is no longer able to look after herself and even seemingly-neglected places have to be carefully managed. There are a huge number of conservation bodies, both large and small, who not only carry out practical work but who also promote public awareness of their need. Some are very localised while others such as the National Trust and RSPB are well known. The latter has over one million members and owns in excess of a quarter of a million acres (103,000 hectares) of land around Britain.

The Farming and Wildlife Advisory Group (FWAG) was formed in 1969 to provide conservation advice to caring farmers about such things as woodlands, hedgerows, water courses, wetlands, moorland and field margins. It also now advises about the many grants available for such things as tree planting; and the long-term Countryside Stewardship Scheme. There are several cost-free conservation measures that farmers can apply to aid wildlife such as leaving autumn stubble unploughed as long as possible, leaving odd rough corners and delaying hedge cutting

Hedgehogs introduced to the Outer Hebrides were decimating the ground-nesting birds. The proposed hedgehog cull caused a public outcry

Many crops of cereals grown today are now sown in the autumn, denying wildlife the stubble that once helped support them through the winter

until February so that birds can feed on the berries left on them during the winter.

However every bird, animal and insect has a complicated life-cycle in which each part of the so-called food chain needs to be in place. For example all birds, whether insect eaters or seed eaters, need grubs and bugs to feed their newly hatched chicks. This supply itself usually needs a specific food source by way of certain plants which in turn need certain habitats. For instance blue tits frequently feed their young on the tiny green caterpillars of an oak moth which hatches from eggs laid on oak leaves. This means that sometimes the blue tit chicks' survival may depend on an oak tree.

Difficult choices

Conservationists are very often faced with a moral dilemma, for while their intention is to preserve, they may also have to destroy. In order to restore heath land or certain species on it they may have to cut down overgrown bushes and scrub which are themselves home to woodland birds. Some wardens on reserves for waders and other ground nesting birds take it upon themselves to control foxes, mink, crows and blackbacked gulls which have been known to almost wipe out tern and avocet colonies. Other species such as hedgehogs, herons and kestrels also take their toll but they are protected by law so wardens can do little about them. In Scotland deer are culled heavily on some nature reserves to protect the habitat in the old Caledonian forests. These are home to blackcock and the few remaining capercaillie although it is thought the main reason for the latter's demise in recent years has been the miles of deer fencing surrounding conifer plantations which they fly into and kill or injure themselves.

Foxes are a constant threat to any bird or animal that lives on the ground. While many conservationists have no time for gamekeepers and at times are even hostile towards them, in many cases they do benefit from the predator control that keepers carry out. Shooting estates cull an estimated 100,000 foxes each year. Recent research shows that golden plover, lapwing and curlew are up to six times more common on keepered moorland than on the equivalent not managed for game. Grouse moor gamekeepers also carry out extensive management of heather by rotational

Above Water vole, pushed to the brink of extinction by mink and habitat loss

Below Little owl with mouse: a gain for one species is often a loss for another

Hurdle making: there has been a revival of interest in country crafts

controlled burning which benefits many species of wildlife besides grouse as well as the heather itself.

Bracken, an invasive plant that excludes all others, is controlled by conservationists and moor managers. Aerial spraying is one method used. Flying as low as 2 metres above the ground, helicopters can spray an acre of otherwise inaccessible ground in as little as 15 seconds. These helicopters are also sometimes used to sow heather seed at the rate of 600 seeds per square metre on areas of ground to re-establish the plant where it has died out.

Fieldsports contribution

In lowland areas many shooting estates grow cover crops for their pheasants and partridges which also greatly benefit other species both as food and on occasions nesting sites. Around the coast wildfowlers, who shoot only truly wild ducks and geese, do much to preserve the marshy habitats that are attractive to them and often work closely with conservation organisations. Shooting estates for the last century, whether intentionally or not, have contributed a great deal to the conservation of the countryside and much of the wildlife in it. Although there are inevitably a few exceptions, most shooting people respect and take more than a passing interest in nature and some estates go to great lengths to improve habitat and take other conservation measures. Ten years ago the Game Conservancy took over the running of an 800 acre

Otters have been successfully reintroduced to some areas and are now naturally increasing and extending their range

CONSERVATION *Useful Words*

BAP Biodiversity Action Plan.

BIODIVERSITY The wealth of wildlife – plant and animal – to be found on land, in water or in the sea.

CA Countryside Agency. A statutory government body.

CAP Common Agricultural Policy (Europe).

COPPICING Cutting back certain trees in a small area each year which allows new growth to regenerate thus ensuring that the species lives on and does not die of disease or old age. This generally improves wildlife habitats and was once carried out by such people as hurdle makers who regularly cut hazel growing in woodland.

CSS Countryside Stewardship Scheme. A scheme offering payments to land managers and farmers to improve the natural beauty and diversity of the country-side.

DETR Department for the Environment, Transport and the Regions.

EN English Nature. A statutory government service that is responsible for looking after Britain's flora and fauna. It advises the government, landowners and managers.

FAUNA Animals.

FLORA Plants.

HABITAT The natural home of a living thing.

LNR Local Nature Reserve.

MNR Marine Nature Reserve.

NNR National Nature Reserve.

PREDATOR A carnivorous animal or bird that hunts and eats other living things.

PREY Victim of a predator.

RAMSARS Wetland sites of international importance.

RAPTORS Birds of prey such as hawks, falcons and harriers.

RIGS Regionally Important Geological and Geomorphological Sites.

RSPB Royal Society for the Protection of Birds.

RURAL Relating to the countryside.

SAC Special Area of Conservation (European).

SPA Special Protection Area for the conservation of the habitat for rare and vulnerable birds (European).

SSSI Site of Special Scientific Interest.

SUSTAINABILITY Meeting the needs of the present generation without compromising the ability of future generations to meet their needs.

URBAN Relating to towns and cities.

WADERS Birds of various sizes that generally have long legs and are usually found near shores, bogs or marshes. Many are winter visitors and those that remain to breed nest on the ground in woodland, farmland or moorland. They feed on insects, worms and molluscs.

Rabbits on a Norfolk heath

farm at Loddington in Leicestershire. They appointed a keeper and have since run it as a study to see how profitable farming and conservation can work together. Detailed records have been kept and have shown that numbers of song birds on it have more than doubled, as have the game birds.

Harnessing the weather

Some things however are beyond the control of anyone and, in particular, that includes the weather. It can be so cruel and a year's work can be undone in a day. A cold spring will not only

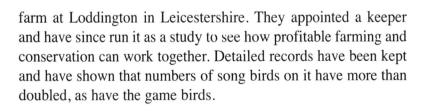

It takes one thousand years for six inches of peat to form from decaying vegetation

kill newly hatched chicks but will also mean that there are few insects or grubs for them to feed on and summer flooding too can wipe out ground nesting birds. Late frosts may damage tender plants and drought may kill others. All wildlife is extremely vulnerable during the breeding season in spring and early summer. Chemicals, noise, pollution, rubbish and disturbance are the enemies of conservationists and measures are being developed to reduce these. Electricity is now being generated by turbines harnessing the wind. Eco-friendly power stations using waste or surplus materials such as straw, wood chippings and poultry litter or renewable sources from fast growing willow trees and other plants are being built.

The conversion of so many barns into houses has deprived barn owls of their homes

Tapping decades of knowledge

There are many traditional skills and tools that conservationists can make use of. Much wisdom is available in the countryside which hasn't been learnt in universities. People who have spent their lives working alongside nature possess an invaluable knowledge which also needs preserving. While theories abound, it is often the non-academic locals who could tell boffins what would work and what wouldn't, were they to be asked. Redundant skills that once earned a countryman his living can now be utilised through conservation funding. There are over 70,000 miles of dry stone walls in England alone, many in disrepair. When these need mending or re-building it is a very skilled job. One experienced man may slot as much as ten tons of stone painstakingly into place in a day. Coppicing and general care of woodlands and marshes also need specific expertise, as do many other jobs. However the backbone of many conservation organisations are the volunteers who do an amazing amount of work throughout the year clearing, tidying, mending paths, recording and manning visitor centres.

Released mink have been largely responsible for the near extinction of the water vole whose numbers have fallen by 90% in the last decade. Trapping this non-indigenous predator is an important conservation measure

Nature mends itself

Plants and their seeds can remain dormant and unharmed in the ground for an surprising length of time. Primroses and foxgloves not seen for years sometimes suddenly appear in newly coppiced woodland. Arable fields that have been included in conservation schemes may suddenly sprout poppies and other wild flowers even though they have been regularly sprayed with herbicides in the past. 98% of the original wild flower meadows in Britain have been ploughed up but in areas like the Yorkshire Dales where they still exist farmers are paid to make hay after July 7th instead of cutting the crop for silage in May. This allows the plants time to flower in June and then seed. 80% of heaths have been lost but moves are now being made under the Heath Restoration Project to restore land back to heath.

A start is being made with the removal of conifers from 300 hectares of Thetford forest so that the land can be restored back to the heathland it was less than a century ago. The preservation of peat bogs is also receiving priority attention as very few lowland ones remain. English Nature has bought up 2,500 acres (1,000 hectares) but there is great concern that peat abstraction is still being allowed to continue on land that has been designated Special Sites of Scientific Interest (SSSIs).

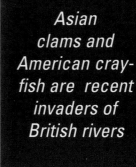

Asian clams and American crayfish are recent invaders of British rivers

It is ironic that thirty years ago grants were being paid to drain wetlands when now they are being paid to restore them. Bogs are unique for their unusual plants – so many of them are being destroyed by the removal of peat of which 70% is used by gardeners to grow plants. It takes one thousand years for six inches of peat to form from decaying vegetation and it can be removed by machines in a very short time. Alternatives are available so gardeners would be wise to use these rather than being party to decimating unique wildlife sites.

The hedge flail enables farmers to maintain miles of hedgerow. The timing of the cutting is important if wildlife – particularly nesting birds – are not to be disturbed, and their winter food (berries) preserved

Harnessing animals for conservation

Animals are also used as conservation tools on many reserves. Local breeds of sheep are particularly suited to certain areas and are often kept in reasonable numbers to control scrub on heaths, moors and fells. Without them unpalatable rank grass would begin to appear after about two years, scrub would be abundant after ten and the whole landscape would have changed within fifteen. Cattle are grazed on marshland in summer and their droppings enrich the soil and encourage the invertebrates that many wild birds need to feed on. Other reserves use ponies to control the vegetation.

Species at risk

There are more than 200 species of birds and 69 species of wild animals living in Britain and some are under serious threat of extinction. Of particular concern is the water vole, already a victim of habitat destruction, whose numbers have been further decimated by mink and have fallen by 90% in the last ten years. The red squirrel has all but disappeared from England and Wales, displaced by an immigrant from America, the grey squirrel. Dormice are becoming scarce through loss of habitat as is the harvest mouse; three-quarters of the known colonies have disappeared during the last twenty years. The removal of many old or dead trees has reduced nesting sites for bats and some species of birds and the conversion of so many barns into houses has deprived barn owls of their homes.

Many farmland birds have been badly affected by agricultural changes including the English or grey partridge. It is a species that has long been revered by sporting estates but now shooting people are contributing a great deal of money into research to find out why their quarry which was once so abundant has become a precious rarity. It certainly isn't because they have been over-shot as the shooting fraternity have always made sure they only reap the surplus of wild stock and leave sufficient for breeding. Other threatened species are the natterjack toad, the great crested newt and the otter although otters have been successfully reintroduced to some areas and are now naturally increasing and extending their range.

Introducing exotic and alien species

The consequences of reintroducing beavers and wolves to Britain, as has been suggested by some conservationists, may well cause unforeseen ecological damage. The human population of the country was very much smaller when these animals last roamed wild here. Exotic and alien species are increasingly appearing in our countryside and can cause unimagined harm as

A mallard and her brood, beneficiaries of the new reserves and wetlands

There are more than 200 species of birds and 69 species of mammal living wild in Britain

the mink and grey squirrel have done. Garden plants are becoming endemic as are aquatic ones dumped from ponds and aquariums and which are now choking some waterways. Asian clams are rapidly invading rivers and a massive colony has become established in the Norfolk Broads. American signal crayfish are threatening the smaller British crayfish because they carry disease and are more powerful. A large group of ring-necked parakeets are flourishing in the London area.

It is illegal to release into the wild any species that is not native to Britain but there are many people who don't realise the long-term consequences of doing so. Although an individual item may seem very insignificant, in the scheme of things its impact on the environment may not be.

Birdwatching

Birdwatching has become an extremely popular hobby but some of the most fanatical observers show little respect for the rarer species that occasionally visit Britain. Many reserves, particularly wader and duck sites, have specially built hides from which birds can be viewed without causing any disturbance to them. Perhaps one of the most unique (and unlikely) reserves is situated in the middle of London. An old reservoir site belonging to Thames Water was purchased by the Wildfowl and Wetlands Trust and has recently been transformed into a 140 acre (57 hectare) nature reserve. Within reach of Hammersmith tube station it enables people from all over London to observe a wide variety of wildlife without having to leave the city, particularly in winter when migratory birds visit the centre.

Birds in the garden

Town and country householders alike do their bit for conservation by having bird tables in their gardens which attract a multitude of species. Conversely these people often also keep cats of which there are about 7.5 million in Britain accounting for the deaths of an estimated 75 million small birds annually. Sparrowhawk numbers have increased in the last few years and a lot of people get quite upset when one grabs an unsuspecting blue tit off their bird table. A bird table must seem to be like a convenient 'take away' to a sparrowhawk who has such a choice of menu from one

Lapwing, a beneficiary of predator-control by gamekeepers

Cats kill an estimated 75 million small birds annually

place. At their present level, sparrowhawks kill approximately 16 million birds a year, and when a parent bird is caught, it is likely that its young will also die through not being fed or kept warm. It must come as a shock to some people to witness that one of the raptors they admire so much actually catches and eats other birds.

Langholm Estate experiment

A five-year research project began in 1991 which examined the relationship between birds of prey and red grouse. It was conducted on an established and well-recorded estate at Langholm in south-west Scotland by several

Grouse populations respond directly to the careful control of moorland predators

conservation bodies including the RSPB and the Game Conservancy. The experiment studied the impact of birds of prey on red grouse.

The season before the project began, 2,000 brace of grouse had been shot and when it started there was a good stock of breeding grouse left and an abundance of pipits, other birds and small mammals as well as 2 nesting pairs of harriers and 3 pairs of peregrines. The year after the study ended (1997) there were 20 pairs of harriers nesting and 6 pairs of peregrines, very few grouse, 4 gamekeepers had lost their jobs and the estate had lost an important part of its income. The study showed that in the last two years, harrier numbers were rising: they killed 30% of the breeding stock of grouse and took over a third of their hatched chicks. While in the nest the young harriers' diet consisted of 45% pipits and 12% grouse chicks.

Peregrines brought 10% grouse chicks to feed their broods and over half their diet was made up of feral and racing pigeons. Since the experiment ended, the populations of harriers have shown a dramatic decrease because without proper management there is insufficient food left on the moor for them to survive and their nests are raided by foxes. Although the findings from this

Golden plover, lapwing and curlew are up to six times more common on keepered moorland

experiment are obviously open to different interpretations, depending on whether grouse or birds of prey are wanted, it seems obvious that a balance needs to be achieved to ensure the future for all our flora and fauna.

If this can be used as an example there is apparently no room for extremism. It shows that compromise is needed by everyone concerned with managing our countryside. Possibly in areas where an increase in raptor numbers is desired and shooting estates have moors that are barely productive enough to employ a full-time keeper, the conservation organisations concerned should contribute towards the wages of one, for they undoubtedly need somebody's services for predator control and heather management. Despite impartially recorded findings conservationists can occasionally suffer from tunnel vision when it comes to their particular field.

Protected birds

Under the Wildlife and Countryside Act 1981, British birds were given various degrees of protection. The less common ones included in Schedule 1 Part 1 are fully protected at all times while others species are offered seasonal protection under Schedule 2. Pests such as crows and wood pigeons can be killed or taken by authorised persons at any time. Schedule 3 covers certain species of birds that can be sold alive at all times provided they are leg ringed and have been bred in captivity. Schedule 4 lists birds that must be registered and leg ringed if kept in captivity. Animals are afforded protection under Schedules 5 and 6 and plants under Schedule 8.

For the benefit of the British countryside and all that is in it, tolerance, an open mind, a broad view and a willingness to work together, combined with common sense, are very much needed.

"The wildlife of today is not ours to dispose of as we please. We have it in trust. We must account for it to those who come after."
King George VI

Below Heather can now be re-seeded by helicopter as part of the management of moorland

FORESTRY

The woodlands of Britain, which cover less than 10% of the countryside, can be divided into two categories – softwoods and hardwoods. Their management techniques are very different. Over half the woodland in England consists of broad leafed/deciduous hardwoods (trees that lose their leaves in winter). Nearly all are privately owned. They are regarded as a long-term investment, for the trees are slow growing and not even thinned out until they are 30 or 40 years old. Most are probably at least a hundred before becoming mature and ready for felling. Oaks in particular can live for centuries.

The recent swing towards conservation policies and the provision of financial grants has meant that many new plantings of broad-leafed trees have appeared in the last few years. Saplings or whips as they are called are planted approximately 3 metres apart in straight lines and individually protected against rabbit, hare and deer damage by wire surrounds or, more commonly, plastic tubes. Weed growth is controlled mainly by spraying with a herbicide and attacks by insects and disease have to be dealt with by using pesticides.

The trees are intentionally planted close together, often with a mix of species, so that they shelter one another and grow straight. In time as they become bigger they are thinned and the remaining ones can then mature into fine specimens. Quite often

Nearly all broad-leaf woodlands in Britain are privately owned

Woodlands cover less than 10% of our countryside

Above Huge computerised machines are now used to harvest softwood

a few evergreens such as holly and laurel may be included in plantings to provide a varied and sheltered habitat for wildlife.

Until the middle of the 20th century woodland was utilised in much the same way as farmland and many of the broad-leafed species were used for specific purposes with very little going to waste. Firewood was in far greater demand than it is now and small diameter stem and branch wood was cut into lengths and stacked to dry out in accessible places. This is known as cordwood because it is sold by the 'cord', a cubic measurement of 4ft by 4ft by 8ft.

Until the early 20th century the coppicing of hazel was an important part of woodland management and created a huge diversity and richness to the wildlife habitat within a wood. Every six to twelve years an area of hazel would be cut back to within a few inches of the ground. The 'stool' as the resulting stump is known soon throws out new shoots which grow thicker and taller in each successive year. A newly coppiced area is suddenly opened up to the light and, incredibly, plants such as primroses and foxgloves suddenly appear which had lain dormant beneath the shadow of the leafy canopy for many years.

The production of charcoal was also carried out within the broad-leafed woods. Not only did it provide work for many country people but it was also part of the management system. Large iron cylinders with lids allowed a slow controlled burn of the wood inside, producing lumps of charcoal, a product of great importance to industry long before barbecues were invented.

Planting hardwood trees: a long-term investment

21st century forestry

All broad-leafed trees can be used for firewood and also for processing as wood pulp. When they are thinned out or when older trees are felled, the smaller diameter lengths are usually sold for these purposes. However, the large mature trunks of most familiar woodland trees are used for other specific purposes and some are quite valuable.

A few decades ago the forests of Britain provided a living for many people but in the 21st century they are now as important for conservation and leisure purposes as they are for their timber. Timber, like many other products, has become less economic to grow in the face of cheap foreign imports.

The elm has all but disappeared from the British countryside because of Dutch elm disease, spread by the elm-bark beetle

THE COMMON HARDWOODS OF BRITAIN

ASH is probably the best for firewood and is also used for turnery and making handles for such things as axes and hammers. It is also used for veneer, furniture and planking. Ash is a popular choice for sports items such as hockey sticks, skis and cricket stumps.

BEECH has a multitude of uses including turnery, joinery, furniture making, flooring and in plywood. It also produces excellent charcoal.

BIRCH is generally considered to be the 'weed' of woodland but it still has its uses. Many of the jumps used in National Hunt racing and Point-to-Points are constructed from birch and until plastic became commonly used, most brooms and besoms were made from it.

HAZEL is invaluable and of all the trees and bushes that grow in a wood, none is more useful to country folk than the hazel bush. Gardeners use it for pea sticks, bean poles and plant supports, gamekeepers use short pieces to prop up snares, angled bits to peg down wire netting and traps, and longer length sticks to beat the cover when out shooting or to mark where the shooters have to stand.
Hazel is used for the shafts of fancy carved walking sticks, and thatchers use it to make short 'spars' which hold in place the reed or straw – 3,000 may be

needed for one roof. It is used to make wattle fencing and hurdles. Untrimmed lengths are tied into 'faggots' for use as sea and river defences and barrel hoops are made from it. Its familiar yellow catkins herald the arrival of spring and, if squirrels don't get there first, the nuts are a tasty delicacy in late summer.

HOLLY is a popular choice for turnery and carving and also makes a strong stick to walk with.

HORNBEAM is used for flooring, turnery, carving, mallet heads and for making the action in keyboard instruments such as pianos.

OAK is very slow growing and is often over a hundred years old before it is mature. Its great strength makes it useful for such things as beams, fencing, gate posts and sea defences as well as veneers and furniture.

POPLAR Distinctively tall and slim, it is often grown as wind breaks in exposed areas but the wood from this tree is put to very lowly purposes. Before the advent of cheap plastic cigarette lighters, poplar was used for making matches and the wafer thin 'chip baskets' and punnets in which soft fruit was sold. Now it is turned into vegetable crates, wood 'wool' and plywood.

SWEET CHESTNUT Familiar for its prickly cased nuts roasted at Christmas, sweet chestnut is commercially grown to be made into pale fencing and fencing posts when it is about twenty years old. Plots were sold at auction to be coppiced (cut) during the winter months and then made into posts during the summer in the woods close to where it was cut. Plots were harvested in rotation, and like hazel, new shoots of sweet chestnut quickly grew from the 'stools' and the wildlife habitat was greatly enhanced by the rotational clearing of patches within woods. But most chestnut is now imported from France. Sweet chestnut can be cut again after only two or three years when it is used for making walking sticks.

SYCAMORE is commonly used for flooring, furniture, turnery and veneer.

WALNUT and **WILD CHERRY** are some of the most valued timber in Britain. Both are used for high quality veneers and decorative purposes. They both make beautiful furniture and the wooden stocks (butts) of the best rifles and shotguns are carved out of walnut.

WILLOW is famous for making cricket bats and about 12,000 mature trees are felled each year for this purpose. It is also used in industry and in the past was used to make artificial limbs.

Much of the woodland in existence today was planted and preserved by wealthy landowners for the pursuit of fieldsports, at first for the hunting of deer and foxes and, since the mid 19th century, for pheasant shooting. Much of the British landscape, its woodlands and its parks, remain the same today as when they were fashioned by those people centuries ago.

The public has right of access to 60% of Forestry Commission land

Pine forests

Nearly a quarter of all British woodland is owned by the government and managed jointly by the Forestry Commission, who are responsible for the day-to-day management of the actual trees, and their agent Forest Enterprise which deals with all other aspects. Softwoods (conifers) are predominately grown but a few hardwoods are mixed in as a conservation measure.

Much of what was once open moorland and many hillsides, particularly in Scotland, are now covered with blocks of conifers planted in regimental lines and whose dark canopy eventually eliminates the growth of all plants beneath them. Soft pine needles carpet the ground and the species of creatures that live in these forestry blocks are entirely different to those that once lived on the open moorland. The value of soft wood timber has decreased in recent years and the purely commercial aspect of growing huge tracts of one species (monoculture) is no longer so attractive and has generally been replaced with an emphasis on conservation and diversification for the benefit of wildlife.

Over 5 million cubic metres of softwood timber is harvested annually on a rotational basis, but Britain's timber industry is finding it difficult to remain competitive against cheap imports from Sweden and the Baltic States. Approximately 85% of all wood products are now imported from abroad. Softwoods are pulped to produce panel board, chipboard, paper and paperboard. About 60% of the conifers planted in Britain are Sitka spruce, the remaining 40% include Douglas, Scots and Corsican pine as well as larch, the only conifer in Britain to shed its needles in winter.

How forestry is managed

Young trees are grown in nurscries from seeds collected in the forests. When the young seedlings have become established they are planted out either in fresh ground prepared by ploughing into ridges or on ground that has been felled. Often these new plantations have to be protected from hares, rabbits or deer with wire netting fences. At first many plants such as bramble and birch will invade the open ground and need cutting back or spraying so that the young conifers are not overwhelmed by the unwanted growth. However, the trees grow rapidly and soon smother the undergrowth. At this stage they are 'brashed', which means the

> *Larch is the only conifer in Britain to shed its needles in winter*

Young hardwood trees are individually protected wit plastic tubes

> *Softwoods or conifers are evergreen, cone-bearing, needle-covered trees which grow quickly in areas where it is impossible to cultivate any other crop*

lower branches cut off, and then left untouched until they are thinned after about 20 years. The remaining trees are left to grow straight and strong until they are ready for felling when they are mature at between 50 and 70 years old.

Roots from the felled trees are dug up and placed in rows. Once they were left to decompose but frequently now a big machine is used to grind them into wood chips which can be used for horticultural purposes or fuel for power stations, with the ash being returned to the land. Disposing of the roots in this manner greatly reduces the risk of fungal diseases spreading to newly planted trees.

Gigantic computerised machines are now used to cut the mature trees and are fast displacing men who used to do the felling with chain saws. Not only do these machines work very quickly, cutting down the trees, but they also remove all the side branches as well as sawing the trunks into the exact required lengths. One of these super-efficient giants can do the work of 25 men and in remote areas such as parts of Scotland, where job opportunities are very limited, their use is causing serious economic problems to many isolated rural communities reliant on forestry work.

The Forestry Commission employs nearly two and a half thousand people to care for the forests. Some are wildlife rangers who have a variety of duties including controlling pests such as deer, rabbits and squirrels which in excessive numbers can cause serious damage to young plantations. The rangers are also involved in education as well as wildlife and environment protection.

Forest Enterprise, the agency for the Forestry Commission, manages more than two and a half million acres (one million hectares) of land and includes over 700 ancient monuments situated on Forestry Commission land. It is also responsible for large areas of non-forested land including nearly 150,000 acres (60,000 hectares) for agriculture and grazing and more than 400,000 acres (160,000 hectares) of mountain and moorland.

Re-introducing the red squirrel

A large part of Forest Enterprise's activities involves conservation measures and one particular interest is the red squirrel. Reintroduction is being attempted in Thetford Forest (Norfolk). In Scotland, where there is still a good population but where road

Walnut blocks waiting to be carved into gun stocks

Britain imports about 85% of all wood products

casualty rates were high, rope bridges have been erected so that they can cross without having to come down on the ground. Woodland habitat, plants, birds of prey and wildlife in general are all concerns of Forest Enterprise, but their greatest concern is recreational activities.

60% of Forestry Commission land has the right of public access and attention has to be paid to way-marking forest roads and tracks for walkers and horse riders. They manage Forestry cycle tracks, picnic sites, car parks, play areas and visitor centres. Thetford Forest is the largest man-made forest in England extending to nearly 50,000 acres (20,000 hectares) and attracts 1.5 million visitors annually.

Besides all these facilities there are also camping sites, self-catering log cabins and touring caravan sites that have been recently set up by Forest Enterprise in partnership with the private sector. Educational projects include 31 forest classrooms. Field sports are strictly regulated on Forestry Commission land: shooting is permitted in some areas, fox hunting takes place under licence, but no deer hunting with hounds is permitted.

Other sports welcomed include drag hunting (following a scent trail laid by man with hounds or bloodhounds), husky racing, horse endurance racing events, car rallying, orienteering, and many more.

The forests are full of hidden secrets that are there to be discovered. Most of the conifers have been planted since the end of the First World War (1918) and have dramatically altered the local landscape encompassing ancient monuments, the ruins of old crofts and other sites of human habitation.

The poor sandy soil of Thetford Forest in Norfolk was open heathland before becoming submerged beneath a sea of trees. Dotted throughout the forest, hidden away in small clearings, are little flint cottages. These were once the homes of warreners whose working lives revolved around the wild rabbits that thrived on the dry heaths. These formed the principle industry of the area, and several factories were built in Brandon (Suffolk) to deal with the skins; train-loads of rabbit meat were regularly sent to Cambridge and London.

Nearly a quarter of Britain's woodland is government owned

50 million people a year visit Forestry Commission land throughout Britain

Below Charcoal was used in industry long before the invention of the barbecue

HORSES AND PONIES

There are an estimated one million horses and ponies kept in Britain and only a very small minority are kept solely for working purposes. Many of the workers such as the shepherd's pony and the garron, which carries shot highland stags off the hill, have been replaced by ATVs (all-terrain vehicles) although there are a few estates that still maintain the old traditions. Heavy working horses like Shires and Suffolks are now mostly kept as a hobby and can only be seen working at shows or organised ploughing matches. A few may still be found working in agriculture or forestry, or hauling brewers' drays, pulling carriages along sea fronts or on ceremonial occasions and of course there are the highly trained and much respected cavalry and police horses.

However all the rest are kept solely for their owners' personal pleasure whether for riding, driving, racing or merely as pets.

There are several breeds of ponies native to Britain. The sturdy little Shetland, as its name implies, originates from the Northern Isles off Scotland. Stocky Fell, Exmoor and Welsh Cobs as well as the lighter-framed Dartmoor and New Forest ponies are all unique to their areas. Some of these breeds can still be found roaming free in their natural habitats. Dartmoor and New Forest ponies run wild and each autumn are rounded up and the

By December 31st 2003 every horse or pony in Britain will be required to have a registration 'passport'

Above Throughbred mares and foals on a stud farm

117

unwanted foals and yearlings are sold at special sales. A few of these find homes as pets for children but many end up being exported for the continental meat trade. There is not enough grazing to support the additional young stock and when stallions are allowed to run free with the mares it is inevitable that most will conceive.

In Britain an estimated 10 to 15,000 horses and ponies are processed for pet food or human consumption each year besides those old, injured or unfit ones that are utilised by Hunt kennels.

Horses: enjoyed by many

The equestrian industry employs thousands of people and is reported to contribute £2.5 billion to the rural economy. Horses need feeding, stabling, veterinary attention, shoeing and tack. Their owners require clothing, hats, boots and transport for their animals. If they are not merely turned out in a field, as hardy ponies sometimes are, their care can be costly and time consuming, although interesting and satisfying. Very young children can enjoy riding and here the diminutive Shetland finds its niche. Many disabled children find it extremely stimulating to ride, enabling them to experience a freedom otherwise denied them. As children grow there is a wide choice of breeds or crosses to suit their size. In fact in Britain there is a breed of horse or pony to satisfy every purpose.

Ponies are hardy, resilient and sometimes strong-minded, rather like terriers. They are an excellent choice for those who do not have much spare time or money. Many are just kept so that their owners can enjoy an occasional ride out. Livery stables will care for an owner's horse or pony if they don't have the facilities, and for those who can't afford to keep a horse of their own, riding stables offer the opportunity to hire an animal. Pony trekking holidays are another way the occasional rider can enjoy riding.

Donkeys are no longer common although they are sometimes kept as pets or companions for another horse or pony or used at the seaside for giving rides to children. There are many Pony Clubs across Britain. Gymkhanas offer a chance for children to ride competitively. Numerous mounted games can be played and jumping over fences is always popular. At a higher level the events become more defined with show jumping compe-

A horse or pony can live in excess of 30 years, often long after the end of their usefulness

Below Exmoor ponies can be identified by their mealy-coloured noses

HORSES & PONIES *Useful Words*

AT LIVERY Kept in livery stables.
BAY Brown horse often with a darker mane and tail.
BREAK Train a young horse to be responsive and used to being ridden.
COB Small stocky horse of no defined breeding.
COLT Entire male under 4 years old.
DAM Mother.
DRAUGHT/HEAVY HORSE Cart horse.
FARRIER Person who cares for a horse's feet, blacksmith.
FILLY Female under 4 years old.
FOAL Under one year old.
FOAL AT FOOT Mare with a young unweaned foal.
GAIT Pace: walk is the slowest, then trot, then canter and finally the gallop which is the fastest pace.
GARRON Highland pony used by deer stalkers in Scotland.
GELDING Castrated male.
GYMKHANA A show where children can ride in competitions.
HAND Measurement of height equal to 4 inches eg 16 hands high is 5 feet 4 inches (163cms) at the withers.

HORSE Over 14 hands high.
INDOOR SCHOOL Barn used for riding tuition or practise.
LIVERY STABLE Place where owners can pay to have their horses or ponies kept for them.
LUNGE Exercise on a long rein in a circle around the handler.
MARE Female over 4 years old.
PIEBALD Horse with black and white markings.
PONY Under 14 hands high.
RIDING STABLE Place where horses or ponies are kept for hire or tuition is given.
ROAN Horse whose main colour is flecked with white.
SCHOOL Practice.
SIRE Father.
SKEWBALD Horse with brown and white markings.
SOUND Fit and healthy.
STALLION Entire male over 4 years old.
TACK Equipment for a horse, eg saddle, bridle.
WITHERS Shoulders.

New Forest ponies have not enough grazing to support all the additional young stock

titions as well as dressage, which involves intensive training to display the obedience and suppleness of the natural movements of a horse.

Eventing combines these disciplines with a cross-country course over natural solid fences and hazards, testing the all-round fitness and ability of the horse. Eventing competitions are often spread over three days with dressage on the first day, the cross country which includes a set distance covered on roads and tracks on the second followed by show jumping on the last day.

The main sport played on horseback is polo but this is costly and only for the well off or armed forces. Many less wealthy people enjoy hunting and relish the opportunity to ride out in different parts of the countryside with a purpose for being there.

Many breeds of horse and pony, including native ones, can

Dartmoor and New Forest ponies run wild and each autumn are rounded up and the unwanted foals and yearlings sold at special sales

be used for carriage driving. In this popular competitive hobby the skills of a carriage driver are put to the test as he steers the horses (often two or four) round a difficult cross country course or obstacles set up in a ring. It requires great precision and control. Trotting has never been as popular in Britain as it is in the States, but nevertheless these specially-bred horses, with an unusual gait that enables them to trot extremely quickly while pulling the lightweight frame of a cart, can sometimes be seen.

Pony riding, always a more popular hobby for girls than for boys

Some horses and ponies are kept just for showing as perfect specimens. These are led around the show ring to be judged although some classes, such as child's pony or hunter, may require the animal being ridden in which case the rider will be as immaculately turned out as his or her mount.

Horse racing

The British racing industry is enormous and is financially supported by men and women who have never been closer to a horse than their television screen or local betting shop. Billions of pounds are spent every year in Britain on gambling. It is estimated that important National Hunt meetings like the three-day one at Cheltenham in March and the Grand National at Aintree and the famous Derby and Royal Ascot meetings on the Flat in summer generate one hundred million pounds in betting money at each event. It is a phenomenal amount of money and because of it the racing industry is under great pressure. While it remains traditional in many ways, trainers also embrace whatever modern technology is available to legitimately improve performances.

At the bottom end of the scale are Point-to-Points which are organised by Hunts under the supervision of the Jockey Club and are only open to amateurs and horses that have been out hunting: it is the bedrock on which steeplechasing has been built.

Owners do not have to be wealthy to have a horse that can run in either hurdle races or steeplechases. These are older horses

About 10-15,000 horses and ponies are slaughtered for pet food or human consumption each year

that have either been specially bred, made their mark as point-to-pointers or often those that have not made the grade over the shorter flat race distances. These rejects can prove to be useful animals as they mature and learn the new game but many of the males by this age will have been castrated and therefore have no future value at stud.

While flat racers begin racing when they are two or three years old, those that are bred for jumping are usually about four before they are raced over hurdles and even older before they tackle the bigger steeplechase fences. Not only do they need a certain amount of natural ability to be successful, they also need stamina as well as speed to win over the longer distances. As these qualities can be inherited, their breeding is of great importance. Although the National Hunt season extends almost throughout the year, officially beginning in May, there are very few meetings during the summer while the ground is hard.

Jump racing is often regarded as the poor relation to Flat racing but it really comes into its own between November and early April which is why it is known as the 'Winter Game'. Flat racing on the other hand gets underway in March and continues to November although there are a handful of meetings during the winter on synthetic all-weather racecourses such as Lingfield.

Racing on dirt surfaces is not as popular in England as it is abroad; and because the British prefer grass, much care is taken of the grass courses to ensure a surface that does not get water-logged or too firm when the weather is dry, whereupon irrigation is used to remedy this situation.

Evening Flat race meetings are held as well as afternoon ones and some on Sundays, attracting large crowds. Prize money far exceeds that offered for hurdle races or steeplechases.

A horse that consistently wins top quality Flat races can not only accumulate a vast amount of prize money but also be worth a phenomenal amount for breeding purposes. A top class stallion is worth millions of pounds and is usually retired from racing when he is 3 or 4 years old. He can sire up to 40 or 50 foals a year maybe continuing to do so for 15 to 20 years. If his progeny also prove to be successful his services can remain fully booked at a very high price throughout his lifetime.

Thoroughbred stallion *Nashwan* was retired to stud after winning many races, including the 2000 Guineas and the Derby in 1989; he has sired many winners since

AI (artificial insemination) is never used on thoroughbred racehorses

Training racehorses

Newmarket is the headquarters of the racing industry: the whole town revolves around the racehorse. Famous stable yards occupy prominent positions and lesser ones are tucked away in the back streets. Horse walkways are built alongside pedestrian pavements and there are rider-operated traffic lights in places where horses need to cross busy roads on their way to exercise on the 3,000 acres of heath training grounds. Besides the famous hallowed turf there are also several synthetic training areas. In Britain there are 2,500 horses in training, 530 registered trainers and many private stud farms as well as public ones. Getting a horse fit for racing or any other equine sport is a matter of slowly building up fitness and rarely are horses pushed to their limits during training. It is a gradual process starting first with walking then trotting and finally cantering. Swimming provides excellent therapeutic exercise and National Hunt horses will also be schooled over fences.

A day at the races

Racing stable routines are rigid, with an early morning start when the first lot are taken out. After breakfast a second lot will go out and stables and tack cleaned. A stable lad or lass is expected to look after two or three horses and probably ride them out although some experienced outside riders may come in to help with the exercising. Visits are likely from the vet, the farrier and sometimes owners and most days there are horses to be taken to race meetings, sometimes far away. There may be a chance for some of the staff to have a couple of hours off in the afternoon before the late feeds and other chores are taken care of. Of course the trainer or his Head Lad will also have a look round last thing at night to make sure that all is well with the horses.

Out of the racing season, some horses may go back to their owners for a holiday and have the enjoyment of being turned out to grass. Endurance racing with pure bred Arab horses is becoming increasingly popular involving this elegant ancient breed covering distances of up to 100 miles to fully test their famed qualities of soundness and stamina. They are allowed several breaks during the race in which their physical condition is carefully monitored by vets to make sure they are not becoming over-stressed. Besides Newmarket there are several other major

A recent equestrian survey concluded that 56,000 horses are kept mainly for hunting

Below Breaking a horse (preparing it to be ridden) is a skilled undertaking

training centres notably at Middleham and Malton in Yorkshire and Lambourn in Berkshire. These are areas that offer the chance to exercise on old established gallops where the turf provides good conditions underfoot, rarely becoming too wet in winter or too firm in summer.

The Stud

Throughout Britain and particularly around Newmarket there are stud farms breeding the next generation of racehorses. Pedigrees can be traced back for generations as all thoroughbreds are recorded in a Stud Book. For every racehorse foal born, an enormous amount of research and planning has gone into choosing a sire that will complement its mother's qualities and strengthen her weaknesses.

Most flat racers are retired when they are 3 or 4 years old although some are kept in training longer. The males (colts) will have been kept entire and any that have excelled will be used for breeding. The females (fillies) are not only judged by their achievements but also by their bloodlines so even if they haven't been outstanding as racers they can still prove their worth at stud. The remainder may be sold on for National Hunt racing or personal use such as hunting or eventing and smaller ones may even make good polo ponies. Inevitably some will be put down.

Mares that have been barren or have not previously been mated and those sent from abroad to be mated are kept in an isolation unit on arrival at a stud for 2 to 4 weeks to ensure there is no risk of infection.

Grass very soon becomes an important part of a thoroughbred foal's diet

Breeding

A mare comes into season for 3 or 4 days during a 3 week cycle. Pregnancy lasts for 11 months and on average a mare can be expected to have a foal 2 years out of 3. As January 1st is every thoroughbred's official birthday it is preferable that foals destined for flat racing are born as early in the year as possible. If it is not born until late June then it will be classed as a 2 year old even when it is only 18 months old. However care also has to be taken that it is not born before January 1st. Twins are most unwelcome and if they show up when the mare is scanned 2 to 3 weeks into her pregnancy, it is possible for an experienced horse vet to

Most flat racers are retired when they are 3 or 4 years old

dispose of one of them. Scanning is carried out again after about 4 weeks and again at 8.

24-hour watch

As thoroughbred mares and their offspring are very valuable, when they are near to their time to foal a person sits up with them every night. Signs of the birth being imminent are waxing of the teats and a rise in body temperature. There are devices that measure this rise and trigger an alarm but they are not entirely reliable so most studs still prefer to have someone in attendance.

Some mares are kept at their owner's private studs to have their foals while others are taken to a public stud where the selected stallion is standing prior to giving birth. Here the mare and foal will spend two or three months being expertly cared for, during which time she will have been mated again and the pregnancy confirmed. The services of a top stallion are very expensive and many studs offer a guarantee of 'no foal no fee' within a certain time.

Modern studs usually have purpose-built maternity units with veterinary facilities, special sitting-up rooms and CCTV which is connected to the Senior Stud Groom's house. As soon as a foal is born it is checked over to see that it is healthy. Its navel is disinfected and it is encouraged to suckle, for bonding with its mother is important.

As well as the benefits it receives through the mare's first milk (colostrum), a thoroughbred foal needs to grow quickly and hand rearing on the bottle is never very successful. If the mare is unable to feed her baby then a foster mother is used, who may be of any breed.

Official registration

The foal is registered in the official Stud Book and its markings and coat patterns, as individual as a human fingerprint, noted as identification. Micro-chipping is also now used as a permanent and reliable record of its identity. It is important that a foal is well handled in the first few months of its life. To begin with, mother and baby are turned out for a few hours each day, weather permitting, into a sheltered grass paddock

RACING & STUD
Useful words

ALL-WEATHER COURSE Artificial surface for flat racing.
BROOD MARE Mare kept for breeding.
BUMPER RACE Flat race for amateur riders.
COVER To mate with.
FENCE Permanent substantial obstacle usually constructed from birch boughs and sometimes topped with gorse or fir branches.
HEAD LAD The person responsible for the day to day running of racing stables.
HURDLE Portable low flimsy obstacle.
JOCKEY CLUB Governing body for British racing.
MAIDEN Horse that has not won a race or a female that has not been bred from.
NATIONAL HUNT Racing over hurdles or fences.
PACEMAKER Horse entered in a race to set the pace they go.
PADDOCK Parade ring at racecourse or small enclosure on stud farm.
POINT-TO-POINT Race meeting over fences for amateur riders organised by Hunts under the supervision of the Jockey Club.
SENIOR STUD GROOM The person responsible for the day-to-day running of a stud farm.
STAND AT STUD Term used when a stallion is kept for breeding purposes.
STEEPLECHASE Race over fences.
STRING Group of racehorses.
STUD FARM A horse-breeding establishment.
TEASER Stallion used to ascertain whether a mare will accept being mated.
TRAVELLING HEAD LAD The person responsible for racehorses in transit and at race meetings.
YARD A trainer's stables.
YEARLING Aged between one and two years old.

which has been specially sown with a palatable mixture of grass, herbs and other nutritious plants. Deep rooted ones absorb beneficial trace elements from the earth beneath. Limestone areas are favoured as sites for studs because the foals do particularly well on this type of soil. Droppings in the paddocks are picked up daily with a suction machine to reduce the risk of infection from parasites.

Grass becomes an important part of a foal's diet and analysis of the soil and herbage is carried out so that any mineral or vitamin deficiencies can be rectified when supplementary feeding is introduced at about 2 or 3 months. Foals are weaned at about 5 to 6 months old depending on their condition. Immense care is taken with their health. They are vaccinated against tetanus (which horses are very prone to) and equine flu. Mares and foals are also wormed regularly.

Foot care is of particular importance for a horse cannot run fast if it has anything wrong with its feet or legs. Brood mares are not usually shod unless there is a medical reason to do so but their feet need to be kept in shape. Foals likewise need to have their hooves regularly trimmed and any slight problems or defects in the legs or feet can often be remedied by the way an expert farrier pedicures the feet.

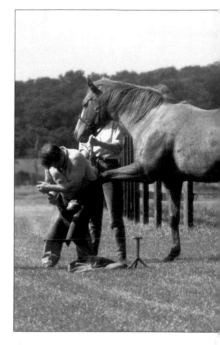

Care of the feet is very important for all horses and keeps the farrier busy

Horse sales

Thoroughbred horse sales begin in September, Tattersalls in Newmarket probably being the most famous. Sales are usually held over several days, often in the evenings after racing, and attract wealthy buyers from around the world for Britain is renowned for the quality of its thoroughbreds. Foals, yearlings, horses in training, older horses and brood mares change hands, some for astronomical prices. Arab gentlemen from the Middle East have shown great interest in horse racing during the last two decades and because of their involvement in this country with both racing and breeding, the industry has gone from strength to strength. Many of the best stallions they own have remained at stud in Britain when they could so easily have been sent abroad.

While some feel that their dominance of Flat Racing has been unfortunate, there are many racecourses, trainers, jockeys and stud owners who have greatly benefited from the amount of

Horses are very prone to tetanus infection

money that has been injected into the sport. Not all foals and yearlings go through the sale ring, a lot are retained by their owners then sent directly to trainers where they are broken in at just under two years old, prior to being raced.

Stud stallions

As may be expected, very valuable breeding racehorses lead a cosseted life and the stallions are no exception. One man is usually employed to look after two stallions with some extra assistance. Regularity and paying attention to detail are part and parcel of the job and the individual temperaments of the stallions have to be taken into account by those looking after them. Such a strong, highly strung, intelligent and sometimes temperamental animal requires sympathetic handling all the time. Stallions at stud are not often ridden although occasionally this is found to be the best way of exercising them.

Exercising begins in earnest in October and includes daily lungeing (exercising on a long rein in a circle around the handler who is stood in the centre) and walking. Not only does taking stallions for a daily walk around the countryside help get them physically fit, it also stimulates them mentally: important because boredom is always a threat to their stability. Some studs also believe that spending a few hours outside running loose in individual paddocks enables them to exercise themselves and gives their lives an added dimension. Tread mills and mechanical 'horse walkers' where several horses are individually secured one behind the other to a circular frame and walked round are sometimes used for exercise but do little to stimulate them mentally.

At the end of the covering season the stallions are rested and allowed to relax for 3 or 4 months before being got fit again for the next season. Diet also

> *Stallions need to be fit to mate with two or three mares each day during the 5-month covering season from 14 February until 14 July*

Judges use horses at hare coursing events

plays an important part in their well-being and each Senior Stud Groom has his own recipe for success. For safety reasons, stallions usually only have front shoes fitted because they can be dangerous with their hind feet, but careful attention has to be paid to their hooves and they are regularly checked by a farrier.

A veterinary examination will usually determine whether a mare is ready for mating and a 'teaser' is used to gauge her acceptance level. Separated by a boarded frame or gate they are introduced to each other and their reactions noted. It is only when she shows her readiness that a mare is introduced to the selected stallion. It was common practice in the past that mares were brought to Public Studs prior to foaling and boarded there for a couple of months, during which time they would foal and be mated again. However with the ease of modern transport and increasing charges it is now more usual for mares to be 'walked in', that is, transported to the stud just to be served.

Vets and racehorses

Thoroughbreds, whether in training or at stud, are subject to continuous veterinary observation. The slightest hint of anything amiss detected by the stable lad or lass looking after the animal or the Trainer, Head Lad or Stud Groom, is immediately acted upon. Blood tests are regularly conducted, swabs and physical examinations are commonplace. Facilities at top stables and horse veterinary centres are superb and the amount of care and attention racehorses receive is unparalleled and puts many aspects of human health care to shame.

Studs, training establishments and racecourses dot the British countryside, particularly in England, and of course the Irish are renowned for their affinity with the racehorse. A lot of top jockeys, especially National Hunt ones, originate from Ireland. Many thousands of acres in the British countryside are manicured to perfection, because the 'Sport of Kings' not only has to maintain its traditions but also its standards. Even so, only about 5% of thoroughbreds in training ever win a race and very few become famous. It is the owner's belief that one of them may be theirs and the willingness of the punter to part with his money that keep the industry going.

Suffolk punches dressed for the show

Only 5% of thoroughbreds in training ever win a race

WORKING DOGS

Most breeds of dogs kept in Britain have been developed for a reason and many in the countryside are still used for the purpose for which they were originally bred.

Training involves developing the dog's natural skills while suppressing undesirable traits and instilling obedience which takes kindness, time and patience. Even those that have been kept as pets for several generations still retain many of the breed's original characteristics.

Some dogs kept for work, especially gun dogs, enjoy the luxury of living indoors with their owners and being treated as family pets. Terriers too are sometimes afforded the same treatment but in most cases working dogs are kennelled outside.

This is not unkind providing their living quarters are dry and free from draughts. The dog has its own 'house and garden' and is not subjected to the continual disturbance that living in a busy

Tail docking of working dogs is purely functional, not cosmetic

Above A hill shepherd feeds a lamb, attended by his trusty sheep dog

household can entail. Some, such as hounds, are kept in communal kennels with maybe 20 or 30 sharing a bedded area and outside run. Others are kept in smaller kennels with an attached run either singly or sharing with one or two others. Working sheepdogs, especially in the north, are often kept tied to their kennels with a few feet of chain, but they are used for work every day so get plenty of exercise.

Terriers, although small in size, are tenacious and brave even to the point of stupidity at times. In particular they play an important role in fox and rat control. Gundogs and hounds on the other hand are usually more biddable and providing they have been trained properly are a useful aid to finding game and hunting foxes.

Working a scent line

The scent dogs rely on can be very inconsistent depending on weather conditions. One day it may be very good and the dogs can work with speed and another day it will be poor which makes tracking very difficult. Scent has often been likened to a light plume of smoke coming from a slowly smouldering fire. It can cling to the ground and surrounding vegetation or it can hang in the air. Scent can vary within yards between areas of sunshine and shade but is generally best on days when there is dampness and a gentle breeze or when the ground is warmer than the air temperature. It is extremely interesting to watch dogs working a scent line, for their noses are as effective for them as sight is for humans. Most people find it fascinating to see a dog puzzling out a situation and it is one of the reasons why so many take an interest in fieldsports.

Because a working dog is kept in a kennel it does not mean to say that it is any less thought of than a pet. Indeed for a shepherd or a gamekeeper, their dog is not only a necessary tool but often the only companion he or she has all day.

Tail docking of working dogs is purely functional and not done for cosmetic reasons. For

It is more practical to keep a long-coated dog outdoors for they can get very dirty when they are working

Sheepdogs on a quad bike, the modern transport for the hill farmer

example a spaniel's natural lively tail action when it is working in thick cover can soon result in the tip of it becoming severely damaged causing the dog great discomfort and a serious risk of infection. Working spaniels usually have their tails docked by only one third when they are two or three days old, which is sufficient to greatly reduce the risk of injury. Most people who work dogs have a great respect for their incredible abilities. Man has utilised and cultivated the skills of different breeds for centuries and probably owes much to them for his survival. A dog can be 'man's best friend' for many different reasons and work is one of them.

WORKING DOGS
Useful Words

ESS English Springer Spaniel.
HPR Hunter, Pointer, Retriever.
GSP German Shorthaired Pointer.
GWP German Wirehaired Pointer.
FTCh Field Trial Champion.
FTW Field Trial Winner.
FIELD TRIAL A trial held under simulated shooting conditions using non-captive live game or rabbits to test a gun dog's obedience and working ability.
COLD GAME TEST Similar to a field trial but using cold dead game instead of live.
WORKING TEST A test held under artificial conditions using dummies to assess a gun dog's obedience and working ability.
DUMMY An artificial object used to teach a dog to retrieve.
CHOKE LEAD A slip lead, a running noose used to restrain a dog.
STEADY Under control at all times.
RUN IN Chase after something without having been given the order to.
MARK Indicate where the quarry is.
FLUSH Make an animal or bird run or fly.
PEG Catch unshot game often when it is sitting tight.
RUNNER Wounded bird unable to fly.
SOFT MOUTH A dog capable of retrieving live game without harming it.
HARD MOUTH Used to describe a dog that kills or bites game etc.
NOSE Used to describe a dog's scenting abilities.
LINE Scent trail left by an animal or bird.
DRIVING IN / DOGGING IN Term used when a dog is used to chase pheasants or partridges away from boundaries or other undesirable areas.
PICK UP Collect shot game with dogs.
PICKER UP Person who picks up shot game using dogs.
COURSE Hunt by sight.

TYPES OF WORKING DOG

TERRIERS are small dogs that will also work underground. They have a strong desire to kill and will defend themselves if necessary.

FOXHOUNDS, BEAGLES, HARRIERS, and **BLOODHOUNDS** have excellent scenting powers and will follow a scent trail for long distances. They are capable of quickly killing a hare or a fox.

GREYHOUNDS, WHIPPETS, SALUKIS are breeds of dogs that hunt entirely by sight, relying on their speed to catch their quarry.

LURCHERS are a mix of breeds that sometimes combine hunting by sight with the use of scent.

COLLIE A breed with a strong natural instinct to gather together animals or birds that can be driven, such as sheep, cattle, ducks and geese. They have a natural stealth, can creep or lay close when driving stock. Collies are often used for search and rescue work such as mountain rescue.

LABRADORS and **RETRIEVERS** have a strong desire to carry objects and are mostly used to find and retrieve shot animals or birds but some are also trained to hunt for unshot game or rabbits. They are invaluable for retrieving wounded game and are very intelligent, often being trained for other uses such as guide dogs and investigative work as 'sniffer' dogs.

SPANIELS are generally very active dogs and have a natural instinct to work the cover with a zig-zagging action known as quartering. They are used to hunt for pheasants, grouse and rabbits which they locate by scent. They then flush (make run or fly) their quarry and are mostly trained to retrieve it to their handler after it has been shot. They are good all-rounders but some can be head-strong and difficult to control. Spaniels are also frequently used as 'sniffer' dogs.

POINTERS are dogs that range widely in search of game which they locate by scent-marking its location by standing absolutely still and looking in its direction. With the exception of English Pointers they are also trained to retrieve after the quarry has been shot.

SETTERS work in a similar fashion to pointers but are not trained to retrieve.

Opposite Springer spaniels are excellent retrievers due to their soft mouths

Left An English pointer flushing grouse

PEST SPECIES

A pest is an animal, bird or insect that interferes with a person's everyday life but the definition and seriousness of one is determined by what kind of life that person leads. Even the most avid animal lovers are appalled at the thought of sharing their home with a rat. Even though it is a living furry animal like a guinea pig, nevertheless it is recognised as a pest because of its habits and it is accordingly disposed of. A cat can be an excellent companion and a much loved pet but out of doors, following its natural instincts, it can become a pest in certain situations.

There are professional pest controllers and in the countryside gamekeepers wage war on most species of pests in order to protect their game birds from predation, for in most cases their jobs depend on there being sufficient game to meet their employer's requirements. For those relying on wild game such as grey partridge and grouse, much of their breeding success depends on how efficient gamekeepers have been in culling predators. Many aspects of fieldsports have developed from the necessity of controlling pests such as rabbits, hares, foxes and pigeons, turning the task into an interesting, challenging and enjoyable one.

An estimated 50,000 badgers a year are killed by traffic

Above The magpie: avid nest-raider and bane of gamekeepers and conservationists

Many pest species are opportunists and have thrived because of the excessive wastefulness that in recent years seems to have become so common in Britain. Foxes, magpies, crows and sea gulls have learned that it is easier to live on scraps discarded in litter bins, dustbins and thrown out of car windows than it is to hunt for food. There is a serious risk of disease for them as well as for pets and humans when they are attracted in unnaturally high densities to urban areas and their health deteriorates as a result of an unnatural diet. The normal food for a fox is meat and occasionally wild berries, not chips and Chinese takeaways.

There is a great deal of legislation concerning how and when pest species can be dealt with and by whom. Some benefit from a close season but none of them are destroyed without there being a genuine reason. As towns and cities grow larger there is more pressure on wildlife and their habitat in the countryside. Some species will undoubtedly disappear if they are not protected. It is inevitable that man has had to become involved, not only for the convenience of humans but also to maintain a balance in the countryside.

It may be distasteful for some but ever since humans first interfered with nature they have had to take responsibility for managing it and controlling pests is part of that.

Mammal pests

FOXES Of all pests, the fox is probably the most damaging to wildlife. They are beautiful but deadly creatures, spread throughout Britain, not only killing other animals and birds to eat but also as a natural reflex. Many a farmer, gamekeeper or conservationist has found bodies scattered around where a fox has been on a killing spree. Townspeople too are not exempt from their attentions, for a cat is fair game to foxes who may well account for a missing pet. The majority live in rural areas but more and more are finding an easy living in towns especially in Southern England.

This has led to a completely unnatural existence for they have learned to scavenge on discarded food and that put out for pets and specifically for them by well-meaning people. Attracted

Greylags, Canadas and pink-footed geese may be shot between 1 September and 31 January but cannot be offered for sale

Stoat, a voracious predator of ground-nesting birds, chicks and eggs, in a spring trap set in a tunnel. All traps are checked daily by the keeper

to certain areas, their density has increased to an unnatural level and their health deteriorates, partly from living on an unnatural diet, and partly because, being in close contact, diseases are likely to spread between them quickly.

Deadly 'mange' from foxes

One of the worst fox diseases is Sarcoptic Mange which debilitates the animal causing much suffering. This can also be caught by domestic animals as well as by humans. Once infected, an attractive-looking animal can soon be reduced to a sad pathetic sight as happened to the group of town foxes in Bristol made famous by the TV film *20th Century Fox* filmed in 1981. By 1996 the group had all been wiped out through contracting mange even though efforts had been made to treat them.

City foxes released in the countryside

Town foxes that have been rounded up at night and those that have been 'rescued' are often taken into the countryside and released by well-intentioned people. There the urban foxes stand little chance of survival and their death is often protracted because they die of starvation. There is also the risk that they will spread any diseases they are carrying to healthy wild animals.

The countryside is not an easy place to survive in. There may seem to be plenty of rabbits about but they are extremely clever and prove very difficult to catch.

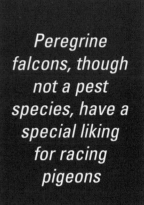

Peregrine falcons, though not a pest species, have a special liking for racing pigeons

Carnage in the poult run: it is naive to believe that a fox will kill only what it needs for food

Foxes that have been hand-fed are poorly equipped to fend for themselves in unfamiliar surroundings, not only having to learn to catch their food but also having to capture and hold a territory in which to hunt. These released foxes are used to scavenging. Raiding young lambs and domestic poultry is often the only way they can find food. It is a complete misconception that it is kinder to release a fox into the wild: probably the perpetrators subject it to a lingering death rather than humanely destroying it in the first place.

There are about half a million foxes in Britain during the autumn and winter; this number is almost doubled in spring with the arrival of cubs. These are born underground and are tended by both parents. When they are a few weeks old and weaned, the family will move around, often laying out on top of ground.

The sad sight of a rabbit with myxomatosis, a horrific disease, first introduced to Britain in an effort to control the ever increasing numbers in 1953

Fox control

Control at any time is vital for conservation purposes and also the rural economy. Although they do good by feeding on rodents and rabbits, they are non-selective and can cause serious devastation to all ground-nesting birds and domestic livestock; poultry and new born lambs being most at risk.

It is estimated that 100,000 foxes are shot each year, 100,000 are snared, another 100,000 are killed on the roads, 25,000 accounted for by terriers and 18,000 by packs of hounds. Even so enough remain to pose a severe threat to the well-being of the countryside and it is extremely important that their numbers are controlled. Few people would wish to see them exterminated but the damage they cause should never be underestimated. Shooting them is often carried out at night from a vehicle using a high powered spotlight and a rifle.

Snaring is subject to strict legislation regarding the type of snare, the way it is used and the fact that it must be checked at least once a day. Trapping is only permissible if large baited cage traps are used. At the time of writing terriers may be used to kill or evict a fox from underground so that it can be shot. Lurchers are occasionally used to chase and catch foxes and packs of hounds are used to hunt them. It is illegal to gas or poison foxes. Using dogs to control them is often the only realistic option in many upland parts of Britain where shooting or snaring is impossible.

Badgers can only be destroyed under special licence. Permission has recently been granted for several thousand to be killed in the West Country

Fox control, the politically correct, modern method. Unfortunately they are not always killed as cleanly as this and a badly shot fox will endure a lingering death by starvation

One pair of rats can produce 800 offspring a year

RATS It is estimated that rats destroy 20% of the world's harvest and, were it not for continuous warfare against them, this could well also be the case in Britain. One pair can produce 800 offspring in 12 months and they inhabit both urban and rural areas. There are millions of rats in Britain and their numbers have increased by 25% in the last few years. Being mainly nocturnal few people are aware of how many there are and in what close proximity they live to humans. Like foxes they scavenge for discarded food in towns as well as land-fill sites and farms in the country. They cause very serious damage to wildlife by taking eggs, chicks and adult birds.

Rat problems
While many townspeople welcome foxes to their gardens, few wish to share them with rats. Their reputation for spreading many diseases is well-founded. Wiels disease is easily caught by humans coming into contact with the excreta from rats. A huge amount of damage is caused to crops and to property particularly in winter time when rats vacate their outdoor living places such as banks and hedges to seek the comfort of living indoors.

Weils disease can be caught by humans from contact with rat excreta

Wherever there is food provided for livestock, then rats are likely to be found in residence nearby. Gnawing is another considerable problem. Rodents have teeth that are continually growing and the only way this can be checked is by gnawing which causes damage to pipes, wood, plastic and many other objects.

Almost any method can be legally used to kill rats as it is extremely important that their numbers are not allowed to become out of control. The use of guns, traps, gas, ferrets, dogs and poisoning are all legitimate. Indeed poison for rats can be bought over the counter but obviously care has to be taken with its use. It is very important that the bait is kept topped up for several days until it no longer disappears for rats can easily build up a resistance to the poison and become immune to it, as has happened in some areas, making continued control extremely difficult. Where there is a heavy infestation such as in banks and buildings, one method used is to smoke them out and use terriers to dispose of them which they do very quickly with one bite.

FERAL CATS It is estimated that there are 7.5 million cats in Britain, one third of which are ownerless. Like foxes they can decimate wildlife. They are ruthless unselective killers and often the death of their prey is a cruel protracted one. Cats delight in playing with their victims before killing them, sometimes not even bothering to eat them afterwards.

However well-fed cats are, most of them still possess an insatiable desire to hunt and may adapt to living in the wild becoming feral, although those dumped in the countryside from towns often do not manage to survive. Some cat owners who are totally opposed to hunting with dogs prefer to turn a blind eye to the habits of their cats. They defend their choice of pet by saying the animal is only doing what is natural to it but they wish it wouldn't. They are themselves condoning the destruction of wild animals and birds by keeping a cat for they fail to recognise the damage one can do.

Cats kill about 300 million creatures annually

In 1997, between April and August, the Mammal Society conducted a survey where the owners of nearly one thousand cats recorded the species and numbers of items their cats brought

A third of all cats in Britain are ownerless

Grey squirrels can cause great damage to trees by stripping the bark and in commercial orchards, taking fruit or nuts. Like rats they will also take eggs and chicks from nests and cause considerable damage by chewing

home. It showed an alarming range of animals, birds, reptiles and amphibians. If the figures are representative, and there is no reason to believe they are not, the total number of creatures caught by cats may amount to 300 million each year. Recorded species included chicks and birds up to the size of a partridge, rats, mice, shrews, voles, squirrels, slow worms, grass snakes, lizards, frogs (a particular favourite), toads and even bats. An average of 16.7 prey items were recorded for each cat during the five month period.

Wildlife is particularly vulnerable to predation by cats between March and August and if this could be reduced it would make a significant improvement to its survival rate, possibly reducing deaths by 100 million during this critical time. Wearing collars with bells on appears to be somewhat ineffectual but a recent survey by the British Trust for Ornithology showed that the use of sonic collars which emit a regular signal significantly reduced the amount of predation on birds, showing a decrease of 65%. Most mammals are nocturnal and the number caught could be reduced by keeping cats indoors at night.

It is the nature of a cat to be independent and therefore its actions are difficult to control, a fact recognised in law as the cat is the only domestic animal for which the owner has no legal responsibilities.

Feral cats (those that have gone wild and have no apparent owners) can be legally controlled by shooting or cage trapping. Like domestic cats any protection they are afforded comes by way of welfare laws regarding cruelty and ill treatment although the domestic cat is also protected by the 'Property Act'. Even though owners may be exempted from legal responsibilities for their cats they should be aware of their moral obligations regarding the preservation of wildlife.

Some cat-owners who are totally opposed to hunting with dogs prefer to turn a blind eye to the habits of their cats

A multi-catch crow trap on a grouse moor. Live decoy birds and/or food is used to entice them in. Smaller Larsen traps, baited with food or a decoy, are also used to catch crows and magpies

MICE are another extremely common pest both in towns and the countryside, causing damage to food stuffs mainly by contamination and also damage to property by chewing. Control is usually by trapping or poisoning.

GREY SQUIRRELS Native to North America, grey squirrels were first introduced to Britain in 1876 when some were recorded as having been released into the wild in Cheshire. Between 1902 and 1929 hundreds more were deliberately released across the country. By the 1950s it became apparent that they were devastating the population of native red squirrels and despite an attempt to control numbers, they have thrived. Now there are few areas in England and Wales where red squirrels can still be found. Grey squirrels are the equivalent of a tree-climbing rat but because they are more attractive in appearance are more likely to be tolerated.

Rabbit shooting is best done at night using powerful lamps. Sometimes large bags like this can significantly reduce numbers and provide a useful source of good meat

However control is very important because they can cause extensive damage to trees by stripping the bark and by taking fruit or nuts. Like rats they will also take eggs and chicks from nests and cause considerable damage by chewing. Control is by shooting, trapping or poisoning which is subject to certain restrictions.

MINK are another unwelcome introduction from North America. They were first imported for fur farming in 1929. The industry boomed in the 1950s but is shortly to be completely banned in Britain. The first wild colony became established in Devon and was recorded in 1953. Since then, because of escapes and misguided releases, mink have spread the length and breadth of Britain having a devastating impact on wildlife. Most to suffer has been the population of water voles which has decreased from 7.3 million to less than one million in a matter of only a few years; they have disappeared completely from 88% of their known sites in Britain during the 1990s.

There are probably millions of mink now living wild and

Hares may not be sold between 1 March and 31 July

they are ferocious killers threatening animals and birds in the proximity to the waterways in which they live. Moorhens are another species to have particularly suffered and domestic live-stock including small animals and game birds are also at risk. Mink are very difficult to catch and gamekeepers, water managers, farmers and conservationists are continually trying to trap them. Packs of hounds have been specially formed and these too help with controlling the numbers.

STOATS and **WEASELS** These are ferocious hunters and despite their small size can easily kill birds or animals far bigger than themselves, posing a particular threat to all ground-nesting birds. A stoat is capable of killing a young hare or full-grown rabbit many times larger than itself which it does by biting the back of the neck to paralyse its victim. Control is by shooting or trapping; most frequently spring traps are used set in natural or man-made tunnels.

HEDGEHOGS Although beneficial to country gardeners, hedgehogs can cause considerable damage to ground-nesting birds, stealing eggs and chicks as well as sometimes the adult bird. South Uist, an island off the West Coast of Scotland, was a well-known breeding site for wading birds but in 1974 five hedgehogs were introduced to stave off a plague of garden slugs. Since then their numbers have multiplied, and there is now esti-mated to be between 5 and 10,000 of them and the success of the nesting birds has fallen dramatically. It is also feared that the hedgehogs may be able to access other neighbouring islands at low tide causing even more devastation. Although they are extremely common in some areas, legitimate means of control are strictly limited.

RABBITS are believed to have been introduced to Britain by the Normans during the 12th century and ever since have multiplied. In the 1800s some large country estates had vast areas set aside as 'Warrens' where rabbits were farmed as a valued source of meat. Elsewhere they were killed by every method available, to control numbers to protect crops from their prodigious appetites and to provide an additional income from their meat. In the 1950s

PESTS
Useful Words

AVIAN Birds.

CAGE/BOX TRAP There are many designs used to catch animals or birds.

CLOSE SEASON Period when it is illegal to kill certain animals or birds.

CORVID Member of the crow family.

FERAL Domestic animal that is living wild.

GAS Chemical substance which when exposed to air releases a poisonous fume.

LARSEN TRAP Cage trap designed to catch one or two corvids by using a live decoy.

LETTERBOX or **MULTI-CATCHER** Large cage trap designed to catch a number of corvids at one time using bait and/or live decoys.

MAMMAL Animal that suckles its young.

POISON Toxic substance. Can only be used under licence for pests other than rodents.

RODENT Gnawing animal such as a rat, a mouse or a squirrel.

SNARE A noose made of wire used to trap certain animals.

SPRING TRAP There are many designs used to catch specific animals. They all do so by springing shut and crushing the body. Strict legis-lation controls type of trap, where it can be set and target species.

TUNNEL Natural or man-made tunnel in which a spring trap is set.

rabbits were causing very serious damage to much-needed food crops, and myxomatosis, a horrific disease, was introduced to Britain in an effort to control the ever-increasing numbers. This had a devastating effect and very nearly wiped out the entire population of rabbits but a few survived and despite continuing sporadic outbreaks of the disease, once again there are millions of them throughout the countryside.

A new disease called Rabbit Haemorrhagic Disease (RHD) was discovered in tame rabbits in 1992 and was first recorded in the wild in 1994 but this does not seem to cause the dreadful suffering or to be spreading as rapidly as did myxomatosis. Because of their excavations, rabbits can also indirectly cause injury to livestock and damage to machinery.

Almost any method except poisoning can be used to kill rabbits. Shooting at night using a spotlight from a vehicle is a popular sport, accounting for a lot of rabbits in a comparatively short time. Ferreting is another country pursuit although a more time-consuming way of catching rabbits. There is no close season for rabbits, but ferreting is not carried out during the spring and summer because it is impractical.

HARES Although regarded as a game species, hares on arable land can also become a pest and are not afforded the protection of a close season. However they may not be offered for sale between 1st March and 31st July.

In some areas of Britain they are present in sufficient numbers to cause serious damage to crops and young tree plantings, so controlling numbers is necessary. This is most frequently done by organised shoots that mainly take place in February. Hunting with beagle or harrier packs takes place between October and March.

Coursing hares with lurchers or greyhounds is only allowed from 1st October to 28/29th February.

DEER The population of all species of deer throughout Britain is increasing and measures have to be taken to ensure they do not cause excessive damage to gardens, crops and woodland or become too many in number where their food source is limited such as in the Highlands of Scotland. Red deer are hunted with

Mink have pushed the water vole to the brink of extinction

The spring trap is still the most effective, least-polluting way of controlling moles. But it is labour intensive and several traps need to be set to tackle a large infestation

hounds in the West Country at the time of writing: otherwise control is restricted to shooting within designated seasons using specified high powered rifles and types of ammunition.

MOLES As every gardener knows, moles can be a serious pest with regards to crop growing and grassland; likewise to horse owners and farmers. Deterrents and gadgets are mostly ineffectual and do not alleviate the problem. The only real solution is to destroy the moles which is mainly done by trapping although in certain circumstances poisoned worms can be used if a special licence is successfully applied for. It is suspected but not proven that moles may be carriers of tuberculosis.

The extermination of a pair of crows or magpies in early spring will save the lives of hundreds of other birds

Bird pests

CROWS Crows are probably the most serious threat to wildlife and a pair can devastate the wild bird population within their territory by deliberately searching for nests and taking eggs and chicks. They will also attack weakly young animals such as new-born lambs, characteristically removing the eyes first even before the animal has died. Control is by shooting and trapping using cage traps such as the Larsen or Multi-catchers.

Below Carrion crows can be a real menace at lambing time on a sheep farm, and to nesting birds

MAGPIES This attractive but lethal bird is adept at systematically searching out nests in the springtime and, being agile, will climb in and out of hedgerows looking for those of small birds to steal the eggs or young chicks. Few will survive if they nest within the territory of a pair of magpies. Like crows they are either shot or cage trapped, Larsen traps being particularly successful.

JACKDAWS are opportunists and groups of them will gather to steal food from cattle, pigs or that which is put out for game birds.

They too have a taste for eggs and chicks and can also be a nuisance when their choice of nesting site is a house chimney as often happens. Control is by shooting or cage trapping.

JAYS are usually more tolerated than crows or magpies although they too will steal eggs or chicks from nests when they have the opportunity. They are most often shot although they can also be caught in cage traps.

ROOKS Although often mistaken for crows, rooks are in fact completely different in nature being gregarious birds. Communal rookeries built high in the trees are a common sight both in urban and rural areas and their raucous calls a familiar sound. They will scavenge in towns, having a particular liking for bread, but in the countryside they steal the food put out for livestock as well as on occasions carrion and can cause severe damage to arable crops by digging up the newly sown seeds. They too will take eggs and young chicks so at times may become enemies of farmers, game-keepers and conservationists alike. Shooting and cage trapping are the methods used to control numbers, the multi-catch type trap being the most successful.

A brood of Canada geese. An attractive introduction to Britain but in very large numbers they can cause damage to crops and grassland

The jackdaw is the corvid most likely to nest in your chimney pot

PIGEONS, FERAL PIGEONS and **COLLARED DOVES** There are an estimated 18 million wood pigeons in Britain. They are common in towns as well as the countryside and will decimate cabbage and sprouts planted in gardens. Their phenomenal appetites mean that they cause severe damage to agricultural crops particularly by feeding on cereals when they are ripening in summer and rape crops in winter when there is a shortage of food; they find the green leaves particularly attractive. Various deterrents are used to keep them off fields including plastic bags, scarecrows and gas guns which are set to make very loud bangs at regular intervals. Shooting is the only efficient method of disposing of pigeons and it is also a popular sport.

This strange object, seen particularly in arable fields, is a gas gun – for scaring pigeons and other pest species

GEESE Geese arrive in their thousands in late autumn to many coastal regions of Britain to spend the winter. Once here they look to feed on grassland and arable crops. Not only do they cause a lot of damage from the amount they eat but also from paddling up the wet ground with their large feet. Deterrents are used as for pigeons, and goose shooting is another popular sport. Greylags, Canadas and Pink-Footed geese may be shot between September 1st and January 31st but cannot be offered for sale. Other species have full protection throughout the year.

GULLS Gulls are attracted inland by landfill sites where they scavenge for food. They will also take eggs and chicks: sea shore nesting birds are particularly at risk. Great black-backed gulls, lesser black-backed gulls and herring gulls are all recognised pests and can be legally destroyed by certain methods.

COOTS and **MOORHENS** If present in excessive numbers coots and moorhens can become a pest by eating crops or taking eggs or chicks. They are subject to a close season from 1st February until 30th August when they must not be killed.

Woodpigeon numbers have doubled in the last 25 years

STARLINGS and **SPARROWS** They were once present in the countryside in such large numbers that they were considered to be a pest. However they are not so common now and modern methods of crop growing and grain storage have greatly reduced their ability to steal food and are probably part of the cause for their decline in numbers. Where food is freely available such as in outdoor pig units, flocks of starlings can still be found. In large numbers they are unwelcome guests because of the mess they make and, as many migrate to Britain from the Continent in winter, there is a risk of spreading disease. Shooting or cage trapping are the methods used where it is necessary to control numbers.

Insect pests

INSECTS There are hundreds of different species of insect to be found in the countryside. Most of them do little harm but those that specifically damage crops such as aphids, carrot flies and some insects in their caterpillar and grub stages have to be reduced or eradicated with the use of chemicals or natural substances applied as sprays, granules or a coating on the seed. Horse flies, blow flies and other smaller flies that bite also plague livestock during the summer months. Honey bees can be found in the wild and are rarely a pest to humans except when they swarm in inconvenient places. They can be destroyed by using chemicals or, better still, removed by an experienced beekeeper. Common wasps are a greater threat, being attracted to sugary food and ripe fruit. They are widespread and more prolific in some years than others. As they build nests in or on buildings or in holes in the ground, they can be accidentally disturbed and as a result they become extremely angry and vicious.

Potentially the most harmful insect of all is the minute tick which commonly lives on sheep, deer and many other animals and birds. They are mostly found on rough grassland habitats such as heaths and moors but can be present almost anywhere. The tiny spider-like insect attaches itself by its jaws to its victim and proceeds to suck out the blood. Within a few days it will

Crows are solitary birds, but rooks are gregarious

The noisy rook is a great scavenger and well adapted to both town and country life

become bloated and about the size of a blackcurrant, before dropping off. If numerous they can cause great distress to their host. Sheep are dipped to prevent this happening but it is impossible to treat wild birds and animals. Ticks often get on humans and pets – at first they may be mistaken for a wart. They need to be removed and if they are pulled off it is important that the head is not left buried in the skin. Ticks can carry a disease known as Lymes disease which can be very debilitating to humans if they should become infected.

An infestation of slugs in the ground can cause serious damage to freshly sown seed and is treated with an application of slug pellets.

The maggots of blow flies burrow deep into the flesh of sheep if they are allowed to hatch from eggs laid on wool that is dirty or wet. This can lead to a slow horrific death if not prevented by way of trimming, dipping or spraying with chemicals and shearing in early summer.

The magnificent goshawk, a protected species and still rare in most parts of Britain

Pest Species Protected by Law

HAWKS, HARRIERS, FALCONS and **BUZZARDS** All birds of prey are fully protected by law and most species are increasing in numbers. They are all predators that will take other birds, animals and insects. Some species will also feed on carrion. Sparrowhawks probably cause most harm to the bird population,;they are ruthless hunters as many a bird table owner has discovered and will take not only small birds but those the size of a pigeon or a partridge. On upland ground, the hen-harrier can be a great nuisance, taking not only birds as large as grouse but also the eggs of ground-nesting birds. Peregrines can be a menace to pigeon keepers as they have a special liking for racing pigeons.

OWLS Most species of owl hunt at night and live primarily on small mammals such as voles, although they will sometimes take small birds when they have the opportunity. They are not generally regarded as a significant pest: in fact the ghost-like barn owl is a particularly welcome sight in the countryside.

Sheep ticks carry Lymes disease which can be very debilitating to humans if they become infected

BADGERS They now enjoy full protection and their numbers have increased accordingly. They are becoming established in areas where they have not been regularly seen before and in some places where there is a high density they are causing grave concern to many local people. Their excavations in fields hedgerows and woodlands can be very damaging; they are not adverse to eating eggs or birds if they can find them and there is also a strong suspicion that they are carriers of bovine tuberculosis which can be transmitted via cows' milk to humans. Badgers can only be destroyed under licence and permission has recently been granted for several thousand to be killed in the West Country, where the population is very high, in order that definitive research can be carried out. In 1997 records showed that 25% of badgers carried bovine TB in one area. In Ireland a 5-year study concluded that where badgers were culled, the spread of bovine TB was reduced by 90%. A good indication of how common they have become is the number of badgers seen dead on the roads. It is estimated that 50,000 a year are killed by traffic.

PINE MARTENS live in forested upland areas of Scotland and Wales. They eat birds, eggs and small mammals and are increasing, which concerns conservationists who are trying to preserve the red squirrel and capercaillie. Polecats are similar but smaller in size.

An uncontrolled dog is a menace in the countryside

A dog worrying sheep can legally be shot

DOGS It never ceases to amaze country folk how ignorant dog owners can be as to the harm their pets can cause in the countryside, particularly in the spring and summer. Obviously dogs that go off on their own for the day are the worst offenders but those that are allowed to run loose in the woods, supposedly chasing rabbits, are capable of causing a lot of damage in a short while. Deer are often the target of their attentions and can be severely injured. Farmers, gamekeepers and conservationists are only too aware of the dangers to both animals and birds. Mere disturbance can have devastating consequences. Even those dogs kept on extendible leads are quite capable of frightening a bird off its nest so badly that it will not return and as a result its offspring perish. Both the owner and the person in charge of a dog that worries livestock (farm animals and poultry including game birds if they are inside a pen) on agricultural land are by law responsible for its actions and are committing an offence.

A dog can legally be shot if it is caught in the act but all too often the results of an attack are only discovered afterwards. It is the nature of most breeds of dogs to hunt and chase. While having a good run around in the countryside may be fun for the dog, it isn't for the residents.

In Ireland a 5-year study found that culling badgers reduced bovine TB by 90%

There is a strong suspicion that badgers are carriers of bovine tuberculosis which can be transmitted via cows' milk to humans

A flock of starlings descending on pig huts, one of the few places where they can still find food with relative ease

FIELDSPORTS

The principle reason that people participate regularly in field-sports is simply because they enjoy them. Only a few take part because it is 'the thing to do'. There are several different reasons why fieldsports appeal to so many people and they are nothing to do with having a sadistic barbaric personality as the media so often portrays. In fact paradoxically many feel a certain affinity with their chosen quarry and are very conservation-minded, for to exterminate that for which they hunt would deprive them of their future sport.

Thousands of years ago, humans survived because they were 'hunter-gatherers' living off what they could find and catch. That urge is still quite strong in many people and they gain much satisfaction from enjoying what they have caught or shot as a Sunday roast or a Wednesday stew. Controlling pests that threaten their livelihood or that of fellow countrymen also seems quite natural.

Some aspects of fieldsports offer a personal challenge, to outwit the fish or be accurate enough with a gun to put food in the bag. For others it is the pleasure of watching a dog using its sharply honed sense of smell, a thousand times more sensitive than a human's, to work out a scent trail and catch its quarry whether it be a hound after a fox or a gun dog finding shot game. One thing all fieldsports have in common is that the outcome is never predictable. When a field sportsman or woman ventures forth in the morning they never know what the day holds in store.

Grouse are never reared artificially for shoots

Above Mallard in flight – a sight to quicken the pulse of the wildfowler

This is another attraction, just as is the prospect of a day spent in the countryside.

Fieldsports are steeped in tradition and it is something that those who participate generally take great pride in. There are unwritten guides to etiquette, dress and the way in which things are done. The vast majority of people who participate have a great admiration for their quarry. This seems extremely difficult for many townspeople to understand but when someone is matched against an animal or bird in the wild and it has outwitted and got the better of them, then it is regarded with an element of respect.

Hunting is one of the most traditional sports; the unwritten rules have changed little in two centuries although the environment in which it takes place has altered greatly. Hare coursing is another old and traditional sport that has changed very little. Fishing, especially some aspects of game fishing, has its roots steeped in the past but has been overtaken by commercialism which, while making the sport available to all, has tended to change the manner in which it is conducted. A few shooting people go out purely to satisfy their lust to kill but these are a small minority and for all the rest it is regarded as a challenge.

Great changes in modern shooting

Of all fieldsports, shooting has probably changed the most. The invention of modern shotguns and cartridges in the middle of the 1800s, which dispensed with laboriously preparing the gun for each shot fired, created a surge of interest in shooting. From then onwards a vast amount of money was spent by wealthy landowners on improving their estates and employing game-

There are over 700,000 people in Britain who hunt live quarry with guns

Hare coursing, probably the oldest of British fieldsports

keepers to protect and rear pheasants and partridges. The huge investment in shooting caused a landscape that had been fashioned by agriculture and hunting, to be redesigned to suit driven shooting. A century ago King Edward VII, then the Prince of Wales, was at the centre of the shooting scene and spent part of each winter in a social whirl of country house shooting parties, staying a few days at one big estate before progressing on to another. Such was the pressure on wealthy landowners at that time to live up to expectations that some were forced to live beyond their means and subsequently they got into financial difficulties.

But what was once the realm of the very rich a century ago is now just the opposite and there is shooting available for anyone whatever their social status or salary. After the second World War it took a few years for shooting to become re-established for there was little food to spare to feed game birds and most estates had been neglected because gamekeepers and farm workers had been away fighting. Since then, the format for shooting has gone through a series of alterations which are linked to social changes.

Shooting syndicates

Because of the post-war economic situation, very few landowners were in a position to bear the costs of running a shoot purely for invited guests. The answer was to form a syndicate, usually of 8 or 9 people, who would share the annual costs in return for an agreed number of days shooting each season. This seemed the next best thing to inviting guests because there was a regular team of guns and everyone soon got to know each other. This system was popular and many shoot managers would add to their ground by renting the shooting from neighbouring farmers.

Since that time in the 1960s and 70s, the demand for shooting has steadily increased and estates began to let shooting by the day instead of the season. This also proved popular and gave people the opportunity to sample shooting on many different estates. Goose and pigeon shooting by the day was also made available and now even February hare shoots are occasionally let.

The demand for shooting still exceeds supply especially in areas such as the West Country and some parts of Scotland where the natural terrain means that high flying birds are the order of the

Driven pheasant shooting, on farmland an important supplementary source of income. To run a large driven shoot, a pheasant keeper will be employed

The pheasant shooting season opens on 1st October

day. Because of Britain's reputation for tradition and quality sport, many foreigners come to enjoy the shooting.

The last decade has seen a dramatic downfall in farm incomes and a number of estates have discovered that more money can be made by giving priority to pheasants and partridges over agriculture. This has led to some shoots in particularly favoured areas being run as commercial enterprises releasing thousands of reared partridges and pheasants (grouse are never reared artificially) and offering let days several times a week throughout the season.

In some cases this has even extended to corporate hospitality which some consider to be a step too far if inexperienced guns are invited to shoot. There is disquiet among much of the shooting fraternity at the development of commercialism in their sport and the pursuance of 'big bags' where what is considered to be an excessive number of birds are shot in a day. However the majority of places, even though they rear and release pheasants and partridges, are organised in a more traditional manner holding a shoot no more than once a week and not going over the same ground in consecutive weeks. Many smaller farms only have a few days in the whole season when personal friends are asked and in return there are invites back.

At the end of the season on most shoots there is usually a 'keepers' day set aside as a thank you for those who have helped on shoot days

Newly released pheasants on a stubble field – at this time they are susceptible to predation from many quarters

The hunter and the hunted

Many people are opposed to fieldsports but few have spared the time to discover if the reasons for their dislike are based on fact or hearsay. All the fieldsports organisations have a wealth of information available and can arrange for those who have a wish to learn more to actively participate. Balaclava-clad saboteurs are normally students who are paid a few pounds, provided with transport, a packed lunch and encouraged in their hobby of causing trouble. Many antis consider fieldsports to be cruel, but in nature there are the hunted and the hunters, and man is just another predator which the hunted naturally have to contend with.

Scottish hunting with dogs

In 2002 hunting with dogs was banned in Scotland by the Scottish Parliament under the Protection of Mammals (Scotland) Act and as a result one of the packs, the Dumfriesshire Hunt, famous for its black and tan hounds, was disbanded after a history lasting 150 years. The other 9 official Scottish packs, in order to survive and obey the new laws, have resorted to strategically placing a few marksmen carrying shotguns around covers they draw, to shoot any foxes that are put to flight by the hounds. The new law permits hounds to search and put up a fox but not to catch one, deeming it more humane for it to be shot, not necessarily fatally, than be killed almost instantaneously by the lead hound.

Everything that is hunted or shot has lived some, if not all, of its life completely wild, in its natural state. It has not been kept penned up nor been subjected to the stress of being loaded into a lorry, transported long distances and having to wait in a yard or a crate prior to being slaughtered. Death in fieldsports is in natural surroundings and usually instantaneous. If not, every effort is made to despatch the quarry as quickly as possible. In the case of predatory pests such as foxes, they suffer an identical fate they themselves have administered to their prey. Even pheasants and partridges that have been artificially reared for the purpose of

Red-legged partridge and chicks

Compared with mass-produced poultry, pheasants and partridges have had a long and stress-free, outdoor life

153

shooting have had a better life than table poultry crammed in a large shed. They will have spent a fair proportion of their lives in complete freedom and when the time comes to harvest the crop, because that is what shooting does, they are killed in surroundings that are familiar to them.

As the average annual return for reared game is only about 50%, then they also have a reasonable chance of surviving the season if they do not get eaten by predators or killed on the roads.

Tickets to a premiership football match cost as much as a day's fieldsports in many cases

A classless pursuit

Another reason why people are opposed to fieldsports is because they view it as the prerogative of the wealthy and therefore indicative that a class system still operates in the countryside. This is very far from the truth in the 21st century. Although it helps to be well off, it is no longer a necessary qualification to participate in fieldsports. Of course there are a few snobs and toffs around but a genuine keenness is all that is needed for acceptance to be guaranteed for the average working man. Inevitably there are still exclusive hunts to follow, and places to fish for salmon, shoot pheasants, partridges or grouse – but there are also plenty of other places to go. For the dyed in the wool working bloke there are always ferrets, lurchers and terriers with which to enjoy some countryside sport.

Keeper feeding pheasant poults on a straw covered track

A free country?

Most people today have far more money to spare for leisure than their grandparents did. Now it is just a question of priorities of what to spend it on. For some it is a premier football league season ticket or dining out and for others it is shooting or hunting. It often costs little more to keep a pony and have a few days out with the local hunt than it does to smoke 20 a day.

Hen pheasants normally lay between 30 and 40 eggs beginning in late March

The choice of a hobby is up to the individual and in this age of human rights and civil liberties, country folk find it difficult to understand why their sports should have become such a contentious issue with politicians.

The detrimental effects of a fieldsports ban

Banning fieldsports of any kind would put many people directly employed out of work and also their homes, as most fieldsports employees live in tied cottages that go with their jobs. It would also seriously affect the rural economy as many local businesses rely on trade passed on to them indirectly through fieldsports.

Land owners and farmers would no longer be willing to finance the many private conservation projects which they conduct in aid of hunting or shooting and which also benefit other wildlife, so that too would suffer. If hunting and shooting were to be banned there would not be the incentive, other than publicly-funded government grants, to preserve woodlands, hedgerows and field margins. Nor would set-aside areas continue to be utilised for game cover from which many farmland birds benefit through the winter.

When fieldsports involve pest control, banning the sport would not save any birds or animals' lives for their numbers would still have to be controlled by other means which are not necessarily as humane as the methods now used. Certainly in the case of foxes there would be less tolerance shown towards them if people could not have the pleasure of hunting, for there would be no reason to put up with the damage they undoubtedly do. Added to all that, thousands of dogs would have to be put down for the owners of those kept purely for work could not afford to keep them as pets nor indeed would many of them be at all suitable to keep as pets. A recent equestrian survey concluded that 56,000 horses are kept mainly for hunting.

Rotten apples

There is an odd rotten apple in every barrel and sadly for fieldsports these are the ones that make headline news and yet overall fieldsports enthusiasts are law-abiding people. The most publicised incidences usually concern poison that has been laid out by gamekeepers or occasionally farmers. This is an extremely

A well ordered game larder: much of it destined for European markets

The tax payer would have to pay for much conservation work which lovers of fieldsports do for free

foolish and irresponsible thing to do and inevitably attracts a lot of media attention and bad press for shooting, even though there is a minute number of people prosecuted each year. There is a lot of pressure on keepers these days to deliver the goods (ie. provide quarry for fieldsports): if they don't then they are liable to be out of a job and their home, so continued predation on a serious scale can easily influence but not justify their actions. Sheer frustration too is another factor, for it is heartbreaking to see the results of what one has worked so hard for months to achieve, being decimated in a matter of days.

Although keepers have to answer to their boss they normally enjoy a certain amount of freedom of choice on how they manage their shoots. They all have their own individual methods and opinions which are usually tolerated by the landowner, providing they achieve good results and don't fall foul of the law.

Some on low-key shoots lead a reasonably relaxed way of life apart from the inevitable worries caused by predators, disease and the weather. But those on commercial and high profile shoots are under a lot of pressure most of the time. Their jobs are very different to the usual image people have of a gamekeeper strolling through the woods with a gun under his arm and a faithful dog at his heel. Modern gamekeeping is seldom like that.

A pair of English partridges and chick: a newly-hatched English partridge is little bigger than a large bumblebee

Gun crime

The shooting fraternity has been heavily penalised following two or three serious incidents when people and children have been murdered by gun shot. As a result, all hand guns were banned in Britain and stringent rules for licensing and storing brought in for other firearms, all of which have been obeyed to the letter of the law by shooters.

However, incidents of guns being used for crime, including hand guns, has instilled an unnecessary fear of guns in people and has risen steadily ever since, resulting in the shooting fraternity paying the price for something that has not made one iota of difference so far as criminals are concerned. Shooting is not assessed as a high risk sport and incidences of accidental shooting are extremely rare. People who use firearms for sport are responsible people and are only too well aware of safety issues.

For a pest-controller, a gun is his tool, as is a spade to a gardener

An important country get-together

Hunt and shoot days as well as field trial and hare coursing meetings are social events. They are gatherings of like-minded people who share a common interest and enjoy a challenge, so usually a strong sense of camaraderie exists. They are an autumn and winter occupation when crops have been gathered, the leaves have come off the trees and the vegetation has died back.

For country people it is a time to relax after a busy spring and summer and a chance to enjoy a day's sport after the morning chores have been taken care of and before the evening ones begin. Even though fieldsports are confined to certain seasons, social and fund-raising events are organised throughout the year and keep rural people in touch. In small and sometimes isolated communities, this is an important element of country life.

The meet, a place for people as well as beagles to come together

SHOOTING *Useful Words*

AIR RIFLE Type of gun which is not very powerful; it fires a pellet propelled by compressed air or gas.

BAG Term used to describe the total amount of game shot.

BASC British Association for Shooting and Conservation.

BEAT Prescribed area on a shoot.

BEATER Person employed to drive game towards standing shooters.

BIT Plastic device clipped into the nostrils of pheasants or partridges to prevent feather pecking.

BRACE Two birds tied together, if possible one of each sex. The bag is usually counted in braces.

BROOD Family of young birds.

BUTT or **HIDE** Place where people can conceal themselves.

CA Countryside Alliance.

CALIBRE Barrel size of a rifle.

CLAY PIGEONS Small discs that are launched into the air and used for practice or competitive shotgun shooting.

CLUTCH Number of eggs a hen bird lays before her instinct makes her go broody and want to incubate them. If eggs are removed from the nest soon after they are laid this instinct is suppressed and more eggs are laid. Embryos in eggs do not develop until they are warmed to body temperature by the hen sitting on them almost continuously.

CPSA Clay Pigeon Shooting Association.

DECOY Imitation animal or bird used to entice others to come close.

DOUBLE GUN Type of shooting where two guns are used alternately by one person.

DRIVE Area brought in by the beaters.

FLANKER Person on the edge of a beating line who usually carries a flag to encourage birds to go in the right direction.

FLIGHT Movement of birds to and from roosting and feeding areas.

FORE SHORE Area of coastline between high and low water marks.

GAME CART Vehicle used to transport dead game.

GAME COVER Block or strip of a crop especially grown for the benefit of game birds.

GC Game Conservancy Ltd or Trust.

GUN Person carrying a gun on a shoot.

GUN SLIP A cover for a gun.

GUN STAND Clearing cut in thick vegetation for a gun to stand in.

HABITAT Environment in which a creature lives.

HOB Male ferret.

JILL Female ferret.

JUG Applied to pheasants when they sleep on the ground at night instead of in a bush or tree.

KIT Young ferret.

LOADER Person assisting someone shooting with double guns.

MAGAZINE Device for holding and automatically dispensing ammunition.

NGO National Gamekeepers Organisation.

OVER AND UNDER Shotgun with two barrels one above the other.

PAUNCH to remove intestines.

PEG Numbered marker indicating where a person shooting has to stand.

PICKER UP Person with dogs employed to collect dead or wounded game.

PLUCK Pull feathers out.

POULT Young game bird.

RIDE Wide path cut through woodland or other dense cover.

RIFLE A gun that fires a single bullet a long distance with great accuracy. Used to kill medium or large sized animals when stationary.

ROOST Place where birds spend the night.

SEWELLING Strips of plastic tied onto lengths of string hung up to discourage pheasants running past.

SHOTGUN A gun that fires cartridges containing spherical pellets made from lead or other compounds known as shot. This may vary in size according to the intended quarry. Shot size is numbered; the lower number being the largest. A cartridge usually contains about an ounce (28 grams) or slightly more, of shot. Shotguns are used for shooting moving targets at up to about 50 yards range and may have one or two barrels. These are manufactured in several different sizes known as gauges or bores, the smallest being .410 (pronounced four-ten) and the largest is a 4. bore. The most commonly used is a 12 bore.

SIDE BY SIDE Shotgun with two barrels side by side.

SPEX Plastic device that clips into the nostrils of a pheasant or partridge to prevent feather pecking or egg eating.

STOP Person placed in a key position to prevent game birds from escaping out of a drive.

TRAP Mechanical device for launching clay pigeons.

WARREN Group of holes inhabited by rabbits.

WILDFOWL Ducks and geese.

SHOOTING

There are over 700,000 people in Britain who hunt live quarry with guns. Shooting as a sport covers many aspects of country pursuits including pest control for rabbits, foxes and pigeons. Deer control is a necessity and stalking with a rifle provides sport for many. For those who prefer to be out in the worst of the weather, often on their own, the choice will be wildfowling. Others who choose not to shoot at live quarry find their pleasure in target shooting on ranges with a rifle or testing their skill with a shotgun, shooting at clay pigeons. However by far the most popular is game shooting which is conducted on many different levels.

DRIVEN SHOOTING is the most formally organised. A team of beaters, usually no fewer than 10 and sometimes 30 or more, are employed to walk across fields, moors or through woodland to drive gamebirds towards a team of guns, normally 8 to 10, who are waiting at numbered positions.

Before the day begins the guns will have drawn their numbers to decide where they stand and by a system of rotation will not be on the same numbered peg for every drive.

Normally between 5 and 8 drives are done in a day, 3 to 5 in the morning and 2 or 3 in the afternoon. Often a substantial lunch

Game cover strips add greatly to the bio-diversity of the countryside, attracting many other species besides game birds

Above A big day on the grouse moor. At times like this it is difficult to select a bird

THE SHOOTING SEASONS
for England, Wales and Scotland

GAME GROUSE 12th August to 10th December

BLACKGAME 20th August to 10th December

PTARMIGAN 12th August to 10th December

PARTRIDGE 1st September to 1st February

PHEASANT 1st October to 1st February

NB. A Game licence is required to take or kill game, hares, deer, woodcock and snipe.

WADERS and **COMMON SNIPE** 12th August to 31st January

WOODCOCK 1st October (Scotland 1st Sept) to 31st January

GOLDEN PLOVER 1st September to 31st January

COOT/MOORHEN 1st September to 31st January

WILDFOWL: DUCK AND GOOSE 1st September to 31st January (Extended to February 20th below the coastal High Water Mark)

Species of wildfowl that may be shot during the season are as follows:

DUCK Common Pochard, Gadwall, Golden Eye, Mallard, Pintail, Shoveler, Teal, Tufted duck and Wigeon.

GOOSE Canada, Grey-lag, Pink-footed, White-fronted (England and Wales only)

NB. It is illegal to use lead shot to shoot wildfowl, coots and moorhens. The following pest species can be taken or killed by any legal means at any time of the year by the owner, occupier or anyone given permission for specific purposes (eg. protection of crops or livestock): Woodpigeon, Collared dove, Feral pigeon, Great Black-backed gull, Lesser Black-backed gull, Herring gull, Carrion crow, Hooded crow, Rook, Magpie, Jay, Jackdaw, House sparrow and Starling. Other mammalian pests such as Rabbits, Foxes, Stoats, Weasels, Grey squirrels, Rats and Mink can also be taken or killed at any time.

Beaters on the sides of partridge or grouse drives are known as 'flankers'

English partridges always pair up soon after Christmas

is served and a cup of tea offered at the end of the day although sometimes only a short break is taken at midday resulting in an earlier finish, and a more leisurely meal is taken afterwards.

Pickers-up with dogs are employed to stand well back behind the line of guns to collect the shot birds and any that may have been wounded.

Although driven shoot days are formal, they are also very social occasions with usually a lot of banter amongst the guns and the beaters and sometimes between the two. The guns are expected to be properly dressed in tweeds. Sometimes when a large bag (kill) is anticipated, two guns may be used by each person shooting, and a loader is employed to load the gun that has been fired and pass it back. These are always people experienced in handling firearms, often other keepers, and they too will be dressed in tweeds.

However, the people behind the scenes, the beaters and pickers up, can wear any type of clothing possibly even T-shirts in hot weather and any sort of waterproof clothing in the wet. But they do need to wear tough thornproof leggings or over-trousers to protect them from brambles when beating in woodland. They are also expected to equip themselves with a stick to stir game birds out of the cover and to make a noise by tapping to make them run forward.

Beaters and pickers-up

Beaters on the sides of partridge or grouse drives are known as 'flankers' and usually carry a flag which they flap and wave to try to make sure the birds go forward in the required direction. On moors and in thick woodland, beating can be a strenuous job but it is one that both fit pre-teens and even some octogenarians seem able to cope with.

Beating is good exercise but poorly paid. For the young however it is a handy source of pocket money, and for other keepers and working people it is an opportunity to be out in the countryside and go on different shoots, while for pensioners it is often a life-line that keeps them fit.

Many do odd jobs gardening in summer to supplement their pensions, keep them occupied and get them out of the house, and helping out on shoots also serves these purposes for them throughout the autumn and winter, slotting in well with gardening. Beaters are often provided with a can or two of beer and occasionally some lunch. Basically, people go beating because they enjoy going, not for the money they get.

The game cart

For those who are no longer so active, an easier job can often be found helping on the game cart, or either as a stop to prevent pheasants running instead of flying out of the drives, or putting up a line of sewelling for the same purpose. One, maybe two, people are also employed to handle the shot game. It is their job to tie two birds together in braces and hang them up on rails in the 'game cart'. At lunchtime and at the end of the day (more often if the weather is hot and there are flies around) they unload them into a game larder which is cool and fly proof, where the

Grouse chick – a sight of the wild rather than the rearing pens that are familiar to pheasants and partridges

Heather growth is regulated by burning strips on rotation about every seven to ten years

birds are spread out on rails to cool.

The guns will be given at least one brace each at the end of the day and the surplus is collected by or taken to game dealers, some of which process it and sell direct to the public. The British are not generally game-consuming people, so most of it ends up being exported to the Continent.

Selling the game

It seems odd in a country that concerns itself with healthy, wholesome foods as well as animal welfare issues, that more game is not eaten. Compared with mass-produced poultry, pheasants and partridges have had a comparatively long and happy life, most of it spent out-doors and have not been subjected to the stress of being caught and loaded onto a lorry before being killed.

Oven-ready game bought directly from Farmers Markets or game dealers is not overly expensive, it is full of flavour and contrary to popular belief will not have been hung until it smells. Anyone with the inclination to skin or pluck and draw (eviscerate) their own birds will probably get a bargain if they approach their local estate.

There are about 5,000 full-time gamekeepers in Britain, usually employed on the larger driven shoots. Some estates may have several although smaller ones may have only a part-time keeper. Their main job is to control pest and predators, ensure the habitat is suitable, care for the birds and organise shooting.

Game cover strips

On lowland shoots it is common practice to grow several small areas of game cover for pheasants and partridges. Maize is a popular choice, often undersown with millet. Kale is also grown and is sometimes left for a second year so that it goes to seed and becomes even more attractive. There are also many other crops such as buckwheat, mustard and sorghum and mixes of seed-bearing plants including sunflowers and the pretty blue phacelia. Game cover strips add greatly to the bio-diversity of the country-side attracting many other species besides game birds. Set-aside land can be utilised and is a valuable aid to conservation by providing winter food for many small wild birds.

The British are not big consumers of game, so most of it ends up being exported to the Continent

The golden plover nests on open moorland where it benefits from the protection afforded it by grouse-moor keepers

The Yorkshire moors where sheep play their part in grouse moor management

ROUGH SHOOTING is for those wanting inexpensive and less formal shooting. The guns themselves do the work of the beaters by flushing game, usually with the help of dogs, and then shooting at the birds when they have obtained a reasonable height and distance. Only a few, if any, partridges or pheasants are released. Sometimes a part-time keeper is employed, often a retired one who still likes to potter about.

Other rough shoots are organised on a 'Do It Yourself' basis, sharing the chores of pest control, feeding, ride cutting, etc. At the bottom end of the scale are those who have access to a bit of ground and just like to have a walk round with a gun to see what they can get. They are quite happy to get the odd rabbit, pheasant or duck without having had to do any of the work of caring for them.

Shooting may be organised by the owner on his or her privately-owned land. Otherwise it may be run by a tenant farmer on the ground he rents; often the shooting rights are let off separately so land may be farmed by one person and shot over by someone else.

The grouse shooting season begins on the 12th August (the Glorious Twelfth)

Game Birds and their Management

PHEASANTS are found across the length and breadth of Britain, apart from on the highest ground. There a number of strains, many of which have been interbred, and it is not unusual to see pure white or black ones in addition to the more normal colourations. Millions are artificially reared and released each year for shooting but in some areas, particularly the Fens and East Anglia, wild pheasants can do well. Elsewhere they are usually regarded as a 'put and take' commodity.

Shoot-reared birds

On shoots that rear their own birds, hen pheasants are often caught up after the shooting season and penned at a ratio of 7 or 8 hens to one cock bird. Most often they are kept communally in 'flock' pens containing a hundred or more birds but sometimes in smaller groups. Eggs from the hens are very occasionally incubated in the old fashioned way under broody chicken but normally they are hatched in modern incubators in a similar way to poultry and reared by the game-keeper.

Day-old pheasant chicks under a gas brooder

However, many estates now purchase young pheasants (poults) that are 6 to 8 weeks old, from specialist game farms in preference to home rearing. This allows the keeper to either concentrate more on predator and pest control or to cope with a greater number of birds, for he does not have to spend time caring for chicks or erecting and dismantling the rearing field pens.

Game farms obtain their stock from local or imported eggs and chicks; or by keeping their own hen pheasants. These may have been bought in from estates at the end of the season or be over-wintered birds.

The majority of hen pheasants are only kept to lay during their first year and are then released into the wild. Some small 'do it yourself' or part-time keepered shoots buy in ex laying hens

Breeding pheasants can be fitted with 'spex' to stop them egg eating or feather pecking

from game farms in preference to young pheasants as they require less attention.

Penned hens that are kept for laying sometimes have a few feathers on one wing clipped so that they can't fly out of the pens they are kept in. They naturally moult out their old feathers when they have stopped laying and new ones quickly grow so that once again they are able to fly. Alternatively a circle of tape (a brail) is twisted round one wing which keeps it closed so that the bird cannot fly. This is easily removed when the bird is released. Sometimes breeding pheasants are fitted with 'spex' which clip into their nostrils. These prevent the birds from seeing directly in front of them although, as their eyes are on the side of their heads, they still have a good amount of vision. Spex prevent the birds eating their own eggs or pulling feathers out of their companions but do not interfere with their ability to eat or drink.

Even though breeding pheasants are kept outdoors in roomy grass pens both these vices are ones they like to indulge. If a hen loses the feathers on her back she not only loses her protection from the weather but she is also very likely to be damaged when they mate by the sharp spurs which a cock pheasant has on the back of each leg. The spex are easily removed when the breeding stock is released back in to the wild.

Laying

Hen pheasants normally lay between 30 and 40 eggs beginning in late March and continuing until mid-June, peaking in early May. Eggs are not normally hatched much later than the end of June because the chicks will not be mature enough to shoot in the coming season. A pheasant is fully grown when it is 18 to 20 weeks old. If an estate plans to start shooting at the end of October then it usually makes sure that all its pheasants have been hatched by the beginning of June, unless it is large enough to divide into separate areas.

The pheasant shooting season opens on 1st October but serious shooting does not normally take place until much later in the month or the beginning of November although days round the boundaries may be organised or a few pheasants taken in partridge drives before then.

You do not need to be wealthy to participate in fieldsports

Common curlew with chicks, a protected bird which has benefited from conservation measures on shooting land

The growing chicks

The majority of pheasants for shooting are reared in temporary pens outdoors in small batches of 200 to 500 in as natural conditions as is possible. Sometimes old farm buildings are utilised. For the first few days the chicks are kept inside a hut on a bed of wood shavings, shredded paper or chopped straw with food and water close by. Warmth is provided by electric or, more commonly, propane gas heaters.

After a few days, when they have gained strength and are familiar with their surroundings, they are let out into a covered shelter pen often called a 'night shelter'. Food and water utensils are gradually moved out of the hut once the chicks have become accustomed to going outside. For the first few days they are fed a fine crumb before changing to a very small 'mini' pellet. After about 3 weeks they are changed to slightly bigger 'rearer' pellets and then after another couple of weeks to 'grower' pellets which are a size larger.

First days outdoors

When the chicks are about a fortnight old they are allowed access to an open grass pen covered with a net because even at this age they are capable of flying out and also are vulnerable to attack from predatory birds. Because young pheasants are kept as naturally as possible and are semi-wild by nature, they unwisely show a preference for sleeping out at night in the open runs at a very young age so gamekeepers normally drive them back inside the heated huts for the first 3 or 4 weeks so that they do not die from hypothermia.

For a further week or ten days after that they will be driven into the covered pens at night where they have shelter from the weather and access to the huts.

By the time they are about 4 weeks old, their fluff will have been replaced with feathers and it is then they may be given the option of sleeping outside, when the weather is fine.

There is a great deal of work in managing outdoor rearing units, much of which is determined by the weather and note is always taken of the nightly weather forecasts. Young pheasant poults are hardy enough to survive extremes in daytime weather when they are on the rearing field because they have access to

Gamekeepers who rear chicks often work from 5am to 10pm every day in summer

Pheasant poults – a time for the utmost vigilance on the part of the keeper

shelter. However, even though they may be 7 weeks old, off heat and ready to be taken to wood, they can still become victims of exposure or smothering in their efforts to keep warm at night if it is exceptionally cold or wet.

Invariably they will settle down to sleep out in the open runs in large groups regardless of the weather. When birds of this age need to be shut in it is not easy because they cannot be driven like ducks or geese. As they grow bigger, they become quite crowded, so shutting in is a job which is left as late as possible in the evening and they are let out as early as is practical next morning.

Pheasant poults soon learn to go to roost

Gamekeepers who rear their own birds, especially if they have successive batches, work very long hours on the rearing field, usually starting at about 5am and not finishing until the daylight fades which can be as late as 10pm in midsummer. In between there is a huge number of other chores, such as feeding, cleaning and moving birds. Keepers require infinite patience and most go to great lengths to care for their birds to the best of their ability. This is something that those outside the profession find difficult to understand, when the whole object of the exercise is to eventually shoot them, but it is rooted in a mix of conscientiousness and pride.

Pheasants, like poultry, are not exempt from becoming infected with certain diseases and internal parasites. Medication for these is given either in the food or drinking water. Because it is difficult to treat the birds once they have left the rearing field, it is very important that they are healthy when they do so. Being wild by nature they are also susceptible to stress so every care is taken to minimise this.

Once in the release pen, they may be exposed to health risks or diseases carried by wild birds, and it is only possible to give them medication for the first 2 or 3 weeks because once they are out of the release pen, it is virtually impossible to treat them. As with poultry there are strict regulations regarding the withdrawal period between dosing and possible killing, so that there is no danger to human health. But with pheasants there is very little likelihood of any risk because they are free for many weeks before the shooting season.

A pheasant is fully grown when it is 18 to 20 weeks old

Young pheasants are very prone to feather pecking even though they are reared in spacious grass runs. It is common practice to clip a small oval plastic 'bit' into the nostril. This lies inside their mouths between the top and bottom parts of the beak preventing them from closing their mouths sufficiently tight enough to grip on a feather. It is quite similar to putting a bit in a horse's mouth and does not interfere at all with the birds' ability to eat, drink or preen its own feathers. Bitting is done when they are about 2 to 3 weeks old and the bits are removed before the birds are taken to the release pens.

Light beak trimming is occasionally carried out but this is not very effective because a pheasant's beak, unlike a chicken's, very quickly grows again.

Into the release pens

Pheasant poults are usually taken off the rearing field when they are between 6 and 8 weeks old, by which time they are fully feathered; in fact they are beginning to moult out their juvenile feathers and grow their adult ones. Some keepers clip a few of the juvenile wing feathers short on the end of one wing which they hope will temporarily prevent the birds from flying over the release pen fence, which is usually at least 6ft (2 metres) high. The clipped feathers soon naturally fall out and are replaced with the permanent adult plumage.

Sometimes a small numbered metal or plastic tag is inserted into the thin skin of one wing for identification purposes. This is known as a wing tag.

Release pens are designed to be an intermediate step between the protection of the rearing unit and exposure to complete freedom in the wild. The large open-topped pens are built usually in a wood enclosing some good natural vegetation, shrubs, trees and some open areas. Approximately a yard of perimeter fence is recommended for each bird, slightly less where over a thousand are to be released. This amount obviously encircles a large area and allows the birds a lot of freedom. Here they can become acclimatised to their future surroundings, learn to go to roost at night in low bushes to start with, and to recognise danger.

The pens are often protected from large animal predators by electric fencing around the outside and deterrents are sometimes used to discourage the attentions of tawny owls and spar-

Newly-released 7-week old pheasants still need to be securely penned until they have become acclimatised

Young poults are notorious for being able to find their way out of the smallest hole but have great difficulty in finding their way back in

rowhawks. Inserted at intervals into the release pen wire netting are small 're-entry' grilles which allow passage through for the young pheasants that have flown out or otherwise escaped. They are, in theory, narrow enough to exclude foxes.

Short tunnels are built over them inside the pen to prevent the other birds finding their way out. Almost from the time pheasants are put in a release pen they are capable of flying over the pen wire, particularly if they are startled. Escapes also occur if there is a slight gap underneath the wire netting or a strand or two broken in it. Young poults are notorious for being able to find their way out of the smallest hole but seem to have great difficulty in finding their way back in the specially designed re-entry tunnels even when they are fully equipped with funnels to guide them.

Inside the pens, and outside later on, the birds are provided with fresh drinking water and food which is either put in food hoppers from which they help themselves or scattered by hand on tracks cut through the vegetation. Most keepers who hand feed whistle at the same time so the young pheasants learn to associate the sound with food.

Poult feeding

They are usually fed twice a day, quite early in the morning and again in the late afternoon. Sufficient food is given so that the birds will clear it up between feeds without becoming over-hungry.

For the first few weeks in the release pen, pellets continue to be fed, but as the birds grow larger, wheat sometimes mixed with kibbled maize, is introduced. They also find insects and pick at plants that they find palatable such as stinging nettles.

When they are not busy searching for food they delight in dust bathing when it is dry enough. If the weather is wet or windy the poults can usually find shelter amongst the trees and after a few days in the pen, when they have found their way around and settled down, they can tolerate almost any kind of weather.

Although in theory they are protected from foxes by the electric fence, there is always the risk that one may, if it decides to go on a killing spree, manage to dig or climb in, which can result in serious carnage. This can often result in losses of maybe

A strip of sunflowers and phacelia grown for gamecover beside a conservation headland

Stoats, mink, rats, feral cats, badgers, tawny owls, foxes, sparrowhawks: all are poult predators

169

a hundred or more, and those that have not succumbed to the jaws of the fox will be panic-stricken and frightened away. This is one of the reasons why fox control is so important to game rearers.

Pheasant poults, both inside and outside the pen, are also likely to attract the attention of stoats, mink, rats, feral cats, badgers, tawny owls and sparrowhawks. While deaths are not so likely to be on the same scale as from fox attacks these predators may keep returning once they have found an easy source of food. The keeper, apart from setting traps and snares for those he can legitimately destroy and rigging up deterrents for those he can't, may also need to spend many hours at his release pens in order to protect his birds.

After a few weeks in the release pen most of the poults will have discovered how to get in and out and will have become familiar with their immediate surroundings.

Young pheasants are by nature wanderers, and their straying away from the release site is another problem the keeper has to contend with. Eventually, well before the start of the shooting season, the pheasants are given their complete freedom and the keeper begins to leave feed for them in outlying woods and strips of game cover to spread his birds around the shoot and hopefully keep them in the areas he wishes them to be. Pellets are expensive and dissolve in the wet, so they are gradually eliminated

Partridges extend the shooting season by a lucrative extra month

French, or red-legged, partridge with brood; now a popular species which mixes well with pheasants and utilises marginal ground

from the diet once the pheasants have left the release area.

Some keepers feed by hand and others hopper-feed but one of the most popular methods now is to ride round on a quad bike fitted with a 'spinner' on the back which meters out the grain or pellets and scatters them over the ground. The main control a keeper has over his birds is by feeding but when natural food is plentiful in the hedgerows, the game covers and cornfields then his birds may show little inclination to return. It is then that he may resort to using a dog to chase them away from the shoot boundaries and roads.

FRENCH (or Red-Legged) PARTRIDGES have become extremely popular recently on driven shoots and millions are now being artificially reared each year. Many are hatched from eggs imported from France or Denmark. Partridges are birds of open farmland and they also do well on marginal ground such as the edge of moorland, thus utilising ground on shoots to the maximum. They also add variety to the day and as the partridge shooting season begins a month earlier than that for pheasants,

A pair of English partridges – a common sight on farmland a century ago but now in steady decline

Partridges are never wing-clipped so release pens are covered with a net

the season is extended. If shoots are letting the days, this is obviously of financial benefit.

French partridges are mostly reared on grass using a similar system to that used to rear pheasants. However, they are easier to manage providing they remain healthy. Quite often the chicks are kept indoors for the first 2 or 3 weeks before they are transferred outside into the rearing units. They are smaller and more delicate than pheasants and this gives them time to become strong and active and better able to cope with adverse weather conditions. French partridges show little inclination to feather peck so do not normally need either beak trimming or bitting.

They are kept on the rearing field for longer than pheasants, often until they are 10 weeks or older. This is partly because they are released onto arable land and it is advisable to wait until the cereal harvest is underway in order that they do not become lost in standing crops or get cut up by machinery which often works well into the evening. They are also at risk from the same predators as pheasants.

French partridges in and out of their release pen

Because partridges are gregarious by nature, a different method of release is usually employed than that for pheasants. Small temporary pens covered with a net are erected well apart in game cover or corners of fields where they are not likely to be disturbed. This may involve a considerable amount of pens if a large number of partridges are to be released. Partridges are never wing clipped. Approximately 50 or so birds are put in each pen where they remain for only a few days before gradually being released, a few each day. Those that have been let out tend to stay near the pen and it is common policy to retain 3 or 4 as 'call' birds for some time afterwards.

Food and water are provided at the pen site and there is also feeding further away to spread the birds out - this can be done by hand, hopper or quad bike and spinner. Partridges show a preference for pellets so wheat is usually introduced into the diet later than it is for pheasants. Where a seed mixture is grown for game cover or where there is an abundance of weed seeds available then partridges will also relish this natural food.

A broody bantam is commonly used to sit on English partridge eggs

A French partridge is fully grown at about 14 weeks old and they should be released at least a month before shooting is planned, allowing them time to become wild and well acquainted with the surrounding area.

ENGLISH (or Grey) PARTRIDGES are seldom reared in any great number. The captive strains do not stay well in the places where they are released and are difficult to manage on a shoot day. The chicks when first hatched are little bigger than a large bumblebee and are highly strung which makes them more difficult to rear. The best results are achieved using a broody bantam (small chicken) but these are no longer easy to acquire and their care is time-consuming. Released birds from captive strains seem to lack the ability to successfully rear broods in the wild.

English partridges were very common in the wild a century ago on farmland but various factors, most of which stem from changes in farming practices since the last war, have caused a serious decline in numbers and there is now grave concern about how much longer they can survive. Very few are shot these days: in fact most shoots have put a voluntary ban on shooting them. Some estates, especially in East Anglia, are spending a huge amount of money on safeguarding their remaining wild stock by creating the right habitat and conditions needed for them to flourish. However, bad weather at hatching time in June can have disastrous results. Research on the English partridge is also being conducted by the Game Conservancy Trust whose main funding comes from gamekeepers and shoot owners.

The English partridge is probably the most cherished of all game birds and has always been a favourite of those who shoot. It has an independent character and it won't be for want of trying if it fails to survive.

WILD PHEASANTS and **PARTRIDGES** In areas where there is a reasonable stock of wild birds, management is geared to ensure that they have the best opportunities to thrive. Artificially reared birds do not breed and survive in the wild with much

A box of day-old English partridge chicks; wild ones are now so rare that most shoots have a voluntary ban on shooting them

On wild pheasant shoots it is customary to shoot mainly cock birds

success, so those estates that have wild populations preserve them with care.

Management is concentrated on predator and pest control and the provision of good habitat. Game cover crops are not only selected to provide winter food and cover, but also to attract insects which newly hatched chicks need to feed on. Unfortunately these days the unpredictability of breeding success, combined with high overheads (wages, rates, vehicle running costs) mean that it is not economically viable to employ a gamekeeper solely to produce wild birds.

To ensure there is sufficient shooting, the answer on most estates is to purchase cock pheasant poults at about 7 or 8 weeks old and to shoot only cocks throughout the season unless it has been an exceptional breeding year and there is an excessive number of pheasants.

This way, as one cock will mate with several hens, there should be only a few remaining at the end of the season and the chances are that it will be wild ones that have survived to breed. All the hens in theory should be wild and therefore stand a greater chance of successfully rearing a brood in the coming year.

Rarely are young partridges released. The sexes are indistinguishable and they pair up at breeding time, so the system used for pheasants would not be possible to put into practice to safeguard wild partridge stocks.

> *Strips of grouse-moor heather are burned in rotation every seven to ten years*

A keeper keeps a wary eye on heather burning on a grouse moor, a practice that needs careful controlling and a knowledge of expected wind direction

GROUSE are never reared, they are all truly wild. Their survival basically depends on 3 factors: how well predators have been controlled, how well the habitat has been managed, and how kind the weather has been while the hens were sitting on eggs and after the chicks hatch.

Grouse shooting is considered by some to be the elite of shooting. In a good year, when broods have done well and there is an abundance of grouse, the moorland can yield a useful income from the surplus. In the long term the moor can only sustain a certain number and it causes harm to leave too many. However in a poor year shooting may have to be strictly curtailed in order that a viable population is left as breeding stock for the following year.

Heather-burning management

Grouse are moorland birds and heather is a major part of their diet, so heather management is of great importance. Growth is regulated by burning strips which is carried out on rotation approximately every seven to ten years. This work is usually done between the end of October and mid-April although there are actually very few days when the weather conditions are right

Grouse shooting is often considered the most challenging game shooting

Above Grouse on a carpet of purple heather in August

to carry out the operation. Only small areas are burned because grouse are very territorial and need a mix of different stages of growth within each territory, which is normally approximately 5 acres (2.5 hectares) in size. This system provides them with young heather for food and old tall heather in which to shelter and nest.

Grouse are not given any supplementary food but small piles of grit are put out across the moor as they need this to help them digest the fibrous heather. Grouse usually have to share the moorland with sheep which, in moderation, can be an aid to management. Excessive numbers, however, can damage the habitat by overgrazing and also become a health risk.

Disease a threat

Disease in grouse is more prevalent in some years than others. One problem is a parasitic worm called strongylosis that gets into the gut and seriously weakens the bird. It can have a devastating effect on young broods especially when their parents are not able to look after them properly. There is little that can be done to treat them apart from putting out grit that has been medicated with a wormer and hoping that they eat some of it. Sometimes adult grouse are caught up in spring and given a dose of medicine individually but this is difficult, time-consuming and not always very effective.

Another grouse disease is one they share with sheep. Ticks are prevalent on the moors: they get on sheep as well as grouse and can transfer a disease called 'louping ill' between the two. A heavy infestation of ticks themselves can seriously debilitate grouse which need to be in good condition all year round to survive on the open moors. Efficient tick control on sheep therefore plays an important part in grouse management. In some areas serious damage may be caused by beetles that eat the heather, which in turn reduces the amount of food available to grouse and can cause deterioration to their well-being.

The grouse shoot

The grouse shooting season traditionally begins on the 12th August (the Glorious Twelfth) but many estates do not start until later in the month. Grouse are usually driven over a line of guns

Winter conditions on the moor can be harsh for grouse and the birds need to be in prime condition to survive into the next season

Sheep ticks can transfer 'louping ill' disease to grouse

which are concealed in 'butts', built out of stone or other materials, sometimes sunk into the ground. Normally grouse fly forward fast and fairly low, often following the contours of the ground. Early in the season they stay in family groups but later on join together in what are known as 'packs'.

Organised shooting does not usually take place after the end of October although a day or two may be arranged for tenant farmers, beaters and others who have assisted on shoot days.

Walked-up grouse

Where grouse numbers are low and insufficient to justify the cost of driven shooting, then 'walking up' is an alternative. A team of guns with their dogs line out across the moor and walk forward shooting at any grouse they happen to put up.

Medicated grit put out by the keeper on the grouse moor. This is necessary for the grouse to easily digest heather and it is a good way of getting wild birds to take their medicine!

Shooting over pointers

Another option on a lesser scale is to shoot over pointers or setters. These dogs range widely and are trained to stop and mark immediately they scent a bird. They wait until the person shooting has got close enough before the handler gives them the command to flush.

At the end of any day's grouse shooting, the shot birds are separated into old and young to give a ratio of kills. An experienced person can tell them apart by looking at their wing feathers and even sometimes their toenails.

Other duties carried out by a grouse moor keeper, besides predator control and heather burning, are the maintenance of tracks and butts and generally monitoring the condition and distribution of the birds. His beat may cover several thousand acres. He needs to be familiar with every inch of it and to be aware of what is happening on all of it throughout the year.

BLACKCOCK are another member of the grouse family but are not so widely distributed. Their numbers are dwindling and they are very rarely shot as shoot owners wish to preserve them.

The Highland capercaillie, about the size of a turkey, is a protected species, in decline due to modern forestry

177

CAPERCAILLIE is a species of woodland grouse that is the size of a turkey. It is found only in some areas of the Highlands of Scotland. Although there has been a voluntary ban on shooting for the past decade because their numbers were declining, this failed to remedy the situation and they are now uncommon enough to have been removed from the quarry list and placed under special protection by the authorities. One of the principle reasons for their decline appears to be connected with the amount of new forestry planting which has been carried out in the areas where they live: there are fences erected around these plantations to protect the young trees from deer damage, and the capercaillie are killed by flying into them.

WOODCOCK are one of a family of birds that are called 'waders' although in fact they have taken to living on the land and seek out wet ground on which to feed. They are mainly nocturnal and spend the days hidden in thick cover. Rhododendron woods are a favourite haunt. They are quite common in some areas and resident throughout the year, with numbers swelled in winter by the arrival of migrants from Northern Europe.

Usually only single birds are encountered and when flushed they provide a challenging shot as they have a zig-zag pattern to their flight when they rise.

SNIPE are small wading birds, similar to a woodcock but inhabiting boggy or marshy areas. They are quite common in some localities and also offer a sporting shot.

GOLDEN PLOVER are another small wading bird now not as common as they once were. They nest on open moorland where they often benefit from the protection afforded them by grouse moor keepers. In autumn and winter they leave the moors and form large flocks moving south to feed on farmland and river estuaries.

MALLARD are the only breed of duck that are reared artificially in any quantity. They are released onto inland ponds and lakes to create additional and varied shooting on an estate. If not managed properly or if they are of a strain that has become over domesti-

Barley is the best corn to scatter around ponds to attract duck

Rhododendron woods are a favourite haunt of woodcock

Artificially reared mallard do not normally go far from the pond on which they were released

cated (something often seen on village ponds), they can become very tame and unsporting. They do not normally go far from the pond where they were released so can usually be relied upon if an extra drive on a shoot day is needed. Under the right conditions they can make some interesting and very sporting shooting to supplement a partridge or pheasant day, as their season opens on 1st September.

OTHER SPECIES OF DUCK appear on inland and coastal waters, particularly in winter, and can add variety to a day's shooting. Inland ponds and lakes are often 'fed' in winter. Barley is a favourite food, and shooting takes place just before sunset when the wild ducks naturally fly in to feed. Numbers and species are unpredictable which makes it even more exciting for the guns waiting hidden out of sight in hides. This form of shooting is known as 'flighting'.

GEESE Canada and greylag have become common on inland waters in recent years where they now breed. While they may offer a shot when ducks are being driven off a pond or lake, they soon go right away, so numbers killed in this way are minimal. Considerable numbers of greylag and pink-footed geese are also shot in coastal areas by wildfowlers where numbers are swelled in winter with the arrival of thousands of migrants from Northern Europe or Iceland. These vast numbers can cause serious damage to farm crops.

The number of resident woodcock swells in winter with the arrival of migrants

179

WILDFOWLING

Wildfowl, which consists of ducks and geese, frequent many areas of coastal marshes and foreshores during the winter months. They are truly wild birds and most are migrants from breeding grounds in Northern Europe or Iceland that come in their thousands to spend winter in the warmer British climate.

Wildfowling is a solitary sport and not one for the faint-hearted. It involves lengthy waits concealed in hides, drains or boats waiting for the birds to flight from their coastal roosting sites at first light to inland feeding areas, or ambushing them on their return at dusk.

Coastal wildfowlers rely on the mud filled creeks that criss-cross the salt marshes left empty by the receding tide to hide in. They often put a few decoys out before taking up their position long before it gets light and then they wait, not knowing what species, if any, of duck or goose may come over them or whether they have chosen the right place to be. Warm, waterproof and camouflaged clothing is essential, as is a good knowledge of tide patterns to avoid being marooned by the incoming tide which

The worse the weather the better the prospects for wildfowling

Above Pink-footed geese fill the Norfolk sky. A wonderful sight to behold and an indication of the numbers that can at times land on a farmer's field

creeps along the creeks and can easily cut a person off. Deaths have occurred from drowning and exposure, through lack of information and a disregard to personal safety. A strong dog is another item of useful equipment to retrieve duck or geese that come down on inaccessible parts of the marsh.

There are many wildfowling clubs around Britain's coasts and they set themselves high standards. Membership is limited and new-comers are only accepted once they have proved that they have a good understanding of the sport and then have to spend a probationary period with an experienced wildfowler before going out on their own. Accurate identification of protected species is very important and there are strict limits on the number of birds that can be taken at a time. The clubs do a lot of conservation work on their marshes during the close season and often warden them so that breeding birds are not disturbed. They also work closely with local nature reserves and other conservation organisations and exhibit at country shows.

Unlike game birds, wildfowl can see reasonably well in the dark and may continue to flight all night if it is bright moonlight

Generally speaking, the worse the weather, the better the chance of a successful wildfowling outing. Unlike game birds, wildfowl can see reasonably well in the dark and may continue to flight all night if it is bright moonlight. Much depends on the weather conditions. When the wind is howling from the north and bringing with it flecks of snow, most people pull the curtains and turn up the central heating: not so the wildfowler for that is what he has been waiting for.

Widgeon and snipe share a feeding ground in a period of hard weather

Traditional wildfowling, punt-gunning
In times past, men made a living in winter from wildfowling and the history of the sport is full of legendary characters. Besides

large ordinary shotguns, the 'fowlers' of yesteryear used a canon-like gun mounted on the front of a type of boat that lay low in the water. They would lay flat in the bottom of it and stealthily approach a flock of ducks. Once within range they would fire the big gun into the group hoping to kill or seriously injure most of them. This was called 'punt gunning'. It was probably a fairly efficient way of getting a large bag to sell when times were hard but undoubtedly it was a cruel way.

Another method used on some inland waters was to build a long tunnel, wide at the mouth and enclosed at the other end. Wild duck were attracted to the water with food while a fox-like dog, which out of curiosity they would follow, was used to lure them into the cage at the end where they could be captured. Remnants of these old duck decoys can still be found amongst the reeds of some inland waters.

Peregrine falcon on its post, a native British bird and strictly protected in the wild. The birds used in falconry are bred from captive stock

FALCONRY

Birds of prey hold a fascination for many people. Their incredible eyesight, speed and agility make them impressive to watch and falconry is a hobby that is becoming increasingly popular. For those who wish to find out more, it is possible to attend organised courses.

Falconry was being practised as long ago as 2,000 BC and was at one time the king of the hunting sports in every European court. It was thought to have been introduced to England by French nobles in about 860 AD. In the Middle Ages anyone who took a wild falcon or interfered with one at the nest was condemned to death. A scale of values evolved whereby Gyr falcons could only be flown by royalty; peregrines were for noblemen; and goshawks and sparrowhawks for landed gentry and the clergy. In present times falconry is still a major sport in the Middle East.

A lot of time needs to be spent with a young falcon to train it and for it to build up a relationship with its handler. It is natural for a falcon or hawk to chase a moving object and in order to get it to return to the handler when it is flying free, a feather lure on

Falcons and hawks are used at some airfields to scare away other birds because of the danger they may cause to aircraft on landing and take off

a string incorporating a small piece of meat is swung round in the air to attract the bird's attention. When it grabs hold of the lure, the bird lands on the ground and either rests or eats the meat, allowing the handler time to approach it, gently catch it and place a hood over its head and eyes to quieten it. Falcons will also fly straight onto the handler's leather gloved fist when tempted with a piece of meat, usually part of a dead chick. They are held or tethered with a cord attached to leather straps on their legs known as 'jesses'.

Falcons as bird-scarers

Falcons and hawks are used at some airfields to scare away other birds because of the danger they may cause to aircraft on landing and take off, and also sometimes in towns to frighten away pigeons where they have become a pest on buildings.

When flying, a falcon or hawk is able to spot its prey from several hundred feet and then plummet in a 'stoop' to catch and kill its victim with its talons. A falcon can reach a speed of 150mph. It is now common practice to fit a small transmitter onto a bird that is flown so that it can be located if it should disappear from sight.

Approximately 13,000 people keep falcons or hawks, which in Britain have to be registered. About 4,000 people fly them at live prey such as game birds or rabbits in their natural environment, and most will work them in conjunction with a dog to mark or flush the quarry. Pointers and setters are a popular choice on open ground, and spaniels where there is more cover.

FALCONRY
Useful Words

AUSTRINGER Person who flies 'shortwings', ie hawks as opposed to falcons.
BATE Verb for when the hawk tries to fly while still 'jessed' to the fist or block.
BIND Verb for when hawk locks to its prey during the strike.
BUMBLE FOOT A condition to which falcons are susceptible, in which one of the rear talons penetrates the ball of the foot.
CREANCE Long length of cord attached to leash during final stages of training, prior to flying free.
GAUNTLET The padded glove the hawk sits on.
JESSES Leather straps which secure the bird's legs when at rest.
LONG WINGS Falcons.
LURE A feather and a piece of meat on a cord which is swung to attract the falcon.
PETTY SINGLES Individual toes of a hawk.
POUNCES The feet of a hawk.
SHORT WINGS Hawks.
STOOP Action when a bird plummets earthwards to catch its prey.
SWIVEL Connects the leash and jesses to prevent twisting. Removed for hunting.

A falcon can reach a speed of 150mph

FOXHOUNDS

Lowland mounted packs

There are nearly 200 registered packs of foxhounds in Britain. A lowland mounted pack is one that operates in areas where the terrain is suitable for the huntsman and whippers-in to control the hounds from horseback. In hilly and rough terrain this would not be possible.

Foxhound pups are usually born in early spring. When they are a few days old their dew claws are removed to prevent the risk of injury later on. Their ears are tattooed inside with an identification number and all their details are recorded in either the Modern English Stud Book or the Welsh Stud Book (Welsh hounds are lighter framed and rough coated).

By tradition they are named using the first one or two letters of their dam's (mother's) name if they have been sired by a stallion (dog) hound from the same pack. However if a bitch has been mated to a hound from another pack, as often happens to introduce certain qualities or bring in a fresh bloodline, then the first one or two letters of the sire's name are used.

Each individual pack will, over the decades, have been

> There are nearly 200 registered packs of foxhounds in Britain

Above West Norfolk Hunt. The huntsman and masters wear the traditional 'pink'. However the Berkeley livery is yellow

HUNTING *Useful Words*

CHARLEY/TOBY/REYNARD Alternative names for a fox.

COUPLE Hounds are counted in couples ie 22 hounds are 11 couples.

COVERT A small dense area of woodland.

DOG Male fox.

DRAW Send hounds into cover to search for a fox. Look-outs are posted at strategic points to shout out if a fox is seen to break from cover.

EARTH Underground den of a fox.

ENTER (a hound) Introduce a young hound to working as part of a pack.

ENTER (a terrier) Introduce a terrier to working a fox underground.

FULL CRY The sound of all the pack giving tongue while running.

GIVE TONGUE/MOUTH The noise a hound makes when it identifies a scent. It is a resonant sound like a cross between a howl and a bark.

GONE TO GROUND Term used when an animal has taken refuge underground.

HUNTSMAN Person in charge of the everyday management of hounds and kennels and who carries the horn and hunts them when out hunting.

JOINT MASTER Person who shares the responsibility of Mastership.

KENNEL MAN Person who does menial chores around the kennels such as skinning carcasses and preparing the flesh.

LODGE The area in which hounds sleep on raised straw-covered benches. Bitches and dogs are often kennelled separately.

MASTER Person taking overall responsibility for the running of a pack of hounds and all that is associated with the task.

MEET Place where the pack and followers gather, usually a large house, farm or a pub.

MUSIC The sound of hounds giving tongue.

STALLION HOUND Dog hound used for stud purposes.

STIRRUP CUP A drink, often port, handed round at a Meet.

TOD Alternative name for a fox used in Northern England and Scotland.

VIXEN Female fox.

WHELP To give birth or new born pups.

WHIPPER IN Person who assists the Huntsman.

WORK A LINE Follow a scent trail.

Hounds do not go out hunting until they are about 18 months old

Foxhounds in the kennels, not suitable as pets, but perfect as pack animals

developed to suit the conditions under which they operate and the temperaments and characteristics will vary accordingly.

The number of hounds kept depends on how many days hunting there are. Pack size varies averaging about 35 to 45 couple (70 to 90 hounds). Only enough litters are bred each year to provide replacements.

When they are about 10 weeks old, after they have been vaccinated, the puppies are 'walked' by hunt supporters who are willing to take them to live in their homes or out-buildings and look after them for several months. This provides young hounds with the chance to have contact with people and livestock during a formative part of their lives, opportunities they would be less likely to get within the confines of the hunt kennels. The volunteers who look after them also undertake the cost of feeding which helps the hunt's finances.

The young hounds return to kennels when they are about 8 to 10 months old. There they have to learn the disciplines of pack life and for a few weeks are each coupled to an older hound when out for exercise. This continues until the Huntsman judges that they can be trusted enough to run loose. They do not go out hunting until they are about 18 months old when they are mature and responsible enough.

Even so they still have a lot to learn and the first few weeks of the hunting season are spent in educating young hounds in the ways of hunting. On average a hound will last for 6 or 7 seasons, ie until it is 8 or 9 years old, when it is humanely put down, something the Huntsman does not like doing. Old foxhounds are not at all suitable to keep as pets and it would be cruel as well as expensive to keep them in kennels if they were not able to do the job that they had been bred for. A few terriers of different breeds or crosses are also used, depending on individual preference, and they are also kept at the kennels.

A hound will live for 6 or 7 seasons, ie. until it is 8 or 9 years old

These young foxhound pups will not hunt until they are 18 months old

Taking dead animals for farmers

Most lowland packs are fed some flesh (raw meat), mainly dead calves, cattle or horses. Although there are more and more restrictions, the Hunt provides an invaluable service to local farmers, by collecting their dead animals and putting down the sick, old or injured on the farm, thus saving the cost of disposing of them by other means.

Health and Safety regulations apply to the handling and preparation of what is known as fallen stock by kennel staff, just as they do to licensed knackermen. All kennels utilising this free source of food by law have to have an incinerator in which to dispose of the offal, spinal cords and heads. Pigs or sheep are not generally used for feeding hounds because of possible health risks.

Lowland foxhounds are given a lot of exercise by the huntsman and whipper in, mounted on bikes, covering several miles at a session. On non-hunting days during the season and at the end of it, the pack is taken out for an hour or so once or twice a day. As summer progresses, their exercise is increased to 4 or 5 hours a day and as the opening of the new season draws near in late August, the hunt staff change their bikes for horses so everybody gets fit.

Early season hunting to disperse fox cubs
The season begins with autumn hunting when the corn has been harvested, typically late August or early September, continuing through until the end of October. Large woodland areas are chosen where it is likely a vixen and her cubs, now full grown, may be in residence. Look-outs are posted round the outside and the hounds put in. Many of the young foxes escape and are not followed by the hounds. Meets are arranged for soon after dawn, and hunting is finished about mid-morning. This is a time when the young hounds can learn their trade as well as accounting for a few cubs. There may be 6 or 7 cubs in a litter and autumn hunting disperses most of these. If they all remained concentrated in one area, they could cause damage to the local wildlife and possibly livestock.

Preserved hunting woodland
Some large hunts own woods or spinneys specifically to manage for hunting. Their main aim is to preserve the fox population by leaving areas undisturbed for foxes to live and breed in. Secondly, good access is needed within woodland for the movement of the hunt, so tracks and pathways are necessary for the Huntsman and the field to be able to keep in touch with hounds.

Jumps are constructed in the surrounding fences or hedges at strategic places. Coppicing on a 5 to 10 year rotation provides

West Norfolk foxhound

Each hunting location is normally only hunted twice in a season

an ideal habitat for foxes and also an environment in which many species of flora and fauna flourish.

Traditionally the official opening meet of the season is at the beginning of November and from then on they are arranged for an 11am start. Hunting continues on a regular basis several times a week, weather permitting, until the middle of March.

Many foxes lie outside during the day and earths are sometimes 'stopped' the night before a hunt to prevent them from going to ground. This also allows hounds the opportunity to catch their fox which may have taken them several miles before either being caught or escaping. Many more foxes get away than are caught and an area is normally hunted no more than 3 or 4 times during the season.

Shooting foxes which have gone to ground

If a fox does go to ground it is either left unharmed or, if the landowner or farmer specifically requests that foxes are killed on their land, the hunt is obliged to deal with it. Then the terrier man uses one of his little dogs to locate and corner the fox. The terrier barks when it has done so, a locator device attached to the dog's collar pointing the position, so that the terrier man can dig down and humanely dispatch the fox as quickly as possible. Inevitably this sometimes takes a little while as it may be deep underground. It is illegal to put a dog into a badger sett, and fox hunting rules prohibit a fox being dug out in order that the hunt may continue.

Fox hunting is regulated by a very strict code of conduct that has been reinforced over recent years to make the whole procedure as humane as possible. The hunting fraternity are well aware that their sport is under the spotlight and that to transgress the rules may result in some unwanted publicity for they know the media are always ready to publicise any foul practice.

Hunt employees

The hunting year begins on 1st May. Large hunts may employ as many as 20 staff and have contact with as many as 1,000 farms with which they like to build some sort of personal relationship.

The kennel staff includes the Huntsman who is responsible

> The hunting year begins on 1st May

Foxhound kennels provide a great service to farmers by collecting and disposing of 'fallen stock'

> *Hill packs are often light in colour so that they can be more easily seen against the dark hills*

for the day-to-day running of the kennels. He is assisted by one or more whippers in (who control the pack of hounds when out hunting) and one or more kennel men to help look after hounds when not hunting and collect and prepare the meat for them. These all work on a full-time basis and are provided with houses and appropriate vehicles. Most Huntsmen have worked their way up through the more lowly positions to achieve their ambition. As well as these people, a terrier man may be employed either full-time by the big hunts or part-time on smaller ones, who may also act as earth stopper. Often he works in a voluntary capacity but at all times he has to be registered with the MFH Association and operate within their code of conduct.

Several horses will be kept by the mounted packs and one girl or lad is employed for every 3 or 4 horses kept. This may be on a seasonal basis as the horses, which are usually the property of the Masters, will very likely be returned to their owners and turned out to grass for the summer. Some of the larger packs keep enough horses so that the hunt staff can change mounts during a hunt day. The hunt horses are of no particular breeding; it is very much a case of handsome is as handsome does. The only requirements are that they are fit, capable and have the right temperament to cope not only with a pack of hounds round their legs but also traffic, machinery and all the other hazards encountered in modern day living.

Only the Huntsman carries a horn on which different notes are blown to keep both hounds and followers aware of what is happening such as gone to ground, a kill, or time to go home. The whippers in are there to help him keep control of the pack, prevent such incidents as chasing cats and to keep a watchful eye on roads.

Hunt livery

Typically the livery (uniform) of the officials to a pack is red (which in hunting is called 'pink') but a few hunts wear a different colour such as the Berkeley who traditionally wear yellow. Mounted hunt staff wear red as do the Masters and Secretaries. Some subscribers may also be allowed the privilege of wearing the red coat but women rarely do.

A cream or white stock, or cravat, is worn round the neck

> *The official opening meet of the season is at the beginning of November*

Only the huntsman carries a horn and different notes signify different messages: such as gone to ground, a kill, or time to go home and all followers are expected to comply with the formal dress code of proper jacket and breeches. Less formal clothes are worn on autumn hunting days but they are still very smart. Drab tweed coloured jackets known as 'ratcatchers' are worn with a shirt and tie.

Each hunt has its own design of brass buttons worn on the coat so any hunt member can be instantly recognised as to which hunt he supports. Interestingly, the coat buttons also provide further identification as to the role of the wearer. Kennel staff have 5 buttons on the front of theirs, Masters have 4 and subscribers 3. For safety reasons, fibreglass crash hats have generally replaced the traditional bowler or top hat.

Finances of the hunt

Hunts are financed by a variety of means. A few are privately run but the majority are what is known as subscription packs. Each hunt has a chairman and a committee who act in the capacity of a board of directors. They are elected from subscribers, farmers or landowners within the hunt. The Master or Joint Masters act as managing directors and are elected by the Committee on an annual basis from 1st May to 30th April but notice of change is given by 1st February.

The role of the Master

Masters are responsible for the hiring and firing of hunt staff, hound breeding, horses, kennel and staff management and may be expected to make up any financial shortfall if necessary. They also hold a very responsible, time-consuming position in that it is the Master's job to liaise with landowners and farmers within the area covered by the hunt, as well as dealing with the press and organising functions.

On hunt days the Master is responsible for controlling the field (mounted followers). Popular hunts may attract as many as 200 at a time which requires a certain amount of discipline. The Hunt Secretary is responsible for the administration, collecting the 'cap' (the one-off single day contribution) at a meet and subscriptions. He or she often acts as treasurer as well. It is considered to be an honorary position but larger packs may pay some salary and expenses.

> *Kennel staff have 5 buttons on the front of their coats, Masters have 4 and subscribers 3*

> *Each hunt has its own design of brass buttons worn on the coat*

> *It is illegal to put a dog into a badger sett*

It costs a lot of money to run a hunt, on average probably approaching a six figure sum each year. In the case of the large fashionable hunts who meet several days a week, they may need to find a quarter of a million pounds to keep going! An annual subscription may be paid or a daily one for non-regulars. Donations from car followers are on a voluntary basis. Various social events are organised in order to raise money.

Fund-raisers

Each hunt holds a Point-to-Point every Spring. This is run under certain racing rules and provides betting facilities but is a strictly amateur affair. They have derived from the original steeplechases when bets were wagered as to who would win the horse race from one church steeple to another, cross country.

Every horse entered in a Point-to-Point must have qualified by having been hunting a specified number of days during the season, verified by one of the Master's signatures on the day.

The Hunt Ball is a familiar fund-raising event and Puppy Shows are organised in summer, combining a social gathering with an opportunity to view the young hounds that are soon to become pack members. Hounds are also shown and judged at Agricultural Shows as well as the top event held at Peterborough each summer where hounds from all over the country compete for the top honours.

There are Hunt Supporters Clubs who work hard to raise further funds and Parades at local country shows provide a chance for people to come into contact with the hounds and find out for themselves just how friendly and well behaved they are.

Tufters, the name given to the oldest, wisest hounds in a staghound pack

John Peel, in the early 1800s, was probably the most famous huntsman of all

The Foot Packs

There are a number of packs of foxhounds that are hunted on foot, many of them unregistered. In Scotland and Wales there are about 50 'gun' or foot packs comprising of a few couple (hounds are counted in twos) which are kept in heavily forested areas and used to evict foxes. People with guns stand around the outside of the woodland or on wide rides within, and shoot any foxes put up by the hounds that come toward them. Other foot packs hunt the mountainous areas of Britain where it would be impossible to follow on horseback.

The Lake District footpacks are kept and hunted in a very different way to the mounted lowland foxhound packs. Their sole purpose is to kill foxes: any sport and entertainment for the followers is incidental. Often hunting with hounds is the only efficient way to catch foxes in such rugged terrain in order to protect the sheep that roam free on the high fells. It is a tough existence for them and it takes tough huntsmen, hounds and terriers to provide this service to local farmers.

How Fell packs hunt

A Lake District foot pack usually has about 50 hounds. They are often lighter in build and colour than other foxhounds so that they can be seen clearly against the dark fell sides. They work more independently than lowland packs and will hunt for hours on their own, puzzling out the line a fox has taken. Foxes often lay out on the open hillsides in dried bracken beds. The hounds spread out and search every likely place. When one finds the scent it gives

Famous foot packs of the Lake District: Blencathra, Coniston, Lunesdale, Melbreak, Ullswater, Eskdale and Ennerdale

Above The Lakeland foot pack is called to heel by the Huntsman

tongue and the others soon join it.

Fell hounds are very intelligent and if they become separated, are capable of picking up the foot scent of their huntsman or other hounds and following that. Alternatively they have the sense to return to where they were released, go back to kennels or to the nearest farm if they get lost.

Long-legged terriers, often coupled together, run with the huntsman and hounds. These are often of Lakeland breeding or the black Patterdale type. They have to be strong and capable of covering 20 miles in a day, as well as scrambling about in rocks to evict a fox so that it can be shot.

The season begins in early September and continues until April. Each location within the area covered by a pack, which may total 300 square miles, is normally only hunted twice in a season. Packs hunt 3 or 4 days a week starting each day at about 9.30am. When the official season is finished, the huntsman and his hounds remain on 'lamb call' until the end of May so that if a farmer loses a lamb or two overnight to a fox, he can call for the hounds early next morning to track down the culprit.

A proud history

There is no glamour in being huntsman to a Fell pack but it is a position that is held with tremendous pride. John Peel, in the early 1800s, was probably the most famous of all but modern day ones are also steeped in tradition. The Fell packs were formed in the 1800s as private packs before becoming subscription ones. The Melbreak Fell Pack can trace its history back to 1807. The Huntsman of the Coniston is the fifth generation of his family to hold the honour and Barrie Todhunter, Huntsman to the Blencathra is very aptly named, as a fox is called Tod in northern England and Scotland. Fell packs also have a Master and Edmund Porter of the Eskdale and Ennerdale is the third member of his family since 1917 to serve as dual Huntsman and Master, having held the positions since 1966.

Only the huntsman wears a red coat and carries a horn which he uses very little, mainly to call his hounds to him, for they may be working a mile or more away. Whipping-in is usually done by enthusiastic locals who have a good knowledge of the area and

The Coniston foot pack, specially bred and trained for hill work

A fell hound will last for 7 or 8 seasons, maybe hunting more than 100 days each season

193

volunteer their services on hunting days. They act as scouts rather than actively controlling hounds. CB radios are now used to keep in touch to let the huntsman know what his hounds are doing.

The Huntsman has no staff at the kennels except maybe a volunteer and a helpful wife; in fact he receives so little in the way of wages that he has to find casual work during the summer to support his family. Fell packs are run on a shoestring and it's very much a team effort that keeps them going. It is the huntsman who has to take care of the hounds, prepare the food and keep the kennels spick and span. Hounds are fed on maize meal porridge mix and meat that is cooked in coppers. Any dead or 'fallen' stock is collected by the Huntsman. Unwanted dairy bull calves put down at birth, and milk over quota which would otherwise be poured down the drain, are also made use of when available.

Trencher-fed hounds

Fell hounds are what is known as 'trencher fed'. This means that when their services are no longer required in the summer, the pack is split up and taken to people who are willing to look after them for a few months. Like lowland foxhounds, young puppies from about 8 weeks old are usually cared for by 'walkers', who are local volunteers, and who teach them to have respect for humans and livestock. When about a year old, they return to kennels for a few weeks to learn about living a pack life before going back to their walkers until late summer. Older hounds often return to their original walkers for the summer and some, at the end of their working lives, are also provided with a retirement home. The walkers feed the hounds in their care and pay for any vet bills. Sometimes they will also care for a bitch when she whelps.

The Puppy Show

At the end of summer each hunt holds a Puppy Show and here the hounds that have been away on their summer holidays are gathered together and taken back to kennels. Incredibly after a week or so they gel together again to form a pack and are ready to go hunting again despite not having seen each other for 3 months. Older hounds sometimes make their way back to kennels before the Puppy Show: a subtle hint of autumn in the air and an indication they know it is time to start work again. Puppies, by now about 18

Foxhounds are generally extremely friendly

The Melbreak Fell Pack can trace its history back to 1807

months old, have no gentle initiation into hunting, although nearly all of this is instinctive anyway. If any seriously unacceptable faults show up, such as chasing sheep, they are put down.

Providing it stays fit, a fell hound will last for 7 or 8 seasons, maybe hunting more than 100 days each season. They work using their own initiative in some very remote places and may well cover more than 20 miles on the trail of a single fox. Any injuries are usually cut pads caused by sharp stones and through being caught on fences, usually Forestry Commission deer fencing. Hunting on National Trust or Forestry Commission land is permitted under licence, with restrictions on the use of terriers. Notification of hunting has to be given a week in advance.

Fell hounds are fed on a combination of a porridge mix made from maize meal and meat

A community effort

Keeping a fell pack is very much a united effort. While many of the houses in the towns and villages are now holiday homes or weekend cottages belonging to people not resident all year round, there still remains a staunch nucleus of supporters dedicated to keeping the packs going. It is not only local people who enjoy the social occasions that hunting provides at a time of year when there is little else happening: visitors also find this timeless scenario enthralling. Fell hunting, conducted for the purpose of killing a serious pest, set in such breathtaking scenery and with hounds purposefully working a line along the sides of fells and over the tops is a spectacle that many locals and visitors appreciate. There is no pomp and ceremony but just a workman-like attitude to the job in hand along with a wealth of tradition.

Unlike lowland packs, subscriptions are entirely voluntary and the hunts manage on a shoestring. Hunt Balls, coffee mornings, raffles, auctions, sponsored walks, puppy shows and fell racing, both hound and human; all these events help to raise funds while providing social contact between supporters during the summer. Sadly the old tradition is dying out of gathering in the local pub at the end of the day and each in turn standing up to recite a poem or sing a song recounting the exploits of a notable day's hunting, huntsman, terrier, hound or fox.

Patterdale-type terriers when taken out hunting with fell packs are often coupled together

BEAGLING

In England and Wales there are 71 packs of beagles and 9 packs of bassetts that are hunted on foot. Their quarry is the hare. Hares are also hunted on horseback by 20 packs of harriers. The hare is not hunted in Scotland. Many packs of beagles have connections with the Armed Services or public schools. Wye College Beagles in Kent are associated with the University of London and The Trinity Foot Beagles have close ties with Cambridge University. Unlike most student sports they receive no funding. Hare hunting is an even older sport than chasing foxes. The oldest English and Welsh packs can trace their roots back to 1745.

Beagles are little more than half the size of a foxhound, while harriers are only slightly smaller than foxhounds.

Each pack has one or more Masters, a huntsman and one or more whippers in. The hunt staff wear red coats with most foxhound packs, while those who hunt the hare generally wear dark green. The hounds are kept in kennels and exercised by the huntsman and his assistant riding on bikes.

As with fox hunting, the season begins in August or September with meets held soon after dawn, continuing for only 3 or 4 hours and used as an opportunity to educate young hounds.

The livery for hunt staff who hunt the hare is usually dark green

Above The Aldershot and Sandhurst beagles

The main season starts in October and continues until March.

Pursued hares usually run in a very large circle, encompassing several fields. They possess great speed and stamina, while the hounds that hunt them are much slower but persistent. Hounds find the hare either by spreading out, flushing it and following the scent (unlike greyhounds, they hunt with their noses not their eyes) or by picking up on an old scent.

The action takes place in fields as hares are creatures of open farmland and fields offer excellent opportunities for the followers to watch what is going on. Hunting is best in places where there are not too many hares or the pack may split if more than one gets up. In fact hare hunting accounts for very few hares and these are usually the old, the injured or those suffering from some form of sickness.

A fit hare can easily evade a pack of hounds unless it is unlucky. It is for the pleasure and appreciation of watching hounds work at the job they were bred to do that makes people go hunting the hare.

Hare hunting is an even older sport than chasing foxes

The North Norfolk harriers. Hare usually run in a very large circle when they are chased and stamina will be needed as well as a good scent line

HARE COURSING

Official hare coursing is self-regulated with strict guidelines laid down for the sport. Meetings are supervised by an official from the National Coursing Club. Two dogs are run against each other after a hare, and points are scored by the one that turns the hare; this normally happens several times during the course. Points are no longer awarded for catching a hare and most of them escape because as soon as a coursing dog loses sight of its quarry it ceases to be interested in it. They never hunt by scent.

The number of brown hares (the normal quarry) on arable land differs widely across Britain. In some areas they are a rare sight while in others they are so common that they are regarded

A slipper using the slip lead to release a pair of greyhounds

HARE COURSING *Useful Words*

COURSE Chase or hunt by sight.

DRIVEN COURSING Hares are gathered from a wide area by beaters and channelled onto a large open field where the course takes place.

GAZE HOUND Dog which hunts by sight and is used for coursing.

JUDGE An official mounted on horseback and wearing full hunting dress who decides the score.

LAW the distance between the quarry and the dogs before slipping.

LAMPING Searching for rabbits, hares or foxes at night using a spotlight. It is illegal to hunt deer in this way.

LEVERET Young hare.

LONG DOG A cross between two pure-bred gaze hounds (ie. Saluki and Greyhound) A dog used for coursing.

LURCHER Crossbred or mongrel dog used for coursing. Popular crosses used are Collie, Greyhound, Deerhound, Saluki, Whippet and Bedlington. Lurchers can be of any size and used to hunt hares, rabbits, and foxes.

NCC National Coursing Club.

PICKER UP An official who takes the hare from the dogs if one is caught and ensures that it is dead.

RUNNING DOG Collective term for all coursing dogs.

RUNNING GROUND The field where coursing takes place.

SALLY or PUSS Alternative names for a hare.

SHY A barrier that the slipper stands behind when he releases the dogs so that they cannot see the hare until it is in front of them.

SLIPPER An official who wears a red coat and releases the two coursing dogs simultaneously.

SOUGH (pronounced 'suff') Artificial refuge for hares.

THE BEAT The ground brought in by the beaters.

WALKED-UP COURSING The crowd line up and walk across a field with the slipper in the middle who releases two dogs soon after a hare is put up.

Crowds of 75,000 were not uncommon at the Waterloo Cup in the 1890s

as a pest. Hares do not like wet conditions and tend to avoid heavy land. As farming practices changed in the 1960s and 70s, destroying much of their habitat, the overall hare population rapidly declined but modern conservation bio-diversity schemes have reversed this trend and there are now estimated to be about three quarters of a million brown hares in Britain plus the blue or mountain hare which is only found on high ground.

Coursing is one of the world's oldest fieldsports dating back thousands of years. The first British Coursing Club was formed at Swaffham in Norfolk in 1776. The Waterloo Cup, the classic event for coursing, has been (and still is) run every year at Altcar near Liverpool since 1836. In the late 1800s the Waterloo Cup was a major national event and daily crowds of seventy five thousand were not uncommon even though the motor car had not been invented then.

Although it is still very popular, the general interest in coursing declined with the advent of track greyhound racing in 1926.

The method for coursing greyhounds

Coursing greyhounds may be trained either by their owners or by professional trainers. It is the natural instinct of a greyhound to chase anything that moves so it is not necessary to use live quarry to practice on. Training involves getting the dog fit and able to run fast over a reasonably short distance. This is done by one person holding the dogs and another standing in sight of them, about 200 metres away and calling them as soon as they have been released.

There are now about three quarters of a million brown hares in Britain

In some areas hares are a rare sight while in others they are so common that they are regarded as a pest

In Britain today there are 23 greyhound coursing clubs affiliated to the NCC and they are well supported. There are also 4 clubs for whippets, one each for salukis and deerhounds and about 50 for lurchers. The whippet, a small fast dog, was a favourite of coal miners who could keep the little dogs at home and enjoy having some sport with them in the fresh air when they weren't working down the pits. Dogs that are used for coursing are known as 'long dogs' or 'gaze hounds'.

Captive hares are not released from boxes to be coursed. At the majority of meetings hares are driven towards the field on which the coursing takes place, although occasionally they may be 'walked up' by the crowd lined out across a field, then the 'slipper' is positioned in the middle and releases the two dogs once the hare has got up and is at least a hundred yards ahead of them.

A driven hare meeting

Official driven meetings take place in open country. The hares are channelled one at a time through a narrow gap or gateway in a hedge by beaters waving flags who have brought them together from the surrounding fields, an operation that may take in more than 100 acres of ground. Once a hare has passed through this funnel onto a large field where the coursing takes place, it is at liberty to run in whichever direction it wants; the ground is never fenced.

Two dogs are held in readiness by the 'slipper' who waits behind a screen. When the hare comes through the gap he uses his judgement as to how fit the hare is. If he thinks it has anything at all wrong with it he does not let the dogs go. When one comes through that is running well he makes sure the dogs have seen it and gives it at least 100 yards start before running forwards a few paces with the dogs and releasing them simultaneously. They are not freed if two hares come through at the same time.

The dog on the slipper's left wears a distinguishing red collar and the one on the right wears white. A greyhound can run faster than a hare. Even though the hare is given a good start the dogs will catch up with it after about 300 yards.

The scoring

The first dog there will score points. Whenever the dogs get close to the hare it jinks to get out of the way, and the dog's sheer speed

The whippet was the breed traditionally favoured by coal miners

Registered coursing greyhounds have an ear tattoo for identification. Distinguishing red or white collars are worn when a course takes place

causes them to over-run. When they have gathered themselves together again they continue the chase and it may be the other dog's turn to force the hare to change direction which it can do more sharply than the greyhounds. This may happen several times before the hare, which has much more stamina than the dogs, either out runs them or disappears out of sight through a gap in the hedge, over a bank, into a drain or an artificial escape hole specially built.

As soon as a greyhound loses sight of its quarry, it gives up the chase: if it can't see it the dog does not go looking for it. An average course lasts for less than a minute and only about one in eight hares are actually caught. Death is usually instantaneous, but if it isn't there are officials in position around the coursing ground who get to the dogs as quickly as possible to despatch the hare. The courses are judged by a time-honoured code of scoring dating back to Elizabeth I. Three points are scored for the run up (the first turn), one point for the dog that forces the hare to turn through more than 90 degrees and half a point for less. A 'Go By' when a dog clearly outpaces the other dog and gets to the hare first in some instances can score a maximum of three points. No points are awarded if the dog catches or trips the hare. A judge in full hunting dress is mounted on horseback so he can view what is going on and keep up with the dogs. He keeps tally of the points scored by each dog and at the end of the course holds up either a red or white handkerchief according to the colour of the winning dog's collar. He also signals by raising his hat if the course is undecided or the score even. If it is a no-course, he signals by waving his hand across his chest and the dogs have to run again. Other flag signals are used by a steward to indicate what is happening.

The two dogs are judged against each other purely on merit. Coursing events are run on a knock-out basis and the winner each time progresses to the next round. Official hare coursing is designed to be as humane as possible: it is no-one's wish to see a lot of hares killed; the aim is merely to appreciate the speed and agility of dogs who have for centuries been bred for only one purpose. If, for any reason, a lot of hares are killed, then a move is made to a different field where conditions underfoot are better or the event may even be abandoned. Running quickly away from

The mountain or blue hare is found only on high ground in Scotland. It is neither hunted or coursed

If a lot of hares are killed, a move is made to a different field which favours the hare

a predator is completely natural for a hare so having to exert itself for a minute or so when it is coursed is not abnormal.

The National Coursing Club does not permit coursing between March 1st and September 30th so that hares are left undisturbed during the breeding season.

Informal coursing

Other forms of legal coursing are informal but are done with the landowner's consent. Sometimes one or two people will get together with their lurchers or long dogs and walk up the fields for hares or rabbits, releasing their dogs when one gets up. Others let their dogs run free (sometimes called moucher lurchers) to find their own quarry whether it be fur or feather. Some of these dogs are trained to retrieve to hand and many are worked at night with the handler using a spotlight to pin point a rabbit, hare or fox. It is illegal to pursue deer in this manner.

Hares on land that is looked after by gamekeepers usually flourish because foxes, who account for the deaths of many leverets, are controlled.

The idea is to make the hare 'jink' or turn, not to kill it. A hare has more stamina than a greyhound

Illegal hare coursing gangs

Hares are also preserved on land that is used for official coursing meetings but in many other places where they are abundant, as many as possible are shot simply so that they do not attract the attention of illegal hare coursers. These gangs of people travel long distances to hold illicit meetings on land they have no right to be on. They are often unsavoury characters known to the police, who cause damage and destruction wherever they go. They have no respect for property or crops and have no qualms whatsoever about catching and killing hares at any time of the year. The gang's only interest is to win money through betting and a lot of money can change hands depending on which dog kills the hare first. Large dogs are also sometimes used as an aid to illegal deer poaching.

The police, landowners, gamekeepers and farmers are severely disadvantaged in dealing with these situations because the game laws relating to poaching offences date back to 1831 and 1862. Poachers think nothing of intimidating their victims and families. It is a very serious rural problem where hares are

It is estimated that six families of foxes kill more hares in a year than all the official coursing meetings in Britain do

abundant, for unlike other forms of poaching it is not what the quarry is actually worth but the huge amounts of money made through betting. Often the dead hares aren't even picked up. The only places that hares are relatively safe is where there are a lot of sharp stones or flints on the ground: which badly cut the dog's paws when they are running so are more likely to be avoided by hare poachers. The general public's opinion may be influenced more by the cruel acts of these people than by the behaviour of official club members who abide by the rules. A ban on hare coursing would only penalise the legitimate followers of the traditional sport. Those who have no regard for the law anyway are hardly likely to take any notice of a ban. It would not save the life of a single hare; in fact it would do just the opposite because many more would be shot to avoid attracting illegal hare coursers.

MINK HUNTING

In the last two decades mink have become an ever-increasing menace. This vicious non-indigenous species originated in North America and has been kept in captivity in Britain for the production of fur, an industry that will shortly be phased out in the UK.

Escaped animals and those liberated by animal rights activists have adapted easily to conditions in this country and are rapidly becoming a serious threat to the well-being of wildlife on the waterways where they have made their homes. Aquatic bird and animal populations as well as fish are being decimated. Like foxes, mink will kill for pleasure and can also wreak havoc with domestic livestock.

Mink are about the size of a large ferret and much smaller than an otter. They are usually dark brown or black, aggressive and strong. It is estimated that a breeding female needs to make at least one thousand kills a year to support herself and her family. The bulk of these will coincide with the breeding season for other wildlife, making the effects more profound, because if a parent is killed it is likely that the offspring will die as a result.

One method of controlling numbers is by hunting with

Mink are a very serious menace to wildlife

20 packs of mink hounds registered in England and Wales will each account for about 70 mink in a season

203

hounds. This, unlike most other forms of hunting with dogs, is carried out during the summer time. Mink are at home in the water, and are very adaptable: they can burrow underground, climb trees and run very fast for short distances. Hunting is conducted on foot and only a few couples of hounds are needed. As with other hunting, there are a Master and a huntsman (usually a dedicated amateur) who dress in breeches and jackets. Dress code for followers is informal but they must be prepared to jump over ditches, wade through rivers and force their way through dense summer vegetation which lines most waterways if they want to watch hounds working.

The mink hunting season begins in April and continues until October. Meets are usually held on Saturdays and sometimes in the evenings. The huntsman may also be called out at other times of the year if there is a serious problem. A strict code of conduct is followed to ensure that the quarry is fairly hunted in its wild and natural state and with permission from everyone concerned with the waterway in question.

Some of the hounds used are descendants of the old otter hounds that were disbanded in the 1960s. Others carry either English or Welsh foxhound blood. They are trained to hunt only mink which they locate by finding and following a scent trail or by searching every likely place for the scent. Terriers accompany the hounds and are used to extricate the mink from small places such as among roots or in drains. If a mink climbs a tree during the course of a hunt then it will most likely be shot. If it is caught by a hound then death is instantaneous. The pack is out for the purpose of ridding an area of a serious threat but such are the numbers of mink that in a short time it will once again be colonised.

Otters are returning to many rivers and mink hounds are never allowed to hunt in an area where there is evidence of their presence. It is highly unlikely that any disturbance will be caused to these animals.

A female mink needs to make at least one thousand kills a year to support herself and her family

Below Otters are fully protected and are on the increase

STAG HUNTING

There used to be many packs of hounds to hunt either red deer or fallow deer but now there are only three. These hunt only red deer and are all based in the West Country at Exmoor, the Quantocks and Tiverton even though red deer can be found in several other locations in England and extensively in Scotland. Buck hounds were kept to hunt fallow deer and the last remaining pack to survive was in the New Forest.

The stag hounds that hunt red deer are followed by people mounted on horseback. Stags were sometimes 'carted' to a location, released, hunted, loaded up again and taken home. It is recounted that some of stags would enter the trailer of their own accord to be taken home after a hunt. This practice continued until the late 1960s. The last place this was done was in Norfolk and Thetford Forest was one of the areas used as a hunting ground. Today there remains the legacy of a substantial, and ever-increasing, herd of big red deer that still roam the area. There is evidence of this sport in England with many places having the name 'Chase' applied to them.

Deer cause about 30,000 road accidents annually

Above The Devon and Somerset stag hunt, a branch of hunting that has been the particular focus of the proposed anti-hunting legislation

In stag hunting now only one stag or hind is ever hunted at a time by the pack and this is carefully selected prior to a hunt. Local men, often farmers with an intimate knowledge of the area, study the herds of deer throughout the year noting which are suitable candidates to be hunted.

The sequence of the stag hunt

The evening before a meet the 'Harbourer', as he is called, spies out the exact locality of where his selected beast is feeding and checks again early the following morning to see where it has settled for the day. When the hunt meets, usually five and a half couples of the oldest and wisest hounds, known as 'tufters', are taken to the place and used to separate it from the group. Once it is away, the rest of the pack are sent for.

Red deer are not sedentary, they naturally move round a large area taking in thousands of acres of moorland and farmland so the stag or hind is very familiar with the countryside it is hunted in and may run a long way. Red deer are cunning and use their guile to outwit the pack if they can, often making use of streams and rivers. Only the selected deer is followed. When the hounds draw close it will often make for a river where it will stop and turn on them in order to defend itself. Once it does, the hounds surround it and 'bay'. This scenario is known as 'hounds at bay'. The deer is not torn to pieces as is often reported. The deer is shot at close range by an appointed marksman or the huntsman, who are never far behind the hounds and know by their baying when the deer has stopped running. The venison (mcat) is shared out locally in the area it was found and if it is a stag, the head including the antlers is given to the farmer or landowner.

Stags over 5 years old (their age can be told by their antlers) are hunted in August, September and October; hinds (females) from 1st November until the end of February; and young stags, 3 to 5 years old, from early March until the end of April. Only one stag is normally taken in a day but 2 or 3 hinds may be killed.

> *Deer culling is necessary for without it many would starve in winter on the hills and die a slow death*

Red deer on alert in a Norfolk wood

It is essential that red deer numbers are controlled for they are prolific breeders and are not predated on by any other animals. They are large animals, as big as a small cow, and cause serious and wasteful damage to crops as well as eating a lot of the grass grown for sheep and cattle. They also cause damage to fences and hedges, and the hunts will sometimes help to keep the deer off land or even occasionally pay compensation. Farmers within the areas hunted are usually willing to tolerate a certain number in return for the enjoyment of watching hounds hunting and in the knowledge that it keeps the deer dispersed. However, hunting is becoming increasingly difficult to do efficiently, because roads are becoming much busier and there are also more and more pockets of the countryside where access is denied them by private landowners and the National Trust, who have prohibited stag hunting on their land.

Those who do support it are fanatical about their sport and there are many visitors from afar who specifically come to the West Country to watch from cars or participate by bringing their own horses or hiring them locally. All this is a life-line for the local rural economy at a time of year when the fair weather tourists are absent.

Only the roe and the red deer are native to Britain

Red deer in velvet

DEER AND DEER STALKING

There are 6 species of deer in this country, only 2 of which are native to Britain. Deer numbers are increasing and in some areas they are abundant enough to be regarded as a serious nuisance. Nearly all species of deer have white rumps which, when the hair is raised, acts as a danger signal to others when they are startled. New-born deer have spotted coats which act as an excellent camouflage; they are left hidden in cover for long periods with the mother only coming back to feed them occasionally although she is unlikely to be very far away. Males take no interest in their offspring. They lose their antlers annually and new ones grow immediately, covered in skin known as velvet. As the antlers become fully developed this skin dies and is rubbed off.

There are about 15,000 deer stalkers in Britain, and six species of deer

DEER *Useful Words*

ANTLERS A bracket structure that is composed of bone and grows from pedicles on the heads of male deer of most species. Antlers are shed and regrown each year.

ATV All terrain vehicle.

BDS British Deer Society, a registered charity formed in 1963. Dedicated to the welfare of deer. Provides education and training on deer and their management.

BUCK Male roe or fallow deer.

CALF Young of red or sika deer.

CAST When the antlers drop off.

CULL Kill a selected animal.

DOE Female roe or fallow deer.

FAWN Young of fallow, muntjac or Chinese water deer.

GARRON Pony used to carry shot deer off the hill in Scotland.

GHILLIE (Scotland) Person who assists a stalker (or fisherman).

GRALLOCH Remove intestines and stomach (everything below the diaphragm).

HEAD Antlers of a deer.

HIND Female red or sika deer.

KID Young of roe deer.

POINTS The number of spikes on an antler.

PRICKET A yearling fallow buck or red stag in England; in Scotland they are called 'staggies'.

ROYAL A red stag with a total of twelve points on its antlers (6 on each side).

RUT The mating season. Males are usually very vocal at this time.

STAG Male red or sika deer.

STALKER Person who shoots deer or takes a client out to shoot a deer.

TROPHY An extra fine quality head. An official assessment taking into account the length and weight can be made as to whether it is of gold, silver or bronze standard.

VELVET Skin that covers and nourishes the growing antlers; its shedding, when the new antlers are fully developed, causes great irritation to the animal.

VENISON The meat of deer.

Red deer spend much of the year living in single-sex herds

Red deer damage to a Scots pine, caused by stags rubbing the velvet off their antlers

RED DEER are the largest of the native British deer, standing up to 4ft (120cms) at the shoulder. They are the species common in the Highlands of Scotland and depicted in art as the Monarch of the Glen. They have been forced to adapt to living and surviving on the open heather-clad hills although this is not their natural habitat. Red deer thrive better in forests and farmland and can be found in South West England, (where they are also hunted with hounds), Wales, Yorkshire, the Lake District, Dumfries, Galloway, the New Forest, parts of Sussex and in some areas of Norfolk and Suffolk. They are also sometimes kept in parks including Richmond Park where there are some magnificent specimens. In summer their coats are reddish brown with a pale rump and a short tail; in winter they are a more drab colour.

Although gregarious by nature, the sexes spend much of the year living apart in herds.

Only the stags have antlers which they lose in April or May. The rut is about October/November time and the young are born in June. Mature stags grow magnificent branching antlers that are much prized by sportsmen as trophies. Reds are very prolific and numbers have to be rigorously controlled to prevent damage to crops and the threat of starvation through over-grazing on the hills. The stalking of stags is often let, while poorer stags and hinds are generally culled by professional stalkers. The income received from sportsmen and the sale of carcasses is a welcome contribution, particularly to Highland estate owners whose

Stalker with a roe deer

land is of limited use for agriculture. As stags grow older, each year more points appear on the antlers. When there are six on each antler (12 in total) the stag is known as a 'Royal'. Park reds or those that feed on arable crops can reach in excess of twenty points. Red deer are also sometimes kept in large paddocks and farmed for venison.

Roe are unique among deer in being able to delay development of the embryo in the uterus

ROE DEER are Britain's other native species of deer and are much smaller than the red, standing just over 2ft (65cms) at the shoulders. The bucks are territorial and roe are secretive by nature, preferring to spend most of the day hidden in cover. They are most likely to be seen when they come out onto the edge of woodland in the evenings to feed. Their numbers are fast increasing and they can be found throughout most of Britain.

In summer their coats are short and a rich red in colour while growing thicker and turning a mousy grey/brown in winter. They appear to have no tails but have distinctive white rumps on which the raised hair accompanied by a dog-like bark acts as a conspicuous warning to the other deer. Roe often live in small family groups of about five to eight with young bucks being ejected when they are about a year old. They are rarely kept successfully in captive situations. Only the bucks have antlers which are cast in November or December. The rut is in late July or August and roe are unique among deer in the fact that after conception there is a delay and the embryo does not actually become implanted into the uterus until early January when it continues its normal development. After this extended pregnancy the young (kids), usually twins, are born in May.

Severe damage can be caused to young trees as roe eat new growth on the top and side shoots. The bucks also thrash and rub young saplings with their antlers when they attempt to remove the velvet or mark their territories. A good head is a much prized trophy although it normally has only six points in total. Roe stalking is often let on private estates. Some young bucks and those with poor quality antlers as well as surplus females need to be culled. Roe venison is excellent meat.

FALLOW DEER are thought to have been introduced to Britain by the Normans. They are of medium size, standing about 3ft (90cms) high. Gregarious by nature, herds can be found in most areas of Wales and England, but large herds are most commonly seen in the parkland that surrounds stately homes.

Fallow vary greatly in colour. Many of those kept in parks are pure white while others are almost black. The common colour is a sandy brown with white spots in summer that disappear as the winter coat grows although there is a colouration known as 'Menil' where the deer are a lighter shade and retain their white spots throughout the year. All fallow have a characteristic white rump and a long tail which is constantly flicked. Only bucks have antlers which grow fairly large and are of a flattened shape. They are dropped in March. The rut is in October or November and the single fawn is born in June. Like red deer, their antlers grow more points as the animal matures and can make an impressive trophy. Numbers need to be controlled especially in parks where grazing is limited.

SIKA DEER were first introduced to Britain from Japan in the mid-1800s. They are similar in size to a fallow and like them have spotted coats in summer and a white rump. There are scattered groups around Britain particularly in Dorset and Lancashire and there is great concern in Scotland because they are inter-breeding with the native red deer. Only the stags have antlers which are similar in appearance to a red deer but much smaller, usually with a total of only six points. Sika are solitary for much of the time

Fallow deer in a park: where deer are contained like this it is essential to operate a culling policy to maintain the health of the herd

Below A pair of well-camoflaged roe deer at dusk

and only form small groups in winter. The sexes stay segregated and only come together for the rut. Stags lose their antlers in April. The rut is from September to November and hinds give birth to a single calf in May or June.

MUNTJAC or **BARKING DEER** originate from Asia and the wild population has become established partly through a major escape from Woburn Park during the last war when a plane crashed through the perimeter wall and partly through other deliberate releases. They have thrived and are established in many areas. Muntjac stand only about 18ins (45cms) high and are often mistaken for a fox as their coat is a similar colour and they have a relatively long tail which is raised when they are alarmed. They also bark which is how they got their alternative name. They are territorial and very secretive by nature, living either singly or as a small family. The bucks have razor-sharp canine tusks and short antlers with only one point (occasionally two when older) which they usually lose in spring. Muntjac eat almost anything including yew (which poisons many animals) and brambles. They rarely leave dense cover so it is difficult to estimate the population and sometimes to efficiently keep control of their numbers.

Muntjac breed all year round and the does mate again soon after giving birth, so reproduce very quickly. The BDS recommend that juvenile females and heavily pregnant females when identifiable should be selected for culling if at all possible. Adult females in close company with a male should not be culled. If these guidelines are followed the risk of orphaning dependant young is significantly reduced.

CHINESE WATER DEER are the least common deer in Britain. They too are escapees that have become established in some areas, tending to favour wetlands, as their name implies, and marshy areas such as the Norfolk Broads. Slightly larger than a muntjac, they are lighter in colour and in winter their coats tend to look woolly. Neither sexes have antlers although the males have tusks. The rut occurs in

> *Muntjac escaped from Woburn Park during the last war when a plane crashed through the perimeter wall*

The muntjac, a secretive and relatively new addition to Britain's fauna. They thrive in thick undergrowth and eat many plants including ivy, yew and brambles

November or December and the females give birth to as many as six young between May and July. There is no official close season for Chinese water deer but as the sexes look very similar it is recommended that none are shot between 1st April and 31st October to avoid accidentally shooting a doe that is suckling young.

Red deer and fallow deer have been kept in parks for centuries both to enhance the landscape and as a way of providing food. They were also kept for hunting. An individual would be caught and 'carted' to a suitable area where it was released to be hunted with hounds by followers on horseback. Often when the hounds held the stag at bay it would be externally unharmed and could be caught up again and taken home to provide sport for another day. This practice only ceased in the 1960s.

Much of the British stock of red deer has been 'improved' in the past by interbreeding with their larger Continental or North American relatives, producing bigger stags with huge antlers. In medieval times there were over 2,000 deer parks. Fallow deer are still a popular adornment in parkland surrounding stately homes but their numbers have to be rigidly controlled.

There are an estimated two million deer in the UK, and they

DEER
Close Seasons

ENGLAND AND WALES

Red stag, sika stag, fallow buck:
1 May – 31 July

Roe buck:
1 November – 31 March

Red hind, sika hind, fallow doe, roe doe:
1 March – 31 October

Muntjac and Chinese water deer:
No close season (see notes on species)

SCOTLAND

Red stag, sika stag and red/sika hybrid stags:
21 October – 30 June

Fallow buck:
1 May – 31 July

Roe buck:
21 October – 31 March

Red hind, sika hind, red/sika hybrid hind, fallow doe:
16 February – 20 October

Roe doe:
1 April – 20 October

Left Red deer in a harsh Scottish winter

In Scotland sika are inter-breeding with the native red deer

all have no natural predators, except occasionally a very young roe or muntjac may be taken by a fox. Human intervention is necessary to prevent numbers spiralling, for besides causing serious damage to agricultural crops, gardens and woodlands, sika, fallow and red also strip bark from trees, which results in bacterial and fungal damage making the timber unsaleable. Deer are also responsible for an estimated average of 30,000 road accidents and up to 15 human fatalities annually.

Roe deer fawn showing spotted marking which disappears in maturity

Although deer poaching has been an offence for centuries, legitimate culling prior to 1963 was indiscriminate and there was no ruling with regards to the methods by which deer could be killed until the Deer Act was introduced. This Act brought in legislation to ensure that culling was as humane as possible by introducing close seasons, regulating the methods used and banning the use of unsuitable guns and ammunition, although there are different laws in Scotland to those in England and Wales. Moral codes have been introduced to improve the general welfare, and methods have been developed to allow selective culling.

The vast majority of deer are culled by professional or amateur stalkers who control deer within a certain area. However, stalking is also a popular sport with both British and foreign visitors. Guests usually pay according to the quality of the stag or buck, with a lesser amount for females and inferior males which are taken out to improve the quality. Trophy heads are much sought after by sportsmen and women and there is an international scale using weight and length criteria to ascertain whether they fall into bronze, silver or gold categories. The revenue creates a useful income for the landowner who retains the carcass. Stalking is also a way of reducing the numbers of deer although sporting estates that offer trophy stalking often retain a high density of deer in the first place. Non-regular stalkers are usually supervised and assisted by an experienced person.

A shot should only be taken when a deer is completely stationary

Deer control throughout Britain is an important element of the countryside. In Scotland alone, shooting and stalking generate

£100 million annually, a significant proportion of which comes from wild red deer which roam the Scottish Highlands. While venison from these animals cannot claim to be entirely organic, it must be as near as is possible, for they are completely free range. There is only a possibility of indirect contact with chemicals and they receive no medication, a fact that has not gone unnoticed, as consumption of wild venison has recently increased by 40%. Even so, most of the carcasses of deer culled in Britain are exported to the Continent. Males are culled to control quality and females to control quantity.

Deer populations have the potential to increase by about 25% to 30% each year

Stalking methods

There are several methods of stalking deer determined by the species and the terrain. One method where the cover is dense, with open areas, is to erect a high seat about 8 to 10 ft (2 to 3 metres) high on the edge of a clearing. Here a person can sit above eye level and wait undetected, for deer have keen hearing and scenting abilities. This also means that when a shot is fired it is angled towards the ground, which is very important from a safety aspect when visibility is limited. Early morning and evenings are the best times to see deer and they can sometimes be attracted by calls from the stalker.

The other popular method is to carefully approach a suitable beast. This needs a great deal of stealth and cunning especially on an open hillside where it may take several hours to get within range of the selected animal and be in position to take a safe shot. Both ways require an infinite amount of patience, for all deer are wary creatures. Muntjac are particularly difficult to come to terms with because of their propensity for dense undergrowth. Deer are always bled and gralloched immediately after they have been shot.

There are about 15,000 stalkers in Britain many of whom are employed professionally in the Highlands of Scotland. Here the stalking is often a major contributor to estate incomes both from paying guests and from the sale of venison. The employment of a professional also benefits the rural economy by providing work in remote areas. It is a necessity to remove the old and the sick deer and to control red numbers for they would starve in winter on the hills and die a slow death otherwise. The stalker must have the

A garron is a tough, foot-sure pony used for carrying red deer off the hill

right weather, reasonable access to the hunting ground, no disturbance from hill walkers and must of course locate the beasts.

Then, after the deer have been shot, there is the challenge of getting them off the hill. Sometimes if the terrain is very steep or rocky they have to be manually dragged through the heather to the nearest track. Occasionally a pony (a garron) is used and sometimes they can be reached by an ATV (all terrain vehicle). Where it is necessary to remove a large number of deer, one modern way of doing so is to drop stalkers onto the tops of the hills by helicopter. Here they can shoot several deer in a day, usually hinds, which can then be airlifted down to accessible areas for gralloching before being taken back to refrigerated larders.

In England and Wales it is illegal to shoot deer from any mechanically propelled vehicle except with written permission on enclosed land. It is sometimes the policy, especially in Scotland, when shooting a red hind, to take the calf that is running with her as well, for without its mother's milk, the calf would be unlikely to survive the harsh winter; although the close seasons are designed to minimise the likelihood of this happening.

Generally, a shot should be made when the animal is broadside on, so that the bullet will go through the heart or lungs and cause instant death. Neck or head shots can mean there is a danger of a non-fatal injury occurring by hitting the jaw or nasal bone if the bullet is not accurate, resulting in a lingering death. The stalker must have proved himself and his telescopic-sight rifle to be accurate on a target before embarking on a foray to shoot deer. A shot should only be taken when the quarry is stationary and within killing range. Safety is the prime concern at all times. It is recommended that those stalking in dense cover should have a dog with them that has been trained to follow a

Roe deer in the long grass. They always have a great ability to merge into the landscape

In England and Wales it is normally lillegal to shoot deer from a moving vehicle, including a helicopter

There are an estimated 30,000 road accidents associated with deer each year in the UK

blood scent to track any deer that may move away from the place at which it was shot. It is quite possible for a deer that has been shot accurately through the heart (and is effectively dead) to run a hundred yards before actually keeling over. In thick undergrowth this is far enough to make it very difficult to find the animal. Most stalkers make use of the excellent camouflage clothing that is available today and carry a good pair of binoculars so that a suitable animal can be positively identified.

Sika stag surrounded by hinds – the two sexes are only seen in groups like this during the rutting season in October

DRAG HUNTING

Drag hunting is when hounds, sometimes bloodhounds, follow an artificial scent trail laid by a man dragging a bundle impregnated with an attractive smell over a pre-set course. It can be exciting and hectic as the route takes the riders across country, over fences and walls, hedges and ditches, but it is rather like going to a football match when you already know the result.

It does not have the appeal of watching hounds puzzling out a difficult line or the unpredictability of following a live animal that is so much appreciated by those who go hunting. It serves no purpose as pest control, and few farmers out of the large number who now welcome the hunt on their ground would be happy to have a lot of horses galloping across their land for no useful reason. Drag hunting is generally accepted as being an equestrian sport bearing little relation to hunting.

Drag hunting is rather like going to a football match when you already know the result

216

FISHING

Fishing is one of the most popular outdoor pastimes in Britain. Over £3 billion is spent each year by the 3 to 4 million people who enjoy the sport. Many disabled people have found it is an outdoor recreation that is readily accessible to them and there are a number of organisations that represent disabled anglers.

There are 55 species of fresh water fish in Britain divided into two categories – coarse fish and game fish (the Salmonidae family). The latter are the elite: salmon, seatrout and wild brown trout fishing in some renowned areas can command a very high price and the rivers in which they live are generally well cared for.

Land owned adjacent to a river extends to the centre of the watercourse and with it, usually, goes the right to fish, provided it is by legal methods and with a rod license obtained from the Environment Agency. Approximately 1.2 million are issued in England and Wales annually; children under twelve are not required to purchase one. It is the owner's responsibility to maintain and keep clear of obstacles the river bed and banks of the water course and to clear any debris.

There are legislative controls for fresh water fisheries as well as moral obligations regarding methods, introduction of fish, availability of night fishing and application of a close season.

There are 3–4 million anglers in Britain

Flyfishing for river trout is popular wherever there are clear, fast flowing streams

FISHING *Useful Words*

AQUACULTURE Fish farming.

BARBLESS HOOK A type of hook which is not barbed causing little physical damage to the fish when it is removed.

BAIT Edible item attractive to fish such as bread or maggots.

BEAT A defined stretch of river allocated to the game angler, sometimes for a given period e.g. a day or a week.

COARSE FISH All fish, such as carp, perch, chub and pike, found in fresh water rivers, canals, ponds and lakes that are not game fish (salmon, trout). In Britain they are generally returned to the water once caught and are seldom eaten.

COMMERCIAL FISHERY Water (usually lake) open to the general public.

DISGORGER Small tool to aid the removal of a hook from fish's mouth.

FLOAT Device used to keep the bait at a certain depth and to indicate a bite.

FLY An artificial lure incorporating a hook, usually made from fur, feather or man-made material and designed to resemble an insect.

GAFF Hooked tool (now illegal) used to land a fish.

GENTLE Fisherman's name for maggot.

GAME FISH The trout and salmon family, which include grayling and char. They are highly regarded for their sporting qualities and are also very good to eat.

GHILLIE Person employed to assist and row for salmon and trout anglers.

GRILSE First return salmon.

GROUND BAIT Food thrown into the water to attract fish.

KEEP NET Large net used to hold caught fish until weighed and released.

KELT Adult salmon after spawning.

LANDING NET Hand held net used to assist with landing a fish.

LEDGER Weight attached to line near bait for bottom fishing.

LIVE BAIT The use of live fish to catch predatory species such as pike. Now illegal.

PARR Young salmon before it becomes a smolt and heads for sea.

POLE or **WHIP** Lightweight, extending coarse rod to which is attached an elasticated line, nylon and bait. Does not require reel.

PRIEST Small, heavy object used to kill a fish, so-called because it administers the fish's last rites.

RED Area of gravel on which fish spawn.

REEL The receptacle for the line. Comes in many forms from 'centrepin' to 'spinning'.

ROD Term for a person who fishes, or the essential item of tackle he uses for casting.

RUN Passage of salmon or sea trout up a river.

SPAWN To breed. The female fish lays eggs that are fertilised immediately by the male.

SPINNER/LURE Artificial 'bait' that wobbles, jerks or rotates to attract fish.

STRIP The process of manually releasing mature eggs from fish by manipulation.

TACKLE Any or all of the equipment used by an angler to fish.

There are 55 species of fresh water fish in Britain

The close season for coarse fishing in rivers is 16 March to 16 June

The pike, sometimes called the 'river wolf', is the biggest predator in British freshwaters and a prized quarry for coarse anglers

This runs from 16th March until 16th June during the spawning period for coarse fish but does not apply to still waters (ponds and lakes) and, more recently, to canals. The use of lead weights is all but banned due to the risk of poisoning wildfowl and swans. It is illegal to leave a rod unattended while fishing. The Environment Agency is involved with many issues such as intensive stocking of still waters, effects of predators on fish (eg cormorants), the theft of fish, discarded angling litter such as line and hooks, and the impact of releasing live bait and foreign exotic species.

Angling clubs

Much of the coarse fishing on ponds, lakes and stretches of rivers is run by angling clubs who have either purchased, leased or negotiated rights to fish the water. Their objectives are to promote and protect the angling interests of their members and to improve facilities for their benefit. Fishing competitions are commonplace. Designated areas are marked out with numbered pegs every few yards and competitors draw their numbers at the beginning of the day. Angling clubs organise regular clean up days to keep their areas spick and span. They may have to control weed growth in their rivers and on the banks which would otherwise become congested and overgrown. That on the banks can be cut either by hand, by using a strimmer or tractor-operated machinery. Where banks are grazed by livestock, trimming isn't usually necessary. Weed growth actually in the water can be removed by using a rake and a bucket, an old fashioned scythe, a chain scythe worked by two people, one either side of the river, or by boat.

There are two kinds of river plants, rooted ones and floating mats of algae, which need to be completely removed from the water. They may cause blockages that smell as they rot or release toxins into the water creating an unpleasant environment for fish, fishermen and boat users. Disposal of a large mass of vegetation can be a problem. There are restrictions on the methods used if poisonous or alien plants (from another country) are present. Three invasive plants are causing major problems along our waterways. Japanese knotweed grows 6 to 10ft high (2 to 3 metres), giant hogweed can grow up to 15 ft (5 metres) and Himalayan balsam can reach 7 to 8 ft (2.5 metres) and its leaves

Coarse match anglers at their 'pegs'. The rules for match angling (techniques, hook sizes, baits allowed) are very strict and matches like this on canals and rivers attract large numbers of competitors

Excessive weed growth in rivers used for fishing has to be removed

can grow to a similar length. Dry material can usually be burned but the wet needs either to be spread out thinly on the banks or piled in small heaps where it can be left to rot down.

Where vegetation is cut in moving water, a boom can be put in place downstream to collect the debris, which can then be dragged out and either disposed of on the land or taken to a land-fill site. River fisheries usually co-ordinate their weed cutting activities so that debris floating down the river doesn't interfere with other anglers.

Game Fishing (for salmon, trout and grayling)

Game fish (the Salmonidae family) are present in most of the rivers throughout Britain. They spawn in late autumn and early winter and are protected by a close season. For wild brown trout this extends from 1st November to 1st March in England and Wales and from 7th October to 14th March in Scotland although there may be slight variations in some localities.

BROWN TROUT Some of the best trout fishing is in England, and the most sought-after is probably in the pristine chalkstreams of Hampshire and the limestone rivers of Derbyshire, but many rivers once famed exclusively for their wild trout are now being stocked with captive bred fish. These select areas can be very expensive to fish but cheap or even free game fishing can be found in less favoured upland areas. The purists fish only with a fly for wild brown trout.

Later in the summer it is no easy task to persuade a disinterested fish to take a fly. It can prove very frustrating and some knowledge of where they are likely to be laying up in the first instance can be very useful. Although the surroundings may seem idyllic, trout fishing is a very challenging sport. Some mature brown trout living in large lakes and Scottish lochs turn to eating other fish. They may weigh up to 25lbs (12kgs) and grow to a length of nearly 3 feet (90cms). These are known as ferox trout. Artificially reared brown trout can also reach huge sizes, but wild trout from natural rivers and lakes feed mainly on aquatic insects and seldom weigh more than a pound or so.

Harling for salmon on the Tweed in Scotland. This traditional method requires a ghillie holding the boat in the current while the angler fishes from the stern

Duffers' Fortnight, at end of May or early June, is when the mayfly hatches and trout are, theoretically, easier to deceive

RAINBOW TROUT are less prized by the old school of trout fisherman but provide exciting game fishing for many others. Unless otherwise specified, rainbows can be caught all year. They are an introduction from North America and are the common choice of commercial fisheries as they grow one and a half times as quickly as browns and are easier to rear, though they rarely breed in the wild.

Rainbow farming

Rainbows are raised in hatcheries from breeding stock (known as cock and hen fish). These are kept to produce eggs which are hatched in special indoor tanks during the winter. The tiny fish (fry) are transferred to outdoor tanks (stews) in early summer where they are fed high protein rations. They are taken out either for restocking or for the table when they weigh 1 to 1.5lbs (500grams) although some may be kept back to grow to a larger size. Brown trout can be raised in the same way.

Brown and rainbow trout will live in either rivers or lakes and river keepers or water bailiffs are employed in some places to care for the fish and their environment. Banks are mowed regularly and marginal weed growth kept trimmed to waist height.

Predators such as mink, rats and some birds are controlled; also some species of fish which would eat eggs or fry. Electro fishing is often carried out in spring and autumn on trout streams to take out unwanted species such as pike. Eels are sometimes trapped and sold for human consumption between mid-summer and Christmas and many rivers have built-in eel traps. Poaching can also be a problem for riverkeepers, and in this fishing context they have the same powers and privileges as a police officer when dealing with law breakers. Trout, particularly rainbow, stocked in ponds or lakes are relatively inexpensive to fish for.

SEA TROUT are a strain of brown trout that have adopted a life cycle similar to that of a salmon, spending part of their lives in the sea. They are also known as 'sewin' in Wales and 'peal' in the West Country; fishmongers sometimes misleadingly call them 'salmon trout'. Small sea trout weighing a pound or less are variously called 'finnock', 'herling' or 'schoolies'. Sea trout are often fished for at night and can be unpredictable in their habits.

It is illegal to leave a rod unattended while fishing

An angler releases a salmon – a practice encouraged on all rivers, particularly before July

GRAYLING are an unusual member of the Salmonidae family, frequently found alongside trout, but only in rivers. They are odd because unlike salmon and trout, which spawn in the autumn, grayling breed in the spring and share a close season (16th March to 16th June) with coarse fish, meaning that they can be legally caught throughout the winter. The grayling is a sensitive fish and can be a good indicator to the health of a river.

SALMON fishing has long been the ultimate dream for many freshwater anglers. It can be very expensive but in spate rivers or places where angling clubs own the fishing rights it becomes more affordable. Salmon do not live in still waters and they prefer rivers whose head waters are relatively shallow and stony as their eggs are laid in gravel beds. However this is not essential as they will spawn throughout the river including the lower reaches.

The most famous rivers are in Scotland, notably the Dee and the Spey, although salmon can be found in many rivers throughout Britain. They are slow-growing and have a very complicated and hazardous lifestyle which involves spending part of their lives at sea and returning to the upper reaches of the rivers where they were hatched to breed themselves.

Fresh run salmon (and sea trout) can be easily identified by an infestation of sea lice that they acquire only at sea. These parasites can't live for long in fresh water so their presence indicates that the caught salmon has recently arrived from the sea rather than one that is returning to it.

There is a close season for salmon in England, Wales and Scotland generally from about 1st November to 14th January although there may be slight regional variations. Spawning occurs in November and December and eggs, which are fertilised by the males after being laid, hatch out in early spring. Fresh hatched fish are called ALEVINS and as they begin to develop are known as FRY. After 2 to 4 years in the river as PARR they depart in late spring or autumn; at this stage they are called SMOLTS. They will spend a minimum of one year at sea before returning to the river as GRILSE. After spawning, both the male and female fish are exhausted and are known as KELTS. Few kelts are strong enough to survive the journey from the upper reaches of the rivers back to the sea and even fewer ever return to spawn again.

A fresh-run salmon: plump, muscular, silver and sometimes carrying sea lice, an indication that the fish has only just come in from the sea

There may be as many as 40,000 salmon in one cage

Measures to protect salmon stocks

Wild salmon grow to a larger size than trout and are a much-prized catch. It was evident after the 1999 fishing season that stocks in Scotland were becoming seriously depleted and steps were put in place to remedy the situation, for salmon fishing contributes a valuable source of revenue to large estates as well as much-needed jobs in rural communities. Monitoring the period salmon spend in their marine environment at sea is very difficult and their survival is unpredictable. However, by improving the river habitat needed for successful breeding, controlling predators and releasing young fish into tributaries of the main rivers, optimistic results are being achieved.

Buy-out initiatives have limited the amount of netting conducted in river mouths and coastal areas, reducing a serious threat to the already depleted salmon stocks; now the fish have unhindered access to their breeding sites. However the threat from illegal netting still remains. All these conservation measures combined with the voluntary co-operation of anglers by reducing the number of fish they take has hopefully ensured the future for wild salmon. In Scotland over a third have been returned to the water and on the river Dee a policy of releasing every salmon caught has been in operation. In England and Wales a recent by-law has made it illegal to keep rod caught salmon before 16th June in order to protect spring stocks.

Crofters' rights to salmon fishing

During the last few decades the plight of wild salmon in Britain has become of increasing concern to game fishermen and river owners alike and some have done their best to address the problems in order to preserve their sport. Given the lengthy and complicated life cycle of salmon it will be at least 5 years before any rewards can be reaped. In Scotland these rewards may not be forthcoming because legislation by the Scottish Executive in the form of the Land Reform Bill will give crofters the right to acquire, by compulsory purchase if necessary, the salmon fishing rights adjacent to their land. It is feared that this may result in the break-up of sporting estates without which there would probably be both a shortage of money and lack of incentive to continue with the long term conservation measures now in place.

Riverkeepers have the same powers and privileges as a police officer when dealing with law breakers

Typical coarse fishing scene – the large black keepnet extending into the river is more commonly seen at match angling events

Salmon farming

Another continuing threat to the welfare of wild salmon stocks as well as sea trout in Scotland is the presence of numerous fish farms around the West Coast which have sprung up during the last thirty years. Besides salmon farms, there are also intensive units producing oysters and other shellfish. Pollution and disease emitting from all these farms appears to be one of the causes for the decline in wild salmon.

There are now over 300 salmon farms producing 37 million tons of salmon annually. Most are owned and controlled by international companies, particularly Dutch and Norwegian. Originally these farms were supported by government-funding to regenerate rural areas. Not only did they create several thousand jobs in places where there was no work but they also took pressure off the demand for wild salmon. Mass production has meant that salmon is no longer the luxury food it once was. But while providing jobs, fish farming has also been linked to the decline of wild stocks and this in turn has meant the loss of ghillieing work, a decrease in estate incomes and a drop in hotel trade because of fewer visiting anglers.

Salmon are reared in blocks of floating cages anchored in sheltered bays. They are fed high protein rations to make them grow quickly, reaching a saleable size in 2 to 3 years. If genetically modified (transgenic) fish were to be used, their growth rate could be doubled or even trebled.

The food pellets on which they are fed are manufactured from other fish which could possibly already be contaminated with pollutants. The wasted food and faeces from these salmon (there may be as many as 40,000 in one cage) pollute the surrounding water. Further contamination occurs when the caged fish are treated for some of the several diseases or parasites with which they may become infected, many of the chemicals used containing toxic substances.

The major parasite affecting farmed salmon is sea lice. Arctic char are sometimes kept with the caged salmon as they will feed on sea lice and help to reduce the infestation without the use of chemicals. Sea lice are easily picked up by wild salmon and sea trout as their migratory route from the sea back into rivers takes them past the blocks of cages which are sited in sea lochs.

Fish farms in the UK produce 37 million tons of farmed salmon annually

Salmon farms in a sea loch in Scotland, providing local factory jobs but damaging wild salmon fishing, ghillieing work and estate incomes

An unnaturally heavy infestation of sea lice can seriously weaken wild salmon and particularly the sea trout. A further threat to their well-being are the thousands of domesticated fish which escape each year and mix with them, spreading disease and parasites. These escaped salmon possess no survival or migratory instincts, so if they do manage to breed with the wild salmon their young do not survive and the next generation is lost forever.

FERRETING

Ferreting is an ancient sport enjoyed today by thousands of people. Ferrets are descended from the wild polecat which can still be found in a few parts of Britain. Some ferrets are almost identical to polecats, with dark brown outer coats and a cream coloured undercoat. Others are cream or pure white with pink eyes and there are other colourations from crossing the strains.

Ferrets are used primarily for hunting rabbits but are sometimes used to flush out rats. In recent years they have also become popular as domestic pets. They are natural predators and can be vicious but when they have been properly handled they can become very tame and even affectionate. Special dry food is now produced, eliminating the need to feed fresh meat. However many people who work their ferrets still prefer to give them rabbits or road kills as they have in the past. Ferrets themselves and the meat they feed on can become quite smelly, especially in summer, if their hutches are not kept scrupulously clean. The females, known as jills, come into season in the spring and will stay so for several months if they are not mated, which can damage their health. Many ferrets owners who do not want to breed keep a vasectomised hob (male) to satisfy this need or have the jills injected by a vet to prevent them coming into season. Young ferrets are known as 'kits'.

Ferreting is usually carried out in late autumn or winter when the vegetation has died back and there is less likelihood of very young rabbits being about. Ferrets are transported in small, specially designed boxes or ventilated bags. One or two are put

A ferreter prepares to release his ferrets down the hole to flush the rabbits

Jills come into season in the spring and will remain so for several months if they are not mated

225

into the holes of a rabbit warren where they work their way around underground. Rabbits thump their hind legs on the ground when they are alarmed and it is a sound that ferreters listen for. Usually they try to escape by bolting out of the holes although occasionally a ferret will catch or corner one underground.

Locating a laid-up ferret

The old-fashioned way of trying to find where the ferret was laid up underground was to have a length of light cord attached to a collar on the ferret with knots tied in the cord every yard to indicate how far in it was. By this method it could be traced and dug out. Now, with modern gadgets, it is much easier. A collar with a small transmitter attached to it is put on the ferret. The collar emits a signal that is picked up by a locator, enabling the ferreter to pin-point the position.

A good spade or graft and a billhook or saw are still needed because it may be several feet down beneath stones and roots. A sharp pocket knife is another vital part of the equipment as rabbits are usually paunched (intestines removed) soon after they are killed. The thin skin above the hock on one hind leg is pierced and the other hind foot pushed through the hole enabling several rabbits to be carried on a stick that is passed between the hind legs of each one.

There are several ways of catching and killing a rabbit after it has been bolted by ferrets. Most commonly, nets are placed over every hole in the warren which the rabbits become entangled in when they try to escape. They are then grabbed and killed by hand. Sometimes they are allowed to bolt and then they are shot as they run away or a lurcher is used to catch them. Occasionally a long net is placed at a distance from the holes to prevent them from getting away. A good dog will also detect and mark any holes that have rabbits in them and ignore empty ones. This avoids wasting a lot of time by putting ferrets in empty holes.

Ferreting is a sport enjoyed by all ages, usually only involving 2 or 3 people. Like all fieldsports it is unpredictable and the bag for the day may be pleasing or disappointing.

If a ferret decides to lay up underground it may take a considerable amount of time and effort to find it but the good days make up for the bad.

A 'hob' is a male ferret, and a baby ferret is a 'kit'

Before starting, the rabbit holes are netted securely so that when the rabbits bolt they become ensnared and can be quickly killed

WHO OWNS THE COUNTRYSIDE?

Britain belongs to many different people. Of course there are traditionally wealthy families who own large Private Estates but many others are now in the hands of foreign investors and institutions such as insurance and pension companies. At the other end of the scale is Common Land over which some householders have certain ancient rights to graze livestock, dig peat or collect firewood.

The County Councils are responsible for many sites besides roadside verges while railway companies own 20,000 miles of track as well as embankments plus some other unused land. The Countryside Agency oversees both National Parks and Trails, and the Environment Agency is responsible for various sites and activities concerning water. Water companies themselves own hundreds of reservoirs and thousands of acres of land. English

> *By far the largest landowner in Britain is the State*

Above A hedgerow in frost, untrimmed to leave plenty of winter feed for birds

227

Nature also own a number of nature reserves and manage many other sites. The National Trust, besides caring for many stately homes, also owns many farms, over 500 miles of coastline and other sites of natural beauty. Many hectares are owned by smaller concerns such as the RSPB, wildlife trusts, the Wildfowl and Wetlands Trust and a multitude of other conservation bodies. Wildfowling clubs own many hectares of marshes that they shoot over and carry out conservation measures at other times.

Hunts also own small parcels of land which they manage to conserve foxes for their sport. The popular game of golf utilises hundreds of acres of land. The horse racing industry accounts for a sizeable area both for race courses and breeding centres.

However, by far the largest landowner is the State, including Forestry Commission land. Other large areas belong to the Ministry of Defence while extensive agricultural land and forests belong to the Crown. The Church Commission comes eighth in the league, letting farms to 300 tenants and owning many other parcels of land.

An alarming amount of land disappears each year from the countryside as housing estates and new towns are built, industrial sites developed and highways and motorways constructed.

THE COUNTRYSIDE AGENCY

In April 1999 the Countryside Commission and the Rural Development Commission merged to form the Countryside Agency, a new statutory body employing about 400 people, which acts as an 'umbrella' for various public and private agencies to co-ordinate and advise on rural affairs. Their aim is to:

a) Conserve and enhance the countryside by safeguarding the environment for those who live and work there or visit it, taking into account the inter-dependence of town and country. Planning advice is included in this.

b) Promote social equity or economic opportunities for the people who live in the countryside to ensure that rural communi-

7% of British land belongs to the National Trust

County councils are responsible for roadside verges

ties thrive across the board and secure adequate access to such things as shops, schools and healthcare. The Countryside Agency also supports the rural economy with a mix of businesses so that both jobs and homes are available locally.

c) To help everyone, wherever they live, to enjoy our national asset (the countryside) by encouraging plentiful access, recognising that visitors can greatly help rural communities financially by spending money locally.

d) To advise the government on matters concerning the countryside and act on issues such as the environment, economy and social affairs. There is also statutory responsibility for setting the Country Code and designating National Trails and Parks although the Highways Authorities are responsible for defining and way-marking rights of way.

The Countryside Agency designates National Trails such as the South Downs Way, which extends through Hampshire and Sussex

There are 20 National Trails in the UK (including bridle-ways) designated by the Countryside Agency and marked with an acorn symbol. Four are in Scotland, three in Wales and 13 in England, covering hundreds of miles. One example in Norfolk is the linking of two footpaths, the Peddars Way, which starts on the Suffolk border and runs north to the coast where it joins the Norfolk Coastal Path at Hunstanton and then continues eastwards as far as Cromer, a distance of 93 miles (150kms).

National Parks have been set up to conserve and protect scenic landscapes. There are three in Wales (Snowdonia, the Pembrokeshire Coast and the Brecon Beacons) and seven in England (Dartmoor, Exmoor, the Lake District, both the North Yorkshire Moors and Dales, parts of Northumberland and the Peak District in Derbyshire). Two other areas afforded similar status are the New Forest and the Norfolk Broads which embrace the flood plains of five rivers.

The Coastal Heritage Forum is supported by the Countryside Agency and represents the interest of our rural coast-line preserving such areas of Heritage Coasts as parts of the South Downs, West Dorset, Flamborough Head, Bempton Cliffs and many others.

Funding of 75% is received from central government and

There are over 4,000 SSSIs in Britain covering nearly 2.5 million acres

25% from local authorities. 74% of British land is in the hands of private owners, 7% belongs to the National Trust or similar bodies and 7% to the Forestry Commission. The National Parks Authorities only own 2.3%.

A new National Trail has recently opened following the 84-mile length of Hadrian's Wall

COUNTY COUNCILS

County Councils are inadvertently the owners of some of the richest sites for wildlife and plants, being responsible for thousands of acres of land. Roadside verges stretch from the highway as far as a ditch, fence or hedge and the majority of these are left virtually untouched. County Councils do have conservation units who create nature reserves and amenity sites but their prime management factor obviously has to be safety. At least one metre at the edge of the road is mowed on average two or three times a year to provide good visibility. Occasionally an exception may be made where there is a specially recognised conservation site; and the mowing will be delayed until later in the year. The rest of the verge can provide a haven for wildlife especially if the adjacent land is prairie farmed with a huge expanse of a single crop. A large variety of plants and insects survive in verges with minimal interference throughout the year apart from when hedges and ditches are tidied up by the council in late summer or autumn.

Close examination of roadside verges will often reveal a wealth of wild flowers during spring and summer, some of which will later seed and provide food for many little birds. Kestrels can often be seen hovering beside roads and motorways searching for mice and voles who thrive in the rough unkempt grasses. Although the motorways themselves are a scar across

Exmoor, one of England's National Parks

the countryside, the banks beside them create mini nature reserves which rarely get disturbed. Some County Councils have made it a policy recently to sow wild flower seeds in the verges of new roads, producing an annual show of comparatively rare plants such as cowslips that would not normally be seen and adding a splash of colour to an otherwise drab landscape.

There are 350 Country Parks funded by local authorities. These were developed to give people the chance to enjoy the countryside on their doorstep and also to offer educational opportunities for local school children.

Rare stone curlews. A licence is needed from English Nature to photograph any Schedule 1 bird at the nest.

ENGLISH NATURE

English Nature, like its Welsh and Scottish equivalents, is a statutory government service responsible for looking after a wide variety of Britain's flora and fauna and to promote the conservation of wildlife and natural features. It was set up in 1991 and is funded by the DETR.

English Nature employs nearly 700 people divided into 21 regional teams who are responsible for identifying and designating areas as SSSIs (Sites of Special Scientific Interest) or NNRs (National Nature Reserves) which provide legal safeguards. English Nature generally monitors, advises (and organises when needed) the management of biologically sensitive areas of all kinds throughout the country, working with 23,000 land owners and agents and in partnership with such bodies as the Institute of Terrestrial Ecology, London Zoo, the Crown Estate Commissioners, Forest Enterprise, the Ministry of Defence and many other non-governmental organisations. Research is carried out to help endangered plants, animals, birds and insects. Grants are also distributed for management conservation and for this purpose England has been divided up into 120 areas which take into account landscape features, geology, wildlife and climate.

English Nature acts in an advisory capacity to the government and its agencies. All political parties recognise that a healthy environment is at the heart of running the country, believing it to improve the quality of life. EN also stages semi-

80% of old heath land has disappeared

nars and courses on wildlife management.

There are over 4,000 SSSIs in Britain covering nearly 2.5 million acres (1 million hectares) of land and water which represents 7% of the nation's land surface and is mainly privately owned. Of special concern is the fact that 80% of old heath land has disappeared while 97% of the natural fen land which once covered Lincolnshire, Cambridgeshire, Norfolk and Suffolk has been lost to farming.

There are 200 National Nature Reserves. Most have some permitted public access and receive more than seven million visits annually. English Nature also organises a year-round programme of walks, talks and educational days throughout the country at selected NNRs. The largest is the Cairngorms area in Scotland which extends to 65,000 acres (26,000 hectares) and the smallest is a one acre (0.4 hectare) meadow in Cumbria. Less than a quarter of NNRs are actually owned by English Nature.

English Nature is also responsible for approving applications and issuing licences where interference, either possible or deliberate, is caused to any protected species. They are also responsible for assessing requests to photograph any Schedule 1 bird at the nest and issuing licences to do so if approved.

English Nature acknowledges the place of fieldsports in the shared countryside providing they are practised within the law. It also has a particular responsibility for several fresh water areas statutorily designated for their nature conservation value and works closely with the Environment Agency regarding their care and management.

Only 3% of natural Fenland remains in East Anglia

THE ENVIRONMENT AGENCY

The Environment Agency was formed in 1996 to act as a guardian. It incorporated what was the National Rivers Authority (NRA) together with Her Majesty's Inspectorate of Pollution and Waste Regulation Authorities and some units from the Department of the Environment. Its functions span every aspect of the care and control of the water resources in England and Wales including:

The Environment Agency issues over one million licences each year for rod angling and net fishing

FLOOD DEFENCE The EA provides flood warning and flood defences for people and property from rivers and the sea and operates a 24-hour emergency phone line. Their off-shore sea defences extend to approximately 27,000 miles (43,000kms). Inland, EA works to control erosion of riverbanks and other waterways by suitable protective measures. Cattle drinking from rivers must not be allowed to cause damage to the banks.

SITE MANAGEMENT There are over 1,000 sites that are managed for recreational use such as sailing, angling and walking. Education, the provision of information and the conservation of natural resources, animals and plants are all included as is the surveying of rivers and the management of the Thames Barrier.

MANAGEMENT OF WATER RESOURCES EA planning provides a balance between water supply and demand. Income is generated from licences issued for water abstraction, discharging waste into the air or water, the transportation and disposal of solid waste, fishing and boating. Major funding is received from central government and from the levies paid by local authorities for building and maintaining flood defences.

WASTE MANAGEMENT The prevention and control of pollution is conducted to improve standards of waste disposal and to reduce it through recycling. All waste disposal by both water and on land is strictly monitored and controlled by the Environment Agency.

FISHING AND FISHERIES The EA actively encourages fishing and hopes to make it available to all especially in urban areas where they are working to improve still water fisheries (ponds and lakes) and to create new ones. Over one million licences are issued each year for rod angling and net fishing and advice is offered to owners on improving habitat. Action is also taken over poaching and where fish have been killed or died. The EA is responsible for maintaining, improving and developing salmon, sea trout, non-migratory trout, coarse and eel fisheries, their habitat and the quality of the water. Some rivers are responding well to improvements and are recovering from pollution

Over 1,000 sites are managed by the Environment Agency for recreational use such as sailing, angling and walking

The Environment Agency is responsible for sea defences as well as inland waters

including the Tyne, Mersey and the Thames. When water quality becomes suitable, areas are stocked with fish from fish farms owned by the Environment Agency. There are two EA fish farms from which over 1 million fish are sent out annually. Open waters (ie rivers) can only be stocked with fish with the consent of the EA and mandatory health checks have to be made prior to release. This is compulsory due to concern over the risk of spreading disease, parasites and non-indigenous (not native to Britain) species. This does not apply to enclosed waters (ie ponds and lakes)

NAVIGATION The EA is responsible for managing over 500 miles (800kms) of inland waterways and issues licences for approximately 40,000 boats annually.

When necessary, the EA does much work clearing and dredging rivers

MINISTRY OF DEFENCE

The Ministry of Defence Estate covers more than half a million acres (220,000 hectares) of land and half as much again is utilised under various licences. This makes the MOD one of the largest owners and managers of land in Britain. Salisbury Plain is its largest holding extending to nearly 100,000 acres (38,000 hectares). Some of the land is let on an agricultural tenancy or licence which stipulates that the agricultural use is subservient to military requirements. The MOD does actually own some of the most unspoiled areas in Britain. Because of the nature of their use many military training sites have remained virtually unchanged and in a surprisingly pristine condition since their acquisition. There has been no urban development, intensive farming or use of agrochemical sprays.

More than 250 SSSIs belong to the MOD and it almost seems as though time has stood still in some of these places. The policy is to strike the right balance between the military needs of the Defence Estate and environmental and conservation considerations. The MOD is very aware of its responsibilities and works closely with local and national conservation groups as well as

Some areas of Ministry of Defence land are the most unspoilt in Britain

English Heritage regarding the preservation of the Historic Buildings and Ancient Monuments that their land encompasses. There are over 600 in total and some of these are included in the Heritage Open Days initiative when buildings of architectural interest are opened to the public.

Conservation on the Defence Estates is now given high priority. A magazine called '*Sanctuary*' is published annually reporting on the MOD's involvement and achievements regarding the preservation of wildlife and plants as well as their archaeological sites both in Britain and abroad. It also contains reports from around the regions and many interesting features. The 'Sanctuary' Award aims to encourage positive conservation work across the Defence Estate and a 'Silver Otter' trophy is presented each year to the best conservation project on MOD land.

Designated public access is encouraged on parts of the MOD Estate but obviously for safety reasons, guidelines have to be adhered to and there are restrictions on times and some areas. A booklet containing details of 10 walks open to the public is available from the MOD. The areas they cover are Castlelaw (Scotland), Castlemartin (Wales), Watton (Norfolk), Longmoor (Hampshire), Catterick, Otterburn, Lulworth, Thorney Island, Salisbury Plain and Dartmoor. There are also limited opportunities for horse riding and climbing activities.

Lulworth Range walks. There are 10 walks open to the public on MOD land

The MOD is one of the largest owners and managers of land in Britain

THE NATIONAL TRUST

The National Trust is renowned for its work in restoring and maintaining stately homes throughout Britain. All their properties are accessible to the public and it is a privilege for both British and foreign visitors to be given the opportunity to witness at first hand the opulent aristocratic lifestyles of yesteryear.

The National Trust is a registered charity whose purpose is to preserve places of historic interest and natural beauty for the benefit of the nation. Despite having over 2.5 million subscribers and thousands of non-member visitors annually, there is not sufficient income generated to cover the upkeep costs of the properties. The Trust employs over 3,000 regular staff in the form of foresters, gardeners, wardens, administrators etc. These are supplemented by nearly 40,000 voluntary workers. It is money received from gifts, donations and legacies that enable the Trust to undertake essential maintenance and restoration work as well as purchase new properties. Legacies bequeathed to the National Trust often specify how the money is to be used.

Besides the stately homes and gardens which are synonymous with the National Trust, it is also responsible for nearly a quarter of a million hectares of countryside deemed to be of natural beauty including 600 miles of coastline. More than a quarter of the Lake District is owned by the Trust as well as St Michael's Mount off the Cornish coast and Brownsea Island off Dorset. 60% of the Trust's land is farmed by 1,100 tenant farmers. Some financial assistance is offered to these but they have to conform with certain methods and specifications as to how they manage their farms. Fieldsports and pest control are regulated and deer hunting with hounds is prohibited on Trust owned land. Holiday Cottages owned by the Trust are available to rent in some parts of the country.

The familiar oak leaf and acorn logo of the National Trust is a reminder everywhere of the importance many aristocratic families in Britain have attached to the preservation of our heritage for future generations and their wish to share such beautiful places with those who have an interest in them today. The financial burden to keep and maintain these splendid houses, priceless contents and immaculate grounds is immense. Without the Trust's work, which is of such historical and architectural value, and the generosity of its benefactors, many of these magnificent places would have been lost forever and their valuable contents ended up abroad.

The Farne Islands, a well-known sea bird reserve, are owned and managed by the National Trust

The National Trust has nearly 40,000 voluntary workers

WATER COMPANIES

There are 10 Water Companies in England and Wales responsible for supplying safe water and the disposal of sewage. Between them they own hundreds of reservoirs and thousands of acres of land which they actively encourage the public to use. Some of the largest sites have visitor centres and facilities for canoeing, wind surfing and other water sports, camping and cycling. Almost all welcome walkers, fishermen and bird watchers, the latter being well catered for by the provision of hides. The waters are stocked with brown and rainbow trout. Tickets to fish are available for the season, the day or even just for an evening and in some places boats can be hired. The fishing season normally begins towards the end of March and continues until late October. sometimes it is possible to fish for rainbow trout longer than this. Each reservoir has its own regulations and a limit on the size of the catch, usually a generous one. Many are leased to angling clubs.

Wicken Fen in Cambridgeshire, a particular haven for butterflies, is owned by the National Trust

The 10 Water Companies are:

SOUTH WEST WATER LTD owns 50 waters, some of them quite small, in Cornwall, Devon and Somerset.

WESSEX WATER SERVICES LTD serves Dorset and other counties and has its headquarters appropriately in Bath.

SOUTHERN WATER SERVICES LTD spans the commuter belt counties of Kent, Sussex and Surrey and has 4 main sites of interest to the general public.

THAMES WATER UTILITIES LTD is the largest water company serving over 7 million people and dealing with the waste from many more. It owns 39 wetland sites and 365 sewage works, and offers some very important urban sites for wildlife and leisure activities. Staines reservoir is divided by a causeway and can be seen when flying out of Heathrow.

> *Some of the Water Companies' larger sites have Visitor Centres*

ANGLIAN WATER SERVICES LTD owns one of the largest reservoirs, Rutland Water, which offers many facilities and is a favourite haunt for birdwatchers.

SEVERN TRENT WATER LTD provides water to over 7 million people and receives more than 5 million visitors a year.

UNITED UTILITIES WATER PLC (formerly North West Water) is the largest land owner of all the water companies having 180,000 acres (73,000 hectares) in its care which includes moorland, huge tracts of woodland and many farms.

YORKSHIRE WATER SERVICES LTD has some of the most scenic sites in Britain.

NORTHUMBRIAN WATER LTD also offers superb scenery and interesting wetland sites.

WELSH WATER (Dwrcymru Cyfyngedig) has 58 reservoirs, many of which are open to the public.

Thames Water, Britain's largest water company, owns 39 wetland sites

The reservoirs in the Elan Valley in Wales belong to Welsh Water (Dwrcymru Cyfyngedig).

THE COUNTRYSIDE IN THE 21ST CENTURY

The countryside is a complex, interwoven tapestry. Nothing in it is truly isolated, for one thing interacts with another and often leads to a chain of events in which the end result seemingly bears no relation to the original happening.

While the countryside may at times be a tough, hard and even cruel place, it is also surprisingly delicate and needs to be handled with great care. For country folk it is their recreational place as well as their work place and for many, their hobbies are also closely related to their work, such is the interest they take in it – the two are not separate entities. Those who are self-employed and keep livestock are unable to take a proper holiday so they look to spend leisure time on their doorstep with activities that they can fit in around their work.

Most of those seen out and about during the day are not having a 'day off', for they will have done some of their chores before they go out and the remainder when they get home. Even if they could take holidays sight-seeing abroad, they appreciate there are few places in the world that could equal the surreal beauty of a misty September morning soon after dawn when sparkling cobwebs decorate the hedgerows and the sun already holds promise of a beautiful day to come.

Duddon Valley in the Lake District: classic sheep country which, in 2001, like so much of Britain was brought to a standstill by Foot and Mouth disease

Right to roam

The present government is encouraging town people to think of the countryside as a giant playground but it is not, it is a production place (80% is managed and maintained through farming) and a conservation area, both of which welcome public access in moderation within designated areas. The proposed Countryside and Rights of Way Bill (Open Access or the so-called 'Right to Roam') is causing huge concern to those who earn their living from the countryside or are responsible for conserving it. While a complex structure of legislation has been put in place to safe_

80% of the British countryside is farmed

239

guard livestock, wildlife and the environment, it is considered to be inadequate and in many cases unworkable. Every year there is increased pressure on the dwindling countryside as thousands of acres disappear under concrete and tarmac. The population seems to want the best of both worlds, regardless of the consequences.

There are already 120,000 miles of rights of way in Britain and it is questioned just how much more is needed and why people should expect to walk wherever they wish and worse still, let their dogs run free. The disturbance caused and the harm it will do to wildlife as well as the possibility of damage (a discarded cigarette could set alight hundreds of acres of tinder dry forestry, moorland or crops) contradicts the government's emphasis on encouraging conservation. Ignorance can be as harmful as deliberate abuse. Most country folk have no wish to deny the public access to the countryside but they need to know where the visitors are going to be, so that those working in the countryside can get on with their tasks, without walkers being in any danger or causing disruption. Urban dwellers would not wish the public to have unlimited access to their own gardens or offices and so it is with folk who earn their living from the countryside, for it is the equivalent.

While the countryside is recognised as being a work place, a leisure place and a conservation place, the political agenda seems not to take into account the cultural and traditional rights

Bempton Cliffs, managed in conjunction with the Countryside Agency

The cliff path at Lulworth Cove, Dorset is very popular with walkers

that country folk feel they deserve. They dislike it when bureaucrats meddle with country affairs of which they have no knowledge. The balance needs to be right to embrace all those things and it also takes country folk to know what that balance is, not just people in plush offices with university degrees but not a pair of wellington boots between them. No-one can train to acquire a natural empathy with the countryside. It is something in the blood, something that makes that person a part of the countryside, sharing and accepting whatever nature has to offer.

Most country folk possess a lot of practical common sense and natural skills such as field craft, stockmanship and being observant. Their working hours and their sport are most likely dictated by the changing seasons or the welfare of their livestock. For urban dwellers the birth and death of animals is not an everyday occurrence or one they earn a living from. Nor do they realise what a huge part the weather plays in country life: a cold wet day in May or June can decimate young broods of birds and a wet August ruin the harvest. A year's work may be wasted. Many visitors to the countryside only venture out on 'nice' days so they may be unaware what happens or the conditions those who work outdoors are faced with.

Town people who buy houses in rural situations are sometimes appalled at what the locals do. Rural communities are losing their identities, as fewer and fewer people in them actually work in the countryside.

Fieldsports and the countryside

Fieldsports or to be politically correct 'country pursuits' are an emotive subject and under threat but they are responsible for preserving much of the countryside. Without them, Britain would look very different. Far less land is now needed for producing food and much of the existing woodland is not commercially valuable, so what else could it be used for other than being built on? Conservation costs money and most projects rely on grants or charitable donations but fieldsports carry out much of this work at their own expense making an important contribution to the biodiversity of the area as well as creating employment and providing leisure activities. About 4 million people participate in fieldsports and 8,000 are directly employed full time in hunting,

About 4 million people participate in fieldsports and 8,000 are employed full time in hunting, shooting and fishing.
Here the West Norfolk hounds are exercised

There are 120,000 miles of rights of way in Britain

shooting and fishing, another 27,000 are employed in trades directly related to fieldsports and many more in the organisation. There are probably more laws broken by youngsters at one night-club on a Saturday evening than by thousands of field sportsmen enjoying their chosen sport across Britain on that same day. Teenagers who take part in fieldsports are often admonished for enjoying a healthy day out in the fresh air while others can end up in all sorts of trouble at clubs by getting drunk or high on drugs yet escape criticism. When human rights and civil liberties in oppressed foreign countries are such politically important issues, it seems odd to country folk that the same freedoms should not apply to them.

Pest control is another emotive subject but it is necessary in order to retain some sort of balance, for pests in general seem to be far more adaptable to living alongside humans than many other species. There is little room for sentiment in either nature or business. Many pest species are nocturnal mammals so the average person does not realise just how many of them there are, other than by seeing bodies laid by the roadside in the morning.

Dogs have been domesticated for 10,000 years to the mutual benefit of themselves and humans. Working dogs feature a lot in the countryside and they are the most amazing creatures. Each breed has its own characteristics whether it be the collie that possesses an unseen control over sheep, a hound or gun dog with scenting powers a thousand times better than human's, a gaze hound that can run faster than a hare or a brave terrier. They are trained by being taught to recognise human dominance through tone of voice, eye contact and body movements. Rarely is there a need to use any degree of force. When properly trained, the respect for their ability as a working companion by people who work them or who enjoy country sports is immense. Animal activists claim that all animals have rights but country folk who work their dogs also believe that their animals should not be denied the right of doing the job they were bred for.

Community benefits

The sight of a policeman in the countryside is a rare one these days although not so long ago every village had one. Now police stations in most rural towns, where they still exist, are only open

Pest control – an emotive subject

50 years ago 25% of Britain's population were connected with farming. Now that figure is less than 10%

during the daytime. There are 5,000 gamekeepers in Britain who influence the management of 7.3 million hectares of land. They are the people who now police the countryside, for they are about their 'patch' most hours of the day and some of the night. It is often they who help police apprehend criminals. Even so, more than three-quarters of them suffer regular poaching because the police are not at hand when they are needed. Because keepers know every inch of their ground, it is also they who help out when anyone goes missing. It is not uncommon for people out shooting to be the ones to discover a body.

Gun ownership laws in Britain have been tightened and hand guns banned altogether since 1998. Legitimate shotgun and firearm licence holders, who have always obeyed the regulations, have been penalised while the use of illegal guns by criminals has risen 40%. Inevitably, criminals have a total disregard for the law and unregistered firearms are still easily obtained.

Foot and Mouth disease

No-one realised how involved and complicated the countryside situation was until the outbreak of Foot and Mouth disease in 2001 brought the countryside to a standstill. Like a boulder dropped into a lake, the ripples spread ever outwards getting larger as they went. The animals were killed and the farmers despaired, then those who earned their livelihoods from all things

> *There are 5,000 gamekeepers in Britain*

> *Since the tightening of UK gun laws in 1998, the illegal use of firearms by criminals has risen by 40%*

Thwaite, Yorkshire Dales: a balance between farming and tourism

even remotely connected with the countryside began to feel the ripples, such as feed merchants, holiday lets, even hot air balloonists selling trips: the rural economy suffered very badly. Nobody in the country was unaffected by Foot and Mouth disease and many urban dwellers who before had given scant thought to the countryside suddenly realised that what went on in it could also affect them. Local footpaths were closed, holidays in Britain were cancelled and some foreign countries gave the impression that visitors from Britain were tainted. People kept well clear of infected areas, not wishing to either be caught up in what was happening or be guilty of spreading the infection themselves. The countryside was declared open by the government but there wasn't anywhere to go in it. TV viewers were sickened with the harrowing scenes of animals being slaughtered and carcasses burnt but if they could have smelt the stench that the bloated bodies exuded, as local people did, there would have been mutiny at the way the situation was being handled.

Legislation concerning food imports into Britain, especially casual bits and pieces brought back by tourists from abroad, are extremely lax and experts have long been aware that the incidence of serious animal or plant disease was a potential time bomb waiting to explode. Foot and Mouth was believed to have arrived in Britain through imported pig swill and the previous year a serious outbreak of Swine Fever was attributed to a rambler throwing his unwanted sandwich made from contaminated imported ham to a pig in a field. If these incidences are true, and there is no reason to suspect they are not, it shows just how easy it is to unwittingly spread a disease. Although there was a serious risk between April 2000 and March 2001, less than 400 food items were confiscated by airport Customs Officers and there was no mention at all of any seizures made at sea ports or the exit of the Euro-tunnel. In America sniffer dogs are used to detect any item of food that air travellers arrive with and it is confiscated on the spot to protect livestock and crops.

Farmers and red tape

Farmers are mostly regarded as puppets by the British government and also, since 1973, by the European Commission. Like everybody else, farmers are drowning under a deluge of red tape

Heathland owned by the Ministry of Defence, great habitat for small skippers, meadow browns, small coppers and other butterflies of rough ground

Less than 1.9% of the workforce now work on the land yet they take care of more than 75% of it

emanating from both places. It is left to managers and workers to put into action often impractical and sometimes unworkable rulings. Europe's Common Agricultural Policy (CAP) has long been a bone of contention among farmers and has resulted in the housewife having to pay inflated prices for her food. The amount a farmer receives for his crop is a fraction of what food costs in the supermarkets. There are many links in the chain between producer and consumer and this is where the profits are highest. Farmers are at the beginning of the production line. When it comes to price cuts being made, they are expected to supply their goods at rock bottom prices so that companies doing the processing, packaging, transporting and marketing can ensure that their profits are not affected.

Farmers have little chance of getting better prices for their produce especially those contracted to supermarkets. They are told what they will be paid and there is no chance to negotiate. There are now proposals to change the Common Agricultural Policy in preparation for allowing ten more of the poorer countries to join the EU in 2004. Plans have been made to trim subsidies by linking them to food safety and environmental standards rather than production levels. Possibly this will end the trend for big farms to get bigger and small farms to disappear. Once again British farmers will have to rethink their strategies and decide which direction they will have to move in to obey the commands, while knowing that other EU countries will continue to disregard what doesn't suit them.

Small hill farms may seem to be an uneconomic proposition and therefore why should they not be dispensed with? But they contribute to preserving the landscape of the British uplands. Even if each farm only enables one man to scratch a meagre living, their contribution to preserving the environment and to conservation is valuable and is self funding.

Animal welfare

The welfare of animals is always a topic that raises emotions but there are very good reasons why they are managed the way they are. The need for food and the urge to reproduce are the two natural driving forces in bird and animal survival. In an ideal world they would all have the liberty to live a natural existence

Farmers cannot negotiate prices with supermarkets

A 'conservation belt' full of poppies and wild grasses at the edge of a Norfolk field

but the cost would be prohibitive. It is already difficult enough for farmers to compete with foreign producers with standards lower than British ones. It is paradoxical that Britain imports almost as much pork and lamb as it exports. Even trying to ensure that home grown produce is purchased is extremely difficult, as labelling is deliberately very misleading. 'Packed in Britain' does not necessarily mean that it is home produced. The little red tractor symbol and 'Produced to British Standards' is a better guarantee that it is home grown. Much of the food produced on farms has been meddled with subsequently by 'middle men' in some way to make it look better, weigh more or keep longer.

Food scares

Livestock medication and vaccines are also a cause of public concern and yet humans think little of filling themselves up with over-the-counter remedies, doctors prescriptions and vaccinations. Legislation is very strict regarding safety issues, and regular testing is carried out. TB, Brucellosis, BSE, Salmonella and E-Coli are of most concern but there are not so many diseases that can be transmitted directly from animals or birds to humans.

Regular scares occur regarding the use of chemicals in agriculture but the same products are freely available in garden centres for controlling weeds, bugs, slugs or mildew and rust. Even the convenient flea collars for pets are impregnated with chemicals similar to those used for farm animals.

Chemicals and agriculture

There has been a rapid decline of insect life since the 1950s, one of the reasons for diminishing bird numbers. Farmers have been blamed but other changes have also taken place besides the use of chemicals. The countryside as a whole was more utilised by coppicing woodland, peat cutting, dyke clearance. There were once smaller fields, more stubble left after harvest and more grazing land. The habitat was more diverse which meant more variety of insects and larvae and therefore more food for farmland birds. This fact is recognised by those endeavouring to increase their stocks of wild game birds. As part of their conservation management they have created wide grassy mounds, known as beetle banks, across the middle of large arable fields to improve habitat.

The barn owl needs all the help that conservation groups can give as its traditional nesting places are developed for housing

Britain imports almost as much pork and lamb as it exports

Landfill sites

The countryside is the tipping place for all Britain's rubbish and apart from destroying even more land it is difficult and extremely expensive to eliminate the risk of contamination. 25 million tonnes every year have to be disposed of by burying in landfill sites but even when the tip is covered over, methane gas is still released into the air for a long time afterwards.

The genuine old-time Romany gypsies caused little harm to their environment. So-called 'travellers' are a scourge of road-sides and lay-bys. Not only is there usually a spate of crime in the vicinity but also an accumulation of junk and rubbish is left behind when they depart. It is an affront to local people who cannot understand why it is allowed to happen. Fly tipping and throwing rubbish out of car windows epitomises the lack of respect that so many people have for the British countryside.

Unseen contaminants are perhaps even more dangerous. These include hormones released by humans into the water system as a result of Hormone Replacement Therapy (HRT) and the use of the contraceptive pill. Their long-term effect on wildlife remains to be seen. Alarm bells are already ringing with regards to some species of sea fish and the marine animals that feed on them.

Not only is farming in crisis, so is everything else in the countryside apart from conservation and recreational projects which seem to be going from strength to strength.

Country folk feel now that they are little more than pawns in a political game of chess where tactics are supposedly the key to success. While they are quite prepared to move with the times, they also cherish their tradition, heritage and culture and do not want to lose them.

Landfill site: one of many dumping grounds for 25 million tonnes of Britain's annual rubbish

How much damage will HRT-use cause to wildlife?

Below Beetle banks are part of the strategy for increasing stocks of wild game birds and pest control in organic farming

USEFUL ADDRESSES

FIELDSPORTS

COUNTRYSIDE ALLIANCE
(All fieldsports including hunting)
THE OLD TOWN HALL
367 KENNINGTON ROAD
LONDON SE11 4PT
TEL 020 7840 9200
www.countryside-alliance.org

UNION OF COUNTRY SPORTS
WORKERS (UCSW)
PO BOX 129
BANBURY
OXON OX17 2HX
TEL 01327 811066
www.ucsw.org

BRITISH ASSOCIATION FOR SHOOTING
AND CONSERVATION (BASC)
MARFORD MILL
ROSSETT
WREXHAM LL12 0HL
TEL 01244 573024
www.basc.org.uk

GAME CONSERVANCY TRUST
(Shooting)
FORDINGBRIDGE
HAMPSHIRE SP6 1EF
TEL 01425 652381
www.game-conservancy.org.uk/

NATIONAL GAMEKEEPERS
ORGANISATION
PO BOX 107
BISHOP AUKLAND
DURHAM DL13 5YU
TEL 01889 508417
www.nationalgamekeepers.org.uk

SHOOTING TIMES (magazine)
IPC MEDIA
KING'S REACH TOWER
STAMFORD STREET
LONDON SE1 9LS
TEL 020 7261 6180
www.shootingtimes.co.uk

SHOOTING GAZETTE (magazine)
ROEBUCK HOUSE
33 BROAD STREET
STAMFORD
LINCS PE9 1RB
TEL 01780 754900
www.countrypursuits.co.uk

THE FIELD (magazine)
KING'S REACH TOWER
STAMFORD STREET
LONDON SE1 9LS
TEL 020 7261 5198
www.thefield.co.uk

HORSE AND HOUND (magazine)
KING'S REACH TOWER
STAMFORD STREET
LONDON SE1 9LS
TEL 020 7261 6315
www.horseandhound.co.uk

NATIONAL COURSING CLUB
16 CLOCKTOWER MEWS
NEWMARKET
TEL 01638 667381
www.nationalcoursingclub.freeserve.co.uk

BRITISH DEER SOCIETY
BURGATE MANOR
FORDINGBRIDGE
HANTS SP6 1EF
TEL 01425 655434
www.bds.org.uk

HAWK BOARD
29 SOUTH ROAD
TWICKENHAM
MIDDLESEX TW2 5NU
www.hawkboard.org.uk

BRITISH FALCONERS CLUB
HOME FARM, HINTS
TAMWORTH
STAFFS B78 3DW
TEL 01543 481737

FISHING

NATIONAL FEDERATION OF ANGLERS
HALLIDAY HOUSE
EGGINTON JUNCTION
DERBYSHIRE DE65 6GU
TEL 01283 734735
www.the-nfa.co.uk

SALMON AND TROUT ASSOC.
FISHMONGER'S HALL
LONDON BRIDGE
LONDON EC4R 9EL
TEL 0207 238 5838
www.salmon-trout.org.uk

HANDICAPPED ANGLERS TRUST
NORTH LODGE
BURTON PARK
PETWORTH
WEST SUSSEX GU28 OJT
TEL 01798 342222

BRITISH DISABLED ANGLING
ASSOCIATION
9 YEW TREE ROAD
DELVES
WALSALL WS5 4NQ
TEL 01922 860912
www.bdaa.co.uk

ENGLISH DISABLED FLY FISHERS
50 HAZELWOOD ROAD
SOUTH WIGSTON
LEICESTER LE18 4LS
TEL 0116 278 5485

NATIONAL COARSE FISHERIES
CENTRE
ENVIRONMENT AGENCY
ARTHUR DRIVE
HOO FARM INDUSTRIAL ESTATE
WORCESTER ROAD
KIDDERMINSTER
WORCS DY11 7RA
TEL 0645 333111
www.environment-agency.gov.uk

ANGLERS CONSERVATION ASSOC.
EASTWOOD HOUSE
6 RAINBOW STREET
LEOMINSTER
HEREFORDSHIRE HR6 8DQ
TEL 01568 620447

ANGLERS CO-OPERATIVE ASSOC.
23 CASTLEGATE
GRANTHAM
LINCOLNSHIRE NG31 6SW
TEL 01476 561008
www.bhs.org.uk

ANGLER'S MAIL (magazine)
KING'S REACH TOWER
STAMFORD STREET
LONDON SE1 9LS
TEL 0171 261 5778

IMPROVE YOUR COARSE FISHING
(magazine)
BUSHFIELD HOUSE
ORTON CENTRE
PETERBOROUGH PE2 5UW
TEL 01733 237111

TROUT AND SALMON (magazine)
EMAP ACTIVE
BUSHFIELD HOUSE
ORTON CENTRE
PETERBOROUGH
CAMBS PE2 5UW
TEL 01733 456672

LANDOWNERS AND MANAGERS

DEPARTMENT FOR ENVIRONMENT,
FOOD AND RURAL AFFAIRS (DEFRA)
3-8 WHITEHALL PLACE
LONDON SW1A 2HH
TEL 08459 33 55 77 or 0207 270 8330
www.defra.gov.uk

AGRICULTURAL DEVELOPMENT ADVI-
SORY SERVICE (ADAS)
WOODBINE FARM
CARN MARTH
CARHARRACK, REDRUTH
CORNWALL TR16 5SA
TEL 01209 822038
www.adas.co.uk

FARMING AND WILDLIFE ADVISORY
GROUP (FWAG)
NATIONAL AGRICULTURAL CENTRE
STONELEIGH, KENILWORTH
WARWICKSHIRE CV8 2RX
TEL 01203 696699
www.fwag.org.uk

CROWN ESTATES OFFICE
16 CARLTON HOUSE TERRACE
LONDON SW1Y 5AH
TEL 020 7210 4377
www.crownestate.co.uk

HIGHWAYS AGENCY
ST CHRISTOPHER HOUSE
SOUTHWARK STREET
LONDON SE1 0TE
www.highways.gov.uk

COUNTRYSIDE AGENCY
JOHN DOWER HOUSE
CRESCENT PLACE
CHELTENHAM GL50 3RA
TEL 01242 521381
www.countryside.gov.uk

ENGLISH NATURE
NORTHMINSTER HOUSE
PETERBOROUGH PE1 1UA
TEL 01733 455000
www.english-nature.org.uk

ENVIRONMENT AGENCY (EA)
RIO HOUSE
WATERSIDE DRIVE
AZTEC WEST
ALMONDSBURY
BRISTOL BS32 4UD
TEL 01454 624400 or enquiries 0645
333111
www.environment-agency.gov.uk

MINISTRY OF DEFENCE
CONSERVATION OFFICE
BLANDFORD HOUSE
FARNBOROUGH ROAD
ALDERSHOT
HANTS GU11 2HA
www.mod.uk/policy/conservation/

NATIONAL TRUST
36 QUEEN ANNE'S GATE
LONDON SW1H 9AS
TEL 020 7222 9251
www.nationaltrust.org.uk

NT HOLIDAY COTTAGES
TEL 0870 458 4411
www.nationaltrustcottages.co.uk

WATER COMPANIES

THE WATER SERVICES ASSOCIATION
OF ENGLAND AND WALES
1, QUEEN ANNE'S GATE
LONDON SW1H 9BT

CONSERVATION

BRITISH TRUST FOR ORNITHOLOGY
(BTO)
THE NUNNERY
THETFORD
NORFOLK IP24 2PU
TEL 01842 750050
www.bto.org

ROYAL SOCIETY FOR THE PROTEC-
TION OF BIRDS (RSPB)
THE LODGE
SANDY
BEDFORDSHIRE SG19 2DL
TEL 01767 680551
www.rspb.org.uk

WILDFOWL AND WETLANDS TRUST
(WWT)
SLIMBRIDGE
GLOS GL2 7BT
TEL 01453 891900
www.wwt.org.uk

WILDLIFE TRUSTS
THE GREEN
WATERSIDE SOUTH
LINCOLN LN5 7JR
TEL 01522 544400
www.wildlifetrusts.org.uk

COUNCIL FOR THE PROTECTION OF
RURAL ENGLAND (CPRE)
128 SOUTHWARK STREET
LONDON SE1 0SW
TEL 020 7981 2800
www.cpre.co.uk

FARMING

DEPARTMENT FOR ENVIRONMENT,
FOOD AND RURAL AFFAIRS (DEFRA)
3-8 WHITEHALL PLACE
LONDON SW1A 2HH
TEL 08459 33 55 77 or enquiries 0207 270
8330
www.defra.gov.uk

NATIONAL FARMERS UNION
AGRICULTURE HOUSE
164 SHAFTESBURY AVE NUE
LONDON WC2H 8HL
TEL 0207 331 7200
 www.nfuonline.com
 www.littleredtractor.org.uk

NATIONAL ASSOCIATION OF FARMERS
MARKETS
SOUTH VAULTS
GREEN PARK STATION
GREEN PARK ROAD
BATH BA1 1JB
TEL 01225 787914
www.farmers-markets.org.uk

SOIL ASSOCIATION
(Organic farming)
BRISTOL HOUSE
40-56 VICTORIA STREET
BRISTOL BS1 6BY
TEL 0117 929 0661
www.soilassociation.org.uk

MEAT AND LIVESTOCK COMMISSION
(Organic)
PO BOX 44
WINTERHILL HOUSE
SNOWDON DRIVE
MILTON KEYNES MK6 1AX
www.aboutfood.co.uk

THE CROFTERS' COMMISSION
4-6 CASTLE WYND
INVERNESS IV2 3EQ
TEL 01463 663450
www.crofterscommission.org.uk

RARE BREEDS SURVIVAL TRUST
THE NATIONAL AGRICULTURAL
CENTRE
STONELEIGH PARK
KENILWORTH
WARWICKSHIRE CV8 2LG
www.rbst.demon.co.uk

FARMER'S WEEKLY MAGAZINE
QUADRANT HOUSE
THE QUADRANT
SUTTON
SURREY SM2 5AS
TEL 0208 652 4911
www.fwi.co.uk

POULTRY WORLD (magazine)
QUADRANT HOUSE
THE QUADRANT
SUTTON
SURREY SM2 5AS
TEL 0208 652 4020
www.reedbusiness.co.uk

FORESTRY

FOREST ENTERPRISE
WESTONBIRT ARBORETUM
TETBURY
GLOUCESTERSHIRE GL8 8QS
TEL 01666 880220
www.forestry.gov.uk

FORESTRY COMMISSION
231 CORSTORPHINE ROAD
EDINBURGH EH12 7AT
TEL 0131 334 0303   OR 0845 3673787
www.forestry.gov.uk

HORSES

SHIRE HORSE SOCIETY
EAST OF ENGLAND SHOWGROUND
PETERBOROUGH PE2 6XE
www.shire-horse.org.uk

BRITISH HORSE SOCIETY
STONELEIGH DEER PARK
KENILWORTH
WARWICKSHIRE CV8 2XZ
TEL 01926 707700
www.bhs.org.uk

RIDING FOR THE DISABLED
LAVINIA NORFOLK HOUSE
AVENUE R

STONELEIGH PARK
WARWICK CV8 2LY
TEL 024 7669 6510
www.riding-for-disabled.org.uk

DOGS

KENNEL CLUB (Gundogs)
1-5 CLARGES STREET
PICADILLY
LONDON W1Y 8AB
TEL 020 7493 6651
www.the-kennel-club.org.uk

NATIONAL LURCHER AND RACING
CLUB
58 WESSINGTON LANE
SOUTH WINGFIELD
ALFRETON
DERBYSHIRE DE55 7NB
TEL 01773 835291
www.huntinginquiry.gov.uk

ANIMAL WELFARE

MEAT AND LIVESTOCK COMMISSION
PO BOX 44
SNOWDON DRIVE
MILTON KEYNES MK6 1AX

ROYAL SOCIETY FOR THE PREVEN-
TION OF CRUELTY TO ANIMALS
(RSPCA)
CAUSEWAY
HORSHAM
WEST SUSSEX RH12 1HG
TEL 01403 264181
www.rspca.org.uk

PESTS AND PEST CONTROL

BRITISH ASSOCIATION FOR SHOOTING
AND CONSERVATION (BASC)
MARFORD MILL
ROSSETT
WREXHAM LL12 0HL
TEL 01244 573024
www.basc.org.uk

NATIONAL FERRET WELFARE SOCIETY
27 ST MARTINS AVENUE
YORK ROAD
DONCASTER DN5 8HZ
TEL 01204 531189
www.bhs.org.u